·HALLUCINATIONS·
AND THEIR IMPACT ON ART

DR. E. M. R. CRITCHLEY

Publisher's note

The publishers wish to thank all those who have kindly granted permission to reproduce illustrations for this book. Every effort has been made to trace copyright but this has not always been possible. We would apologise for not being able to make contact with copyright holders in every case.

Hallucinations and Their Impact on Art
by Dr Edmund M. R. Critchley

Published in UK by Carnegie Press, 125 Woodplumpton Road, Cadley, Preston PR2 2LS. Tel (0772) 728868
Printed in UK by T. Snape & Co. Ltd., Boltons Court, Preston.

Dedication:

To Mair, Giles, Hugo and Helen

Table of Contents

·HALLUCINATIONS·
AND THEIR IMPACT ON ART

DR. E. M. R. CRITCHLEY

Carnegie Press, 1987

Introduction

IT is claimed that this book is unusual in two important respects.

In the first place, it provides a comprehensive account of the many types of hallucinations that exist and the sheer complexity of circumstances in which they appear. Hallucinations occur in physical and mental illness and can be experienced by perfectly normal, healthy people. They range from the sensations of phantom limbs following amputation to the fantasies of childhood; from dreams and other phenomena of the world of sleep to mirage-like mass hallucinations reported in broad daylight by soldiers on the battlefield.

Secondly, the holistic nature of the scientific study of hallucinations is further broadened by a detailed examination of the impact of hallucinations on art. Many artists have depicted an apocalyptic experience, their nightmares or alterations in perspective which come to them in dreams. A few have been hallucinated as a result of illness and the malign influence of that illness upon their lives is clearly recorded. Others have tried the effect of drugs as a stimulus to art. This was often so in Primitive Art — the creative art of primitive peoples. Childhood art abounds in dream like fantasies and the distortion of the visual image. More sophisticated artists, representing the Surrealist and Constructive movements in particular, have consciously evoked subconscious phenomena in their art, mixing different sensory modalities or deceiving the eye and beguiling the mind.

The artist, in addition to any aesthetic pleasure he may give, commits for analysis a permanent record of his psyche and inspiration. Were we able to understand the human mind in all its aspects there could be no better form of expression to which we could refer. Less ambitiously, we may examine the role of known imaginative experiences as reflected by the artist in his work. It is possible thereby to study every nuance of visionary and hallucinatory experience exemplified by the plastic arts. No more vital and dynamic model exists to encourage the scientist in his endeavour to interpret the processes of the mind.

Hallucinations have never been an easy subject. They lie at the borderland between neurology and psychiatry. The tradionalists docketed hallucinations into three categories: organic hallucinations — released by epilepsy or by focal lesions of the brain; functional hallucinations — conjured forth by psychotic disorders or drug induced states; and pseudohallucinations — in which the person possesses insight into their unreality. Advances in medicine have forced natural scientists to adopt a wider definition of hallucinations, in fact to return to that originally proposed by Esquirol (1817) who defined hallucinations as perceptions without an object. Such a definition provides a continuity with delusions — false beliefs impervious to reason — and with illusions — misinterpretations of the form of external stimuli. The advances which have necessitated a more open definition of hallucinations include research into disorders of the eye and ear, observations of phantom limbs after amputation, pathological disturbances of sleep, sensory deprivation, brain washing, space exploration, the state of mind of hijack victims, memory surges in diseased states and flashbacks with drug addiction.

A broad definition is the only possible one if we acknowledge the fundamental insubstantiality of matter as viewed by modern physicists. Such a definition permits us to explore visions, dreams, hypnagogic experiences as we wake from or fall into sleep, nightmares, and other forms of imagery. Among these are scenic dreams and oneiristic states occurring in the course of delirium; synaesthesia — the splashing over of impressions from one sensory modality to another; disturbances of thought provoked by illness, drugs or deprivation; and the fantasies of childhood and of primitive people.

Visual art is basically a 'thing of the mind', a perception presented in material form. Not only is it possible to gain psychological insight into the mind of the artist but art affords an opportunity to study the very best the human mind and imagination can present. Hallucinations provoked naturally or artificially have often provided the inspiration for art, and in this respect there is a paradox whereby passive or real experience from nightmares, deliria, neuroses, psychoses or intoxications can be reproduced artistically as exact replicas of the form in which they appeared whereas experiences actively evoked by the fertile mind, artifically created from thoughts, fantasies or crystal gazing, need a heightened presentation involving the fullest use of the artist's sophisticated techniques. We should not dismiss hallucinations as inevitably pathological or linked with insanity; for, as de Chirico has argued, 'such abnormal moments can be found in everyone, and it is all the more fortunate that they occur in individuals with creative talents. Art is the fatal net which catches these strange moments on the wing like mysterious butterflies, fleeing the innocence and distraction of common man'.

The first chapters are preparatory to the central theme. The first examines the creativity of art, stressing the need to distinguish between the personal experience of the artist and inspiration derived from literature, legend or historical events or based upon the works of earlier artists. In an historical perspective, attention is given to the medieval diagnosis of madness which clearly excludes hallucinations. At that time visions were accepted as a spiritual rather than pathological occurrence. The essential differences between medieval visions and the hallucinatory experiences of modern psychiatric patients are discussed and compared. We next take a plunge into the fundamental and metaphysical basis of fantasy, imagery and perception, examining the approach of modern physicists into the understanding of matter, what is substantial and what insubstantial.

These early chapters give way to nine chapters which provide a more systematic examination of hallucinations and allied phenomena beginning with the experiences of sensory deprivation, stories told by explorers and lone voyagers, the effect of weightlessness as observed in gliders, in high altitude flying or by free-fall parachutists. Ordinary people in moments of lapsed awareness can experience brief sensations of floating or falling. New aspects are presented by space travel; and a space mission engineer from Cape Kennedy has gone so far as to interpret the Book of Ezekiel in terms on interplanetary U.F.O.s. A mixture of sensory deprivation accounts for mass hallucinations experienced by several people simultaneously in the course of battle and for the peculiar mental trauma which afflicts the victims of hijackings.

Sleep associated hallucinations form the largest single group of visionary experiences that are liable to be experienced by normal people. Hypnagogic hallucinations experienced between waking and sleeping provide patterned and coloured images, pareidolic imagery of half-observed objects, vicarious dreams and feelings of the presence of others in the room beside them. The scientific exploration of dreams began with Freud's *Interpretation of Dreams* (1900). Surrealists pledged themselves to open up the super-reality of fantasy, dream and imagination, but in recent years a new venture has arrived with the critical study of many forms of pathological disorders of sleep such as narcolepsy, catalepsy, Ondine's curse, hypersomnia and twilight states. Art finds a different inspiration in the nightmare than in the dream.

Hallucinations may arise from the special senses. Phantom sensations arise from an amputated limb. Whilst most people with aquired deafness experience troublesome noises or tinnitus, a few may be disturbed by formed music; and those born with profound hearing loss who later come to develop schizophrenia often claim to experience hallucinations involving hearing. Disorders of the eye may generate even more complex phosphenes or visions. Of particular interest are the so-called philosopher's visions that occur in elderly people with intact intellect. It is possible that such visions have been responsible for the increased creativity of three or more prominent artists in their old age.

Disease within the brain is normally associated with a negative loss of function but there can be a variety of positive phenomena. Distortions of vision can occur, with ordinary objects appearing extraordinarily ugly or beautiful, large or small, unfamiliar or highly coloured. Colours may persist or spread. Parts of the body-image may be replicated or distorted. Hallucinations can vary from simple flashes of light to highly complex multi-sensory scenes mingling voices, smells and pictures. Some kinds of hallucinations may be marked by the appearance of animals (zoonoses), others by minute figures (Lilliputian hallucinations). Lewis Carroll based the diversified phantasmagoria of *Alice in Wonderland* upon his personal experience of classical migraine with images that split, swell, shrink, disappear or metamorphose.

The dreams of children and the high art of primitive cultures have been appropriated as inspiration for art, though less so than the personal sufferings of the artists themselves. Drugs, destitution and disease have had an inevitable toll on the impoverished artist. Many have struggled to eke a living whilst suffering from tuberculosis, epilepsy, venereal disease or psychiatric disorders; but, of all the diseases, schizophrenia is particularly interesting in this respect, not only as a source of hallucinations but because those afflicted often find it easier, or have an impulsive desire, to communicate in visual form.

Drugs appear through the centuries to have held greater temptation to the writer than to the artist. Perhaps the artist has been less able to afford a constant supply. Although hallucinogenic drugs may hold a strong theoretical attraction, any positive stimulation to art has been disappointing, so that their impact on Western art has been miniscule compared to their association with primitive art.

Art depends upon perspective as well as perception. Both can be illusory even to the point of hallucination. Thus the devices used by the artist to beguile the mind need to be discussed in the wider context of hallucinations. The scientists can marvel rather than comment on such ambiguities as classical *trompe l'oeil,* visual puns, anamorphosis, impossible pictures and that paranoiac-critical method of Salvador Dali. Scientific comment upon the orchestration of mental associations and intersensory synthesis ranges from discussion of the primitive state of mingling of sensory impressions in early life to the psychological basis of synaesthesia and hormonisation of the sensations as a special talent given to a few, among whom are some of the greatest artists, writers and musicians.

Throughout the text, frequent reference is made to the lives and experiences of particular artists. The personal and visionary experiences of certain well known artists, their diseases and hallucinations are common knowledge and it would be wrong to leave the subject without providing a few selected vignettes in an attempt to explain the illnesses which afflicted Goya, Rossetti and van Gogh, among many others, based upon present day medical diagnoses and knowledge.

Chapter One

Historical Perspective

'Every epoch is given its own measure of artistic freedom and even the most creative genius may not leap over the boundary of that freedom'.
Kandinsky (1911)

IT can be argued that homo sapiens is divided from other animals by his capacity for symbolic thought rather than by his capacity for language; and that language is merely a vehicle for the communication of symbolic thought. In this respect, hallucinations, illusions, delusions, visions, superstition, possession, fetishism and the occult are paranormal phenomena, sometimes physiological but often bordering on the pathological. Early man moved from instinctive behaviour to one based on symbolic bewitchment. Although his talent for symbolic thought elevated him above the beasts, it did not set him free; it merely rendered him subject to a new series of regulators, or governors, of his existence, developed through and from symbolism. Territorially, he could extend his bounds. He had no fear of the stream, but in fulfillment of the aphorism 'look before you leap' he must firstly placate the water spirit before he attemps to cross, thereby approaching the stream with caution. He should not kill recklessly or the animal spirits would ensure that he goes hungry. He must live in neurotic obedience to the sun or the moon or the stars. In his language, as in his religious ceremonies, he must do exactly right; he may have to say 'beware' three times before he is understood or tap wood as he mentions a name. It is characteristic of the more illiterate regions of even quite civilised countries that unless a word is pronounced exactly right by a stranger they will fail to understand what is spoken. Not long ago — a point which well illustrates Jesperson's theory of the advancement of language through simplification — it was necessary to apply the correct collective noun in a host of circumstances: a sege of herons, a flight of doves, a claterynge of choughes, a muster of pacockys, a herde of cranys — to muddle any of these collective nouns would have resulted in total failure to be understood.

The additional symbolic attribution to common objects around early man may be seen as a form of synaesthesia and also as the origin of all manner of superstition, taboo, witchcraft and legend leading to a complex cosmology in which the boundaries between the real and imagined are uncertain. Within a given territory various locations will become known as the site of a killing, where animal bones are buried, where a battle took place or where their ancestors were put to rest. The subsequent attributes of these locations will be known in relation to these facts: the spirit of a deceased yielding good fruit from the trees, a bloodied field producing a poor crop, sour wines at a burial site. Such events and attributes will serve to blur further the distinction between the dead and the living and encourage the development of myths.

We can presume something of the perspective of early man from the experience of children. There is a difference between the childhood environment and the wider world. On returning to one's childhood home everything seems smaller, punctuated by a startling revival of persistent eidetic images. The perspective of the external world as primitive man left his native environment was of giants and great terrors; dwarfs and other little people — good and bad — reside within one's own environment and are rarely seen or recognised by foreigners. However, our perception of the environment is also dependent upon the brain's apperceptive (recognition within the mind) or analytical adjustments. People are not aware of the growth of their own body image, nor indeed do we notice any alteration in the size of our own hands when stretched out rather than close to, although books and other objects held in front of the face and then at a distance alter, appearing larger or smaller proportionate to the distance. The healthy brain avoids confusion by keeping the body image stable in all circumstances. We can presume that this adaptation occurred in tool-using man if not earlier in vertebrate evolution.

If primitive man had difficulty in distinguishing between reality and non-reality in everyday life, the Greeks can be said to have had a similar difficulty in historical perspective in differentiating between mythology, legend and the true history of their peoples. Memory (Mnemosyne or Mnemosure) was the mother of the Muses. Zeus himself was their father; and it is evident that without the parentage of memory no progress in any art or science is possible. The Greek, and even Norse, gods were less fearsome (except perhaps Zeus as the earliest and most primitive). They were effectively of similar size to humans, they shared the same foibles, did the same things, provided at times ideals, oracles and guidance. They could take human form and they could become mortal. It is hard to tell whether an historical personage or event is real or make belief. Stories and art depicting the exploits of the gods or of earlier times were embroidered and elaborated upon; narratives and paintings became congeries with added symbolism.

By the Middle Ages we are able to make a distinction between historical legend, albeit embroidered, and mythology; even though many of the lives of the saints are told in allegorical form. Satan is most commonly symbolised as the dragon or as the serpent: the serpent representing the evil spirit as the wily tempter that first betrays to sin, the dragon as the devouring monster that remorselessly consumes those that have become its victims. The dragon and the dragon slayer appear in many creeds and form the subject of countless legends. The great mass of legend that in the Middle Ages clustered around the names of faithful saints, the local traditions of every land, all point to the fatal presence of some evil principle and record the ultimate triumph of good. The evil spirit is described in the *Book of Revelations* as 'that great dragon'. The conflict between St. Michael and the dragon is a favourite subject in art (e.g. Fra Carnovale's picture). Memling, Tintoretto, Pisanello and Domenichino have all depicted St. George and the dragon. Both St. John of Rheims and St.Cyriacus are represented in art with a dragon held enchained. St. Theodore has a dragon with three heads and St. Germanus of Auxerre one with seven heads. St. Margaret thrusts a staff into the jaws of a dragon and St. Romain has the monster bound with his girdle and captive at his feet.

What is more curious to contemporary man is that the medieval description of insanity does not include hallucinations; and the experience of possession (passivity phenomena) is not described as occurring concurrently with or as an intergral of a visionary state. In Western Europe from AD 500-1500, people who heard voices or saw visions considered themselves, and were considered by their contemporaries, to have had an actual perceptual experience of either divine or satanic inspiration. They were not considered mad and were not dealt with as such. Hallucinations (fantasmata) were only considered as mad when combined with trickery (prestigiae). Non-psychotic religious fervour could be expressed by visions, social withdrawal, (hermits, recluses, incluses) and even self-mutilation or destruction. Several of the medieval visions show angels or saints chastising a person for sins of commission (wrong doing) or of omission (failure to carry out a mission). After the murder of Thomas A'Becket, Henry II was forced to purge himself by oath and penance: he walked three miles along a flinty road barefoot to Thomas A'Becket's tomb and there allowed the monks to scourge him in the cathedral. St Lucy plucked out an eye for her wrong doing.

From historical records it has been possible to reconstruct the 'folk' criteria of the time for madness (Kroll and Bachrach, 1982). It would consist of forms of behaviour such as: losing one's wits or reason; babbling or refusal to speak; wandering aimlessly and unaware of one's surroundings; neglect of person; howling like a beast; thrashing about tearing oneself with one's teeth and violent assaults on others. Similar criteria are to be found among primitive, non-industrial societies, e.g. among the Eskimos and Yrouba peoples in rural Laos; except that these societies all include hallucinatory experiences as aspects of insanity. Kroll and Bachrach were able to compare contemporary American psychiatric patients who 'saw Jesus and various saints', 'claimed that they themselves were Jesus' or 'received commands from angels and devils' with similar visions and legends of medieval times. There were astonishing similarities:

for example, a multiple sclerosis sufferer saw a piece of light break off from a cloud and enter her heart — she attributes her clinical remission to that event — and a schizophrenic patient cut off her right hand with a power saw in response to a vision of Henry Kissinger as the Antichrist.

The major difference between medieval hallucinations and modern psychotic hallucinations is the higher percentage of visual or mixed (auditory and visual) hallucinations (visions) seen in the Middle Ages. The most probable explanation why hallucinations were excluded from the criteria of madness was the universality of hallucinatory experience at that time; but there is also a possible secondary factor in that the degree of insight and recognition of an hallucination depends upon cognitive and apperceptive aspects. It would appear from medieval manuscripts that certain excesses were respected and applauded in the Middle Ages. Future actions depended on establishing a visionary, and often religious, *raison d'être* — just as today in certain strata of the United States of America it is necessary to have had a cataclysmic experience and to have been 'born again'. Heresy and witchcraft, as in *malleus malefactorum,* were the mental preoccupations of that era, just as religious observance was to the Victorians and sexual mores to our own time. In the secular field, Cervantes' Don Quixote parodies the chivalry and adventure necessary for a knight to prove his worth.

There are many other reasons why anyone of note in the Middle Ages would have had personal experience of hallucinations. Medieval Europe was swept by epidemics of fever and hallucinations. In the 15th-17th centuries Italy was afflicted by the tarentella, a rapid whirling dance said to provide a remedy against madness caused by the bite of the tarantula spider. This spider was later shown to be innocuous and the name more probably arose from the city of Tranato (Tarentum) where the disease first broke out. The sufferers made continual contortions and had an insane desire to plunge into water. The cure was music and the patient had to dance until he fell from exhaustion. The traveller could expect plague in the towns, encephalitis in the forests and malaria (marsh fever) in certain habitats. The Black Death had decimated the population where the life expectancy was already brief. Religious ecstacy may well have been stimulated by poisons. When wandering he may have had to feed off berries and poisonous mushrooms or starved, fallen ill in a swoon from lobar pneumonia or suffered sensory deprivation in damp dungeons awaiting a ransom. Albrecht Dürer was prone to dreams and hard drinking. The beverages would have varied widely not only in alcoholic content but in herbal flavouring, impurities and contaminants. The unscrupulous host anxious to search his guests possessions would not have hesitated to drug or sedate his victim. Whatever the cause the higher proportion of visual rather than auditory experiences is in keeping with hallucinations induced by fever, poisons, and metabolic disturbances rather that from schizophrenia.

Four painters, three Flemish and one German, epitomise the atmosphere and tensions of the medieval period.

Hugo van der Goes (1440-82) was a deeply religious lay brother who spent his last six years in retreat in a monastery suffering from a strange sickness with recurrent attacks of nervous depression. In 1481 his religious melancholia gave way to a suicidal mania. 'He could not get rid of the idea that he was damned and would have drowned himself if he had not been prevented by force'. The Prior tried to cure him with music and encouraged him to drink with his guests. A sense of melancholy also pervades his art which revealed a distorted, grotesque and almost expressionistic forcefulness. His technical perfection, use of lighting and sense of movement of the angles bursting into ethereal space are clearly seen in the Adoration of the Shepherds, the Portinari Altarpiece and in his last work, Death of the Virgin, portrayed in blue and livid pallor yet with the apostles gaping and gesticulating around the deathbed of the madonna.

Hieronymous Bosch (Jerome van Aeken, 1450-1516) combined fantasy and observations with an even greater expressionist flavour. Technical inventiveness, instinctive delicacy of painting, exquisite refinement and ravishing colours mirror the hopes and fears of the age and its major preoccupations with Biblical scenes, folly and death. Every bourgeois, every peasant and every child knew his Heaven and his Hell as well as his own room. Bosch 'the most pitiless of ironists' could present in lurid detail a world of sulphur and fire; exploding, bloody, violent visions of hell — the basic themes being simple yet heavily embroidered with narrative and symbolism. Moralising subjects were displayed with esoteric iconography as a tritych, in the segments of a circle or as a mirror 'where each his counterfeit may see'. Concentric rings with Christ emerging from his sarcophagus in the middle represent the Eye of God which is the central feature of the Tabletop of the Seven Deadly Sins and last Four Things. Around the pupil are inscribed the words 'Beware, Beware, God Sees'.

The explicitness of his imagery — sexual, anal and depraved — is such that critics have argued whether Bosch was a secret member of the Heretical Brethren of the Free Spirit — Adamites who, claiming innocence, indulged in rites of sexual promiscuity — or whether, as is more probable, he was a member of a guild of clergy and laity, the Brotherhood of Our Lady, instructed by the bishops and patronised by the nobility such as the arch-conservative Philip II of Spain to produce moralising works which were a salutary deterrent from sin: 'If the fear of God does not restrain you from sin, the fear of Hell at least should restrain you' (Thomas à Kempis).

Bosch's best known work, the Garden of Earthly Delights, possesses everything that human ingenuity has ever conceived by way of misshapen construction and erotico-acrobatic postures (Courthion, 1958); so much so that André Breton declared 'Externally, its subject is the sensual pleasure, treated with a perfect fusion of lewdness and near obscenity . . . The ruler over this dream atmosphere is the Orphic Egg, the principle of metamorphosis.'

Pieter Bruegel the Elder (1525-69), although influenced by Bosch, had a huge material and spiritual appetite for the sensible world. Humorous and realistic peasant scenes were presented with a carnival atmosphere. Such pictures as 'Big Fish Eat Little Fish' and 'Children's Games' cannot but appeal. His skill at fantasy was admired by Huysmans:

> 'There are frogs in paroxysms of laughter, unlacing their bellies
> and letting out eggs; and impossible mammals protrude pikes' throats
> and dance a jig on shin bones fitted into water melons. In his prints
> of the Deadly Sins the wild fantasy is even more accentuated: boars
> are scurrying about on turnip legs and wagging tails interwoven with
> roots and twigs; bodiless human faces roll about on the end of a
> lobster claw which served them as an arm; birds whose opening beaks
> are mussel shells and whose tails are eel-tails hop about on a pair
> of hands, with their heads lowered, running along like wheelbarrows.
> It is a gathering of hybrid creatures, vegetables and masculine, a
> union of tools and cripples'.

Albrecht Dürer (1471-1528) shared the energies and contradictions of
his age. He was the third of 18 children of a Hungarian immigrant and
apprenticed to his father as a goldsmith and wood carver before becoming
a painter. His woodcuts were so renowned that Erasmus, whose portrait
he painted, declared Dürer to be the 'Apelles of black lines'. This classical
allusion is misplaced. Apelles was the most celebrated of Greek painters,
excelling in grace and beauty but, according to Pliny, he painted in just
four colours. Dürer was far more versatile. Scarcely had he mastered the
intricacies of local colour than he threw himself into pictorial construction
based on groups of complementary colours, incorporating Flemish and
Italian art forms. The richness of Dürer's palette with its yellow orange,
blue, violet, red and green had something almost frightening (Waetzoldt)
and his contemporaries regarded the 'winged spirit' of his fantasy as one
of his most outstanding characteristics.

Erasmus was astonished to find Dürer capable of holding his own in
conversation with learned friends such as the patrician and humanist
Willibald Pirckheimer and that he was conversant with the religious,
philosophical, mathematical and astrological literature of his time. In fact,
Dürer wrote on geometry, perspective and fortification and drew his
inspiration from the same sources as the poets, delighting in allegory which
he was able to place alongside more popular illustrative works. The age
in which he lived, and in which his art thrived, demanded a deeply rooted
conscious belief, yet with a fantasy which could soar to philosophical
heights. As with Bunyan's *Pilgrim's Progress,* ideas were personified. His
contemporary Ulrich von Hutton wrote with grim humour and grotesque
imagery a conversation with the personification of the French disease
(syphilis) and many of Dürer's paintings, woodcuts and engravings take
this form. Dürer's biographer, Wilhelm Waetzoldt, devotes a whole
chapter to Dürer fantasy, based on the proverbs, mythology and literature
of all Europe, pagan and Christian. To stimulate his imagination, he
collected the exotic and curious: turtle shells, bones of giants and asses,
teeth said to belong to sea monsters, bezoars, ostrich eggs, a stillborn pig
with eight legs, and parts of a unicorn, walrus and rhinoceros. He could
temper religious expression and pagan beliefs, gentle adoration and bawdy
humour to the service of his craft; transforming ridicule into playful teasing
or biting sarcasm. Laughter and ridicule were necessary counterparts to
the deadly earnestness and harsh sentiments of his time.

Central Germany in Dürer's boyhood was filled by a craze for pilgrimage. Religious fanatics abounded. Some, such as Hans Böheim, were burnt at the stake. The excitement of pilgrimage amounted to a spiritual epidemic or licenced saturnalia and Dürer as a youthful artist in search of experience wandered through Germany and the Netherlands. In the festival atmosphere of these wanderings he became a connoisseur of wine, not averse to drinking bouts and over rich food: the theme of bibulous exhilaration pervaded his marginal drawings for the Emperor Maximilian's prayer book; but when, as a young adult with a definite painterly purpose, he went to Italy to meet Bellini and other artists he was advised against eating and drinking with Italian painters for fear of the danger of being poisoned by competitors. The movement of the masses meant the movement of disease. Thus syphilis spread via Spain through Italy into Germany, so much so that penitential sermons were preached against its evil in Nuremburg. In 1506 Dürer wrote to a friend 'I know nothing that I now fear more, for almost everyone has it. It eats some of them away to such an extent that they die of it'. When, at about this time, he suffered a high fever with faintness, lassitude and pains in the head, he procured 'French wood' (guava wood) which was commonly supposed to be a cure for syphilis. He was probably not infected but survived a further 21 years, dying at the age of 58 from a wasting disease.

His vividly dramatic and fertile imagination, the sublime conception and the wonderful union of boldness and correctness of design of his work are seen to best advantage in his religious works, most of which were created before the rise of his contemporary, Martin Luther. They are still dominated by the ideas of the medieval church, an art of reformation not of protestantism, closing the old world of medieval religiosity before Luther opened the new era of the individual attitude towards faith. Some of his landscapes were actually seen by him and are revealed with photographic objectivity and topographical detail: others were invented as fantasies on landscape themes of great demonaic and visionary power. Many pictures are declared as 'dreams' and there is ample evidence from his own writings that he was haunted by nightmares, visions and apparitions — 'from a soul torn by religious experience'.

Hallucinations are, above all, the property of mystics, particularly of religious mystics. The path of a mystic towards perfection may be strewn with subjective experience guiding them on their journey. Some, such as Martin Luther (1483-1546), may have tremendous confidence in the power of the invisible and yet be troubled by the apparition, or the voice, as he supposed, of Satan: and on one celebrated occasion used his inkstand as a missile against his adversary.

Apparently, Martin Luther and Albrecht Dürer never met but knew of each other's existence. Dürer, 12 years the senior, said of Luther, in hiding following the decision of the Diet of Worms, 'I don't know whether he is alive or has been murdered, but in any case he has suffered for the Christian truth... Oh, God, if Luther is dead, who is going to explain the gospel to us?'

Luther was the son of a miner of precious metals. Two younger brothers died of the plague and the sight of a friend killed by lightning at his side caused Luther to abandon his law studies and dedicate himself to God's service. He became a monk at Erfurt and was ordained as a priest in 1507. Three years later he travelled with a fellow monk to Rome on the business of his order and was horrified by the profligate and blasphemous Italian clergy. On his return he took his doctorate at the University of Wittenberg and was elected a professor. Dürer's age was one of pilgrimage and travel: Luther's of the proliferation of universities and printing presses. His first tract, *'Utopia'* in 1516, visualised an ideal republic discovered by one of Amerigo Vespucci's seamen where everything was done in the light of reason and natural religion and the monks set an example by looking after the sick, repairing roads and bridges and doing the menial tasks to cleanse the town of dirt.

His stern theology made him more aware of the less than ideal behaviour of the church of Rome and especially of the widespread sale of indulgences,

> *'As soon as a coin in coffer rings,*
> *The soul from purgatory springs'.*

Near Wittenberg, the peddling of indulgences was personified by one John Tetzel, a Dominican monk, who is reported to have said, 'Even if you have deflowered the Virgin Mary, an indulgence will free you from punishment in purgatory'. On 31st October 1517, the eve of All Saints, Luther (is reputed to have) nailed to the church door 95 Theses against the doctrine of indulgences and announced his readiness to defend them. 'If the Pope could free souls from purgatory, why does he not do so out of Christian love? Why does he demand money for doing this merciful deed?'

Tetzel obtained a copy of the Theses and transmitted them to Rome where Pope Leo X (Giovanni de Medici, 'God has given us the papacy; now let us enjoy it') ordered Luther to appear. However, the Elector of Saxony demanded that any trial of a German monk should take place in his own country. The trial took place and, after the inevitable decision, Luther went into exile, protected by the German nobility, and continued to produce more and more vitriolic tracts: On the Freedom of a Christian, On Secular Authority, and, notoriously, Against the Jews and their Lies.

What of Luther, the man? We know him to be very sensitive, of a jumpy, nervous disposition. John Osborne's play highlights his constipation and Erickson *(Young Man Luther,* 1958) mentions urinary retention. Others describe his insomnia. The Catholic biographer, J. M. Todd (1964) provides a more complex hypothesis:

> 'Horror of some sort of sexual impurity led to a common opinion in medieval times that a priest should generally refrain from offering Mass on a morning after he had experienced a seminal emission during sleep. In Luther's sensitive mind, always inclined to a certain morbidity, this sort of emphasis on the gross sinfulness or impurity of involuntary acts led to a fear of being in a state of sin which became a permanent dread, weighing him down'.

'I said Mass with great dread', Luther is also recorded as saying, 'I thought I was the only one who had ever experienced these "spiritual temptations" and I felt like a dead man'. Whatever disturbed Luther and accounted for his hallucinations appears to have had a physical basis. Luther talks of his Anfechtung 'combat' rather than Versuchung 'temptation' and speaks of the powers of music — 'Music is the art of the prophets, it is the only other art which, like theology, can calm the agitation of the soul, and put the devil to flight'.

Another Christian philosopher and mystic, Emanuel Swedenborg (Svedberg) 1688-1772, bridges the centuries between the Middle Ages and the Pre-Raphaelites. He conveys his message in the form of visions of the heavenly hierarchy observed with a simplicity and clarity that leaves no reasonable doubt of his absolute conviction of their reality. His New Jerusalem Church (Swedenborgians), based on the tenet of God as a trinity of principles rather than of persons, was founded some years after his death. To many who are not his followers, Swedenborg's visions, illuminations and spiritual experiences are the result of mental illness; but Immanuel Kant who, according to Bertrand Russell (1940), bought one of only 4 copies sold of Swedenborg's massive tome expounding his mystical system, wrote a curious work called *Dreams of Ghost-seer, Illustrated by the Dreams of Metaphysics* (1766), in which, half seriously and half in jest, he suggests that Swedenborg's 'fantastic' system is perhaps no more fantastic than that of orthodox metaphysics.

Swedenborg's life divides sharply into two halves. The son of a bishop, he was, until the age of 58, a notable man of science and an assessor extraordinary of the College of Mines. Some of his works were theoretical, attemping to explain the phenomena of the elemental world in the philosophical manner. He distinguished himself by various mechanical inventions and successful engineering projects, often showing remarkable anticipations of subsequent scientific discoveries in astronomy, physics, chemistry and anatomy. Among his many experimental models was that of a flying machine, but he had the sense to realise that it would never fly.

In 1743, the period of what he called his illumination began, and soon afterwards he openly assumed a new character: 'I have been called to a holy office by the Lord, who most graciously manifested himself in person to me, his servant, in the year 1743, and opened my sight into the spiritual world, endowing me with the gift of conversing with spirits and angels, which I enjoy to this day. From that time I began to print and publish various arcana that have been seen by me or revealed to me as respecting heaven and hell, the state of man after death, the true worship of God, the spiritual sense of the Word, with many other most important matters conducive to salvation and true wisdom'. His *Arcana Celestia* was interspersed with accounts of wonderful things seen and heard in heaven and in hell; and his *Spiritual Diary* contained minute notes of his intercourse with the spiritual world. His works aroused hostility in Sweden but he travelled to Holland and Britain where he felt that there was a greater freedom of speech. He could describe how he was permitted to pass alive through all the experiences which accompany death, visit other worlds of the solar system, meet the spirits of Louis XIV and George II and converse with King David and St. Paul.

The visual nature of his hallucinations, his demeanour, his high intelligence, intact personality and the fact that he rarely referred to his spiritual visions in the course of conversation, except when specifically questioned, is against the more usual forms of schizophrenia. Without further knowledge we would be wiser to marvel at the metaphysics of Kant's *Ghost-seer*.

Spiritualism, mysticism, dreams and idealisation, often of a frankly sensual nature, pervade the inspiration of Blake and the Pre-Raphaelites. Blake was poetic, prophetic, philosophical and experimental. Visionary beliefs inform the whole of his work, given substance through an idiosyncratic and imaginative cosmology. In France, writers and poets such as Huysmans, Mallarmé and Verlaine provided the textual temperament upon which was based the symbolist doctrine applied in an ecstasy of the dream to the plastic arts by Moreau, Bresdin, Redon, Puvis de Chavannes, Carrière and others. The same shadowy outlines and dreamlike symbolism permeated the Pre-Raphaelites Rossetti, Holman Hunt, Burne Jones, Watts and the *fin de siècle,* aesthetic decadence of Aubrey Beardsley. Painters of other nationalities such as Böcklin, von Stuck, Kubin, Munch and Vrubel advanced the symbolist cause whilst William Morris, Klimt and Toorop, perhaps more than others, transformed the sensual, erotic and dreamlike character of the plastic arts of the symbolist movement into the decor of Art Nouveau. The symbolist movement can be regarded as the major precursor of Surrealism and the counterbalance of Realism and Impressionism. It is scarcely surprising that in the early days of Surrealism, a medium and the subject of Théodore Flourney's book *'Des Indes à la Planète Mars* (1900), by the name of Hélène Smith, should in a state of trance speak Martian, describe her adventures on Mars and afterwards draw and paint the plants, houses and landscape which she saw there.

The dream and hallucinatory aspect of the symbolist movement ignored nature and did little for colour. In their different ways Géricault, Delacroix and Cézanne would look at nature to observe its rhythms. Géricault would study corpses and visit slaughter houses as others have done before and since. Kokoschka attempted mentally, if not literally, to psychoanalyse his subjects in order to increase the intensity of his work. Where Cézanne was plodding and obsessional, Gauguin sought to 'pass emotion through a filter'. He advised other artists not to copy too much from nature but to take from nature by dreaming about it, seeking the absolute. 'Dream and then just go ahead and paint. I dream of tremendous harmonies in the midst of natural frequencies which intoxicate me. My dream cannot be formulated, admits no allegory; a musical poem, it needs no libretto'. Van Gogh's dream was more that of the nightmare; as Aurier describes: 'Matter and nature are frantically twisted in a wild paroxysm of distortion; form has become a nightmare, colour is flames of hot spilling lava and precious stones; light is fire, and life itself is feverish and hectic'. Jean Baptiste Carpaeaux displayed a similar 'hectic violence of genius' in a sculptor's skin'. Marc Chagall (1887-1984) is an artist at the transection of the symbolist and expressionist movements. He describes his paintings not as literature, but as persistent arrangements of inner images that obsess him. Recollections are broken up and images juxtaposed as though in a magic kaleidoscope of multi-coloured, riotous dreams. He appears to be haunted by stories of his childhood, springing from Jewish folklore with a rich strain of personal fantasy transforming objects and subjects tumbling from the memory of his early life in Russia. Kandinsky theorised in a similar vein, defining three different types of inspiration: the Impression — a direct impression of outward nature, the Improvisation — a largely conscious, spontaneous expression of inner character, and a Composition — a slowly formed inner feeling, worked out repeatedly and almost pedantically, dependent upon consciousness and purpose.

The historical intent of the Surrealists was to seek to disentangle the dominion of the dream and the role of the subconscious. Thus, their mandate was to obtain inspiration by exploring the subconscious mind through dreams, hallucinations, drug-induced states, by automatic writing, poetry and drawing, by psychological word games and by encouraging the unpremeditated. Primitive vision was examined as expressed by children, idiots, psychotics and uncivilised peoples. Primitive complexes involving mythology, witchcraft and magic were utilised by Victor Brauner, Kurt Seligman and others. Salvador Dali exploited guilt feelings, obsessions, phobic-anxiety states, sexual symbolism and sexual aberration. Each surrealist interpreted his mandate in a different way. René Magritte (1898-1967) invented a repertoire of combinations which have since been overworked and lost their original novelty. He would produce a series of transparent enigmas suggestive of dreams. A detail would appear abnormally enlarged, a mountain take the form of an eagle, shoes would appear to grow toes, a face develop at the end of an arm. The effect was hallucinoid rather than hallucinatory. André Masson (1896 -) reacted to the violence of war. The First World War in which he was wounded and underwent psychiatric observation left him in a permanent state of revolt against society. He symbolised with erotic significance the violence of the Spanish Civil War in a series of works entitled Massacres, Sacrifices and Tauromachies. He painted with deep passion. When his canvases failed to satisfy him he would slash them angrily with a knife. He would use 'support words', as he worked, saying aloud 'attraction', 'whirling', 'transmutation', and used every possible means to invoke a state of trance. He chose rigorously abstract constructions with trance-like mysterious curves communicating his sense of restlessness to the whole composition. His automatic drawing appeared to be obsessed with passion, the sun and the destiny of animals. He scattered sand over glue-coated canvases. From 1937 he painted with a shrill verism desolate, often perverse, dream scenes in a state of abject fury. The style of his paintings altered frequently but the tremendously restless nature of his art remained throughout.

During the early 19th century all manner of 'perceptions without object' were brought together by Esquirol (1817) under the common denomination of hallucination with an application particularly to vision. By examining the nuances of meaning provided through art it has proved feasible to expand the scientific concept of perceptual thought and learn something of the workings of the brain at a subconscious as well as at a conscious level. However, there are many who adhere to the strictest possible definition of hallucinations, so much so that any attempt at discussion comes to an early and sterile impass. I wish therefore to end by justifying the position I have maintained throughout. Firstly, as it is impossible to establish the degree of insight experienced, it is wiser to adhere to a broad definition of these phenomena. This is the position generally held in North America. Secondly, French, German and Spanish psychiatrists consider hallucinations as a subset of delusions (sensory delusions), assuming that both words, hallucination and delusion, subsume a temporary or prolonged disturbance of personality and a fracture in the relationship between the subject and his world. This is a more cognitive and less intellectual (perceptual) interpretation than is widely adopted in Great Britain. And thirdly, all manner of hallucinations are fundamentally disorders of perception. The distinction between 'organic' and 'functional' hallucinations started in the 1950s and created as many problems as it solved (Berrios, 1982). The notion of 'pseudohallucinations' was introduced by V. Kandinsky (Rokhline, 1971) to cope with the clinical anomalies that fitted neither the organic nor the functional categories. It is unfortunate that Jaspers' (1963) idiosyncratic interpretation of Kandinsky led to the official view that pseudohaliucinations constitute a third class. This anachronistic conclusion neglects the fact that Kandinsky proposed the term as a rag-bag for unclassifiable hallucinatory experiences. As Berrios reiterated, the view of hallucinations as a symmetrical and homogenous disorder in all five Senses breaks down in relation to the impossibility of 'pseudohallucinations' occurring in some sensory modalities such as touch.

Chapter Two

Art, The Mind and Imagination

'All art is simultaneously surface and symbol'
Oscar Wilde

THE nature of man's higher mental functions: consciousness, emotion, memory, thought, perception, and their expression through language, through specific talents in music, art and literature, prowess in sport and in the application of developed skills, attracts the wonderment of all. Science cannot use any animal model or experimental paradigm to ape these faculties; the best we can do is to study the effect of trauma, drugs or disease and observe the results of enfeeblement. We can quantify and docket examples of aberrations of the impaired, malfunctioning nervous system, studying the circumstances in which such aberrations arise in order to gain insight into the human mind. The workings of the imagination can thus be revealed through unusual perceptions, subconsciously arising visions, spontaneous hallucinations, distorted imagery, curious illusions and in dream states.

Art offers a different facet of the human story: a chance to study the very best the mind and imagination can present, displayed in a form open to careful and leisurely analysis. Art is the exteriorisation of so many visual perceptions, provided not only by the quaint, the queer, the mystic overmuch, the dismal and the dry, but often by those possessing the greatest talents and intellectual abilities.

Through the centuries, every conceivable form of imagery has been pressed into the service of art. What more ideal source permitting an understanding of the highest human faculties is there available for study? The art historian, Wilhelm Worringer wrote that 'art is generated by spiritual forces, art history properly understood is a history of the human psyche and its forms of expression, the ceaseless shifting of man's relation to the impressions crowding in on him from the surrounding world forming the starting point for all psychology on the grand scale'. E. H. Gombrich describes the history of art as the forging of master keys for opening the mysterious locks to our senses to which only nature herself originally held the keys. Like the burglar who tries to break the safe, the artist has no direct access to the inner mechanism. He can only feel his way with sensitive fingers, probing and adjusting his hook and wire when something gives way. Of course, once the door springs open, once the key is shaped, it is easy to repeat the performance. The next person needs no special insight — no more, that is, than is needed to copy his predecessor's master key'.

The importance of the unconscious in art has not always been obvious but is nowadays an inherent part of the doctrine of self-expressionsm in the arts. Art therapy has greatly assisted the evaluation and rehabilitation of institutionalised patients in disturbed mental states who are otherwise unable to communicate their innermost feelings. Maurice Utrillo (1883-1955), a confirmed alcoholic by the age of 19, first began to paint under constraint from his artist mother, Suzanne Valadon (1865-1938), who felt that this would have a remedial value. Artists themselves, such as Wassily Kandinsky (1866-1944) have sought to connect the visual matter of art directly to the inner life of man. Tolstoy's description of the generative process of art applies to artists from time immemorial:—

'To evoke in oneself a feeling one has experienced, and having evoked it in oneself, then by means of movement, lines, colouring, sounds or forms expressed in words, so to transmit that feeling that others experience the same feeling — this is the activity of art'.

Thus all art, from the most rudimentary to the most sophisticated, of necessity requires the projection of the artist's psyche into his work.

For many generations such projection was muted by patronage. The artist rarely had the opportunity to choose his own subject; this was the prerogative of the patron, whether the church, a potentate, a wealthy burgher, or a corporate foundation. Even so, given the shadowy format of an idea, the artist could use his perceptive experience and technical excellence to ennoble the concept, seizing the soul and essence of beauty, giving aesthetic pleasure through idealism — ideal proportions, ideal harmony — in short, ideal beauty (Herbert Read, 1931). Modern art, where the role of fantasy can be the creative force and not merely the embellishment of the endeavour, provides a more open, obvious exteriorisation of the artist's emotional, psychological and spiritual urges. 'Old drawings', to quote Rutter (1927), 'may strike one as better done and modern drawings as more interestingly seen', but both old and new result from the coordinated application of hand, eye and mind.

From the concept of art as a 'thing of the mind', it follows that any scientific study of art will be psychological. It may be other things as well, but psychological it will always be (Friedlander, 1943). However, a piece of art taken by itself is rarely sufficiently revealing for a stranger to pronounce on the source of its imaginative content. Much else is required: a knowledge of the artist, of the stresses and strains of his life, his inspiration and his interests. Even then, the avarice of the would-be investigator is often curtailed because the intellectual presentation is difficult or subtle and is thus not open to the crude methods at his disposal. The investigator may have to try to place himself in the situation of the artist in an attempt to determine from the available documentation how the artist viewed his own work. In seeking a broader perspective of art and the imaginative experience, we are, at the very least, limited within the confines of the mainstream of Western Art, selecting from the few examples where a positive statement can be made. As the navigator in Virgil's *Aeneid* says, "Alter aliis teneant" (Let others keep to the deep).

The purpose of art is to communicate. Pictorial art developed in Egypt in order to tell a story. The hieroglyphics of that time represent a stage of transition between pictorial symbolism and writing. In the Middle Ages, sequences of pictures, like a comic strip, were used so that the unlettered masses could learn about famous battles, the life of Christ and the visions of the saints. As a means of communication the extravagant and mystic symbolism of medieval art was no more complex than the language of verbal communication. The vernacular was replete with introductory and redundancy clauses, seeking to establish the correct relationship before the essence of the proposition could be presented. Etiquette required exact grammar and the use of the appropriate collective nouns and adjectival phrases. The language of the aristocracy often differed from the common tongue. Sagas took on a complex poetic form: the rhythm or measure was determined by rhyme, by alliteration and by a succession of grouping, feet or stresses, and marked by a definite recurrence of ictus. But symbolism, though often lost to present day observers, was widely understood and determined the identity and life story of each saint. Through fantasy Albrecht Dürer (1471-1528) depicted the visions of St. John with an array of comets, meteors, eclipses of the sun and moon, fire, floods and high tides, battle, plague, famine, martyrdom and death. A modern artist might, in a similar manner, fantasise on the transportation of Ezekiel by U.F.O. from the riverside to the high mountain surrounded by flashing lights and cherubim from outer space (Blumrich, 1974). Hieronymous Bosch (1450-1516) presented in allegorical form sermons against pride, gluttony, greed and ignorance. With the growth of patronage outside the church, artists and their patrons sought inspiration not only from religious subjects but from folklore, legend and literature. As if the symbolism of the Middle Ages lacked complexity, that of the Florentine Renaissance, when the influence of Greek art mingled with Christianity, was adorned by an even more elaborate, ornate and high flown imagery. For example, the human shape of Jupiter could not be presented without attention to certain recognisable features:

He is horn-faced, in deserts placed,
With eagles laced, with palm leaf mazed,
With gold veil graced.
His countenance bright, its colours light,
The thunder he grips, from a horn he sips.
(Gombrich, 1972)

Religious works have always depended almost exclusively upon patronage, but in such works an additional factor, the religious fervour of the artist, enhances his commitment and strengthens the power of his imagination. From the early altar pieces of Chimabue and Giotto, the choice of artist to depict a religious subject, though made partly on the artist's reputation and the school of his apprenticeship, took into account his religious rectitude, depth of feeling and the sincerity which he was able to project into his work. Inferior work which offended the devotees of the shrine was often rejected and the artist's future suffered accordingly. Ruskin was merely reflecting previous dicta in declaring that the Dominican Fra Angelico was not an artist properly so-called but an inspired saint. A similar commitment in the manufacture of holy works survives to this day. Suzanne Massie, in describing the icons of old Russia *(The Land of the Firebird)* provides an excellent example:

'The Orthodox believed that it is possible to recognise the presence of the Holy Spirit in a man and to convey it to others by artistic means. Therefore, the function of the icon painter had much in common with that of a priest, and although it was important for an icon painter to be a good artist, it was essential for him to be a good Christian. Those who painted icons had to prepare themselves spiritually: fast, pray, read religious texts, for it was a true test, not a pictorial work in the usual sense'.

Portraiture, of necessity, will continue to thrive on patronage. Argüelles (1975) makes the unkind comment: 'In the genre of portraiture is the germ of the illusion of history — the glorifying of the individual ego. The bourgeois banker sitting for his portrait is only Napoleon unmasked: the naked, grasping ego!'. Despite our professed love of caricature and such statements as 'any publicity is good publicity', portraiture remains a sycophantic art but the skill and personal touch remains. Jonathan Richardson (1715), a relatively inferior portrait painter, declared that the artist must 'understand mankind', and enter into their character, and express their minds as well as their faces'. The touch of a brush can make the difference between sorrow and a smile, or — as with the recent portrait of Mrs. Thatcher — the presence or absence of a squint. Portraits on currency notes render them harder to fake: an inaccurate copy produces a slightly different expression that is instantly recognised. Portraiture can be an art of the highest order, commanding the empathy, the incisiveness and intellect of the artist. As Ruskin pronounced: 'the best pictures that exist of the great schools are all portraits. Their real strength is tried to the utmost; it is never elsewhere brought out so throughly as in painting one man or woman, and the soul that was in them'.

The first slackening of the power of patronage, leading to the growth of self-expressionism, began in the 19th century with the Romanticist movement. In earlier centuries artists could be broken or bullied. Michelangelo was forced to leave his sculptures incomplete and made to paint fast-drying plaster on the ceilings of the Vatican vaults. The impetuous Caravaggio had several private patrons, including some cardinals, who admired the inspiration and realism of his paintings but he was broken by the criticism and rejection of much of his commissioned work. In the same era, only Dürer appears to have thrived, perhaps because he shared many of the patrons who supported Martin Luther. He was able to broaden his vision, displaying great versatility of subject matter whether religious, literary or legend, and in 1515 depicted in water colour his own famous dream in which he saw the final catastrophe brought about by huge columns of water crashing to the earth.

The burgeoning of self-expressionism in the 19th century was initially shown to best advantage in the new perspective of landscape painting; described by Sir Herbert Read as essentially a romantic art, invented by a lowland people who had no landscape of their own. The doyen of the Romantic movement, the French landscape painter, Caspar David Friedreich (1774-1840) declared that the painter 'must not only paint what he sees before him, but also what he sees within him. If however he sees nothing within him, then he should omit to paint what he sees before him'. Gainsborough was able to concentrate all his powers on the translation of his own continuing emotion into paint and to 'make the vigour, heat and unity of his passion the measure of his art' (Sir Walter Armstrong), and Ruskin's famous defence of Turner echoes the same thoughts:

'In a wildly magnificent enthusiasm, he rushes through the aethereal dominions of the world on his own mind — a place inhabited by the spirits of things; he has filled his mind with materials drawn from the close study of nature and their changes and combines, giving effect without absolute causes, seizing the soul and essence of beauty without regarding the means by which it was effected'.

Freedom of self-expression in the plastic arts became a living force at the turn of the century when the precepts of Modern Art were enunciated by Albert Aurier, writing on Gauguin in 1891. He felt that a work of art should be:

1. Ideative, since its sole aim should be the expression of the Idea;
2. Symbolist, since it must express this idea in forms;
3. Synthetic, since it will express these forms and signs in a way that is generally comprehensible;
4. Subjective, since the object will never be considered merely as an object but as the indication of an idea perceived by the subject; and in consequence,
5. Decorative, since decorative art is nothing other than an art at once synthetic, symbolist and ideative.

An even broader statement which can be equally applied to abstract art, art brut, object trouvé and even to forms of anti-art is that of Gombrich: 'Art, like music, certainly does more than simply restate the intellectual message. In clothing it with forms, it also modifies and articulates the thought'.

From acceptance of the belief that a work of art is a perception presented in material form, it will be appreciated that psychological insight into the workings of the mind can provide a door through which to seek a deeper understanding of the inspiration behind the creation of many works of art. A great many artists have been regarded as eccentric, not a few mad, and yet others have been overwhelmed by horrendous experiences. Could their dreams, visions, fantasies, nightmares, delusions and hallucinations have contributed to their highly developed talents for artistic imagination and characterisation? However, before we accept at their face value examples where there is a recognised or presumed association with such experiences, it is, alas, necessary to temper our enthusiasm and allow the cynic within us to make us aware of potential pitfalls and present a few caveats.

The philosopher, Bertram Russell, in the Analysis of Mind (1921) comments that:

'Behaviourists say that the talk they have to listen to can be explained without supposing that people think. Where you might expect a chapter on thought processes you come instead upon a chapter on the language of habit. It is humilitating to find how terribly adequate this hypothesis turns out to be'.

Even the most famous artists throughout the ages are not exempt from this stricture. They are no less lazy than the rest of us. The art of copying is easier than that of evocation. Consciously or unconsciously they borrow to circumvent the need for thought. Artists use models to paint a portrait, a still life or a landscape; in seeking inspiration they turn to folklore, legend and literature.

In the hierarchy of the arts, music is the most ethereal and all arts aspire to the condition of music; but in practical terms poetry, more so than prose, has reigned supreme, providing the source and inspiration for the major movements in music, painting and sculpture, notably for the Romanticists, Symbolists, Pre-Raphaelites and Surrealists. Among leading painters, Michelangelo, the Rossettis, Blake, Arp, Dali and Picabia were also poets. The Surrealists applied 'automatism' or 'the dictation of thought without control of the mind' to their poetry before extending similar techniques of expression to the visual arts. As already stated, much of the symbolism we recognise in the visions of the early saints amounts to little more than the application of conventional signs and objects by which each particular saint was recognised. Similarly, much of the complexity of the pictorial language of modern art is contrived, furnished from an astonishing familiarity with psychiatry, orthodox and otherwise (Dali), mythology (Masson) and the traditional signs of magic (Brauner, Seligman). Disaster pictures, particularly shipwrecks, may have been born of the experiences of hullucinatory imaginings of Vernet and other; but once they had achieved a popularity they found continued favour as part of the stock trade of Romantic art, exploited and vulgarized by the market. Turner, among others, is criticised for his sensationalism and lack of realism — though as Patrick Trevor-Roper (1970) explains in *The World Through Blunted Sight,* Turner's increasing use of vivid yellows and reds was the result not just of their availability as newly developed tints, but to the diffraction of light through the opacities and cataracts of the ageing eye.

Above all, artists have learnt from and copied the work of earlier masters, sometimes applying different techniques, but copying their ideas nonetheless. Rubens, Seurat, Cézanne, Poussin, Manet, Picasso and Bacon have borrowed, translated or paraphrased Michelangelo, Francesca, Delacroix, Titian, Giorgione, Negro art and Velàsquez. In art, said Gauguin, there are only revolutionists or plagiarists. The young Micheal Ayrton in an essay, *The Master of Pastiche* (1944), which he has only partly retracted, was bold enough to castigate the work of Picasso as cooking, not art:

'Picasso engulfs an existing formula, choosing, it seems, at random from the history of his art. It may be Negro sculpture, Greek vase painting, or the drawings of Ingres. The formula, once digested, he regurgitates, like the albatross feeding her young, accentuating certain characteristics and obliterating others... His constant, mercurial changes of style, which are today extolled as the fruits of a unique and all embracing genius, are not a genuine development but superlative conjuring. He is a master technician and his many 'periods', whilst they may not accord with the development of a real vision are at least in accord with the prevailing hysteria of the times'. (This description runs contrary to others which emphasise the almost hallucinatory nature of the processes whereby Picasso selected and developed his subject matter).

We should not decry all copying as the absence of art. Who but Francis Bacon could 'paraphrase' Velàsquez's Portrait of Pope Innocent X with such horrific brilliance? How was van Gogh able to copy in exact detail and perspective Millet's The Cornfield and yet add something of van Gogh's own style? How was van Gogh able to take a common chair, inexactly drawn and painted in drab colours, and yet make it a work of art? The perception behind such works is undoubtedly present in heightened form but its interpretation defies description.

The major caveat is not that we should discard works of art because their origin is suspect, but that we are limited because so often we are unable to fathom the origin of a work of art's projected content. The theme of wonderment remains and we must accept that man's perceptions are not bound by organs of perception; 'He perceives more than sense (tho' ever so acute) can discover' (Blake). In medicine, as in art, the term hallucination (which will be definded in the next chapter) is not confined to the abnormal. André Breton was able to describe Max Ernst as possessing the most magnificently haunted brain at work today; and hallucinations and illusions as not a negligible source of pleasure, the confidences of madmen, but scrupulously honest. There is a paradox whereby passive or real experiences from nightmares, delirium, neuroses, psychoses or intoxications can be reproduced artistically as exact representations of the form in which they appeared, whereas experiences actively conjured by the fertile mind, artificially created from thoughts, dreams and crystal gazing, need a heightened presentation involving the fullest use of the artist's sophisticated techniques. A further paradox is that the dream content of the imaginative experience of most normal healthy children is more replete and varied than the less ephemeral but stereotyped experiences of the psychotic.

'Imagination outstrips all the world's magicians; it not only places the real before our eyes in a vivid image and makes distant things present, but also, with a power more potent than that of magic, it draws that which does not exist out of the state of potentiality, gives it a semblance of reality, and makes us see, feel and hear these new creations' (Bodmer, 1741).

Chapter Three

Mind Stuff: Its Nature and Reality

'Our knowledge of the visible world lies at the root of all the difficulties of Art'.
Ruskin

THOUGHT depends on two dynamic processes, perception and imagery. Perception is the active gathering and selection of information from the external world. The reality of the percept is then tested by matching against earlier memory traces. Imagery relates to the further processing, storage and retrieval of the information and is defined as an experience that receives or copies a previous perceptional experience in the absence of the original sensory stimulus. Knowing is a prerequisite to seeing and strongly determines what we see. In effect, we perceive only what we can conceive and any rigid distinction between imagery and perception becomes artificial.

The least sophisticated form of thought, and evolutionary the most primitive, is the thought that remains as an exteriorised perception. Such a percept differs from normal sensations in being more persistent and presented in heightened detail. Next in sophistication is the internal but reality-adjusted thought which we might designate as a 'clear' thought and, lastly, fantasy or abstract thought. Fantasy or abstract thought adds considerably to the mental imagery of most individuals, providing thought-vehicles for reasoning, for memory and for the processing of sensory data as when reading rapidly. The quality of visual imagery varies from person to person with every inflexion from achromatic silhouettes to the vivid recollection of colours and hues. According to Galton, people may be categorised into those whose thoughts are principally visile and those whose thoughts are principally audile. He originally used the word 'eidetic' to describe visile thoughts but the term has come to be applied specifically to exteriorised imagery seen in great detail. Thus a strong visualiser with eidetic or crystal imagery may see the image in front of his eyes, as might an artist painting a portrait from memory. Most people with so-called photographic memories reinforce their visual impressions by means of associations; with true eideticism the thought-object has to be seen in actuality and cannot be processed from visual to auditory memory. Very few adults retain eidetic memories. These essentially rigid memory systems are found mainly in children below 11 years of age and in only 1-10% of children above that age. When put to the test, what initially appears to be an exact and complete graphic memory is invariably found to be beset with flaws. Because an eidetic image does lend itself readily to translation into more pliable forms of thought, it has been considered to be a possible factor in children with specific learning difficulties, as, for example, in children with dyslexia. An adept reader, when reading rapidly, takes a jumble of incomplete clues, sequences them, tests them against related memory clues, and then processes them through reality-adjusted thought. When concentrating on a book or a lecturer, thoughts are most likely to take the form of brief, achromatic silhouettes. If interest is lost, the thought processes may be diverted by other thoughts in the shape of completed, highly flavoured images.

Thought processes vary with the alertness or attention of the subject. Few people can maintain the same level of concentration; and disturbances of the mechanisms of thought are frequent but are probably minimised by the mind's own capacity to ignore that which appears unreal. However, percepts or images subjected to intrusive alterations may take on new forms:

as a DELUSION, a false belief impervious to reason;

as an ILLUSION, a misinterpretation of the form of the external stimulus; or

as an HALLUCINATION, a perception in the absence of an external stimulus.

Delusions are often regarded as alien notions that have captured the mind of that person. Examples include that of the man who dare not micturate lest he flood the whole world, or the lady who believes she is Mary, Queen of Scots. Such beliefs only become abnormal if they remain unnatural when measured against the individual's socio-cultural background. If a non-conformist minister born before the end of the 19th century declared from the pulpit that he always felt he had an angel on his shoulder he would have evoked no more comment than a few Amens from the High Seat. It would not be so with a present day clergyman but it was acceptable for a man who travelled the oceans on a raft to entitle a book published in 1966 *An Angel on Each Shoulder.* If I were to explain that I do not smoke, because by inhaling I would be polluting my god, you would look askance; but this is a tenet of the Parsee religion.

Illusions, the conscious or unconscious misinterpretation of the form of external stimuli, provide much of the unexpected in art. The conjuring of visions from natural objects (pareidolia) to stimulate conscious imagery has long been an acceptable and recognised device. Story-tellers have found the theme for a tale by gazing upon a burning fire, artists have seen visions in clouds and soothsayers in tea leaves. Leonardo advised painters to seek chance inspiration from puddles or stars. Bronzino (Agnolo di Cosimo) visited the Florence hospital of his day to draw ideas from the marks of spittle on the walls of its wards. Alexander Cozens (1786) used ink blots as a 'new method for assisting the invention in drawing original compositions of landscapes' and, later, Rorschach was to use similar blobs to probe disorders of thought processes among the psychiatrically ill. Salvador Dali's paranoic art makes great use of tricks in contour, colour or perspective to allow a double or even triple interpretation from a single object.

> *'Sometimes we see a cloud that dragonish,*
> *A vapour sometime like a bear or lion,*
> *A tower'd citadel, a pendant rock,*
> *A forked mountain or blue promontory*
> *With trees upon it, that nod into the world*
> *And mock our eyes with air . . .'*
>
> Shakespeare: *Anthony and Cleopatra:* act iv: scene 14.

The Latin hallucinatio or alucinato means to dream, to talk idly, or to wander mentally and was first used in English by Lavater in 1572 to refer to apparitions — ghostes and spirites walking by night. The modern term hallucinations, describing the apparent perception of an external object when no such object is present, provides a differentiation from illusions which are distortions (or transpositions) of perceptive data, and from delusions, which are false beliefs impervious to reason. The term is less successful in crystallising the unusual nature of the experience as distinct from special kinds of mental imagery which are perceived but evaluated as fictitious (pseudohallucinations).

Differences in the degree of insight or substantiality, the presentation in external objective space or internal subjective space, the consciousness of the real environment, and the ego content of the event have all been invoked to separate psuedohallucinations from hallucinations proper. Thus, it is claimed that a pseudohallucination is usually ego-centric and arises as a result of cogitation, e.g. wishing a dream to continue; true hallucinations are perceptions of a memory abnormally released or excited by an unusual stimulus, possibly due to instability of brain cells. Three examples of my own from schizophrenic patients will suffice to explain just how difficult it may be to quantify the degree of insight.

(a)   A worker on a production line started to hear voices. He knew they were nonsensical because they kept telling him to work overtime.

(b)   A deaf patient saw a figure he called Molly, who signed to him. The doctors were trying to persuade him to stay in the unit; he wanted to leave to go to London. In desperation they asked what Molly said. He signed to her and she signed back, 'Stay here'.

(c)   The assessment of the degree of insight may rest heavily upon the examiner. One patient described two hallucinations. She saw St. Theresa who said that she would go to Heaven and she felt elated. She also saw the devil who said she would go to Hell and she then became depressed. The social worker, a nun, was asked what supportive treatment should be given. She answered, 'Send for the priest'.
'What for?'
'To exorcise the devil.'
'What about St. Theresa?'
'Oh, that's just lovely'.

Presumably, the devil was an hallucination and the saint a pseudohallucination!

Hallucinations, pseudohallucinations and illusion may impinge upon the consciousness of normal people in dreams, in hypnagogic states (falling off to sleep or just waking), in wish-fulfilment hallucinations of the bereaved, under stress or sensory deprivation, or as organic symptoms of illness — the phantom limb phenomenon following amputation, or from spontaneous, central pain. Most British psychiatrists now favour the American usage of word hallucinations in its broad, lay sense to cover dreams, hypnagogic experiences, and other forms of imagery. Only if the term hallucinations is used in a restricted sense can there be said to be a proper place of pseudohallucination, and if so there is no word left to cover other subjective sensory experiences such as tinnitus (noises heard in the ears or head) which are also interpreted normally.

The traditional view of European psychiatrists, especially, was that all fantasy was abnormal and that 'true' hallucinations were frankly pathological, occurring only in specific circumstances as with organic or psychotic disease of the nervous system due to intoxication or with pathological disturbances of sleep. Whilst it was accepted that some children developed a high flown fantasy life, their hallucinations were presumed to express repressed experiences, wishes and conflicts too painful to the social ideal to be allowed the usual free conscious outlets. Deprived children, problem children and high grade defectives indulged in such behaviours at times when the environmental stress became overwhelming. These behaviours represented either a compensation for unsatisfactory reality or a regression to more primitive experiences. From the 1930s, a contrary view began to gain acceptance, namely that fantasy play provides a normal process whereby the child prepares himself for the future rather in the manner of a playful kitten who stalks and attacks inanimate objects to become a champion mouser at a later age. Fantasy in childhood according to this theory is not an escape but an approach to reality with the function of strenghthening inadequate knowledge by acting out a hypothetical scene. There is increasing evidence that normal people can and do experience hallucinations. In childhood this is a universal attribute which we eliminate in the process of social adjustment as we grow older. The wealth of literature describing imagery companions in childhood far exceeds that of the more sinister döppelganger of later life.

The imaginative experiences of normal people often contain a simple hallucinatory content. McKellar, a psychologist working in Aberdeen, found that as many as 76% of people questioned admitted to sensations of falling, 69% sometimes had *deja vu* sensations of undue familiarity, 63% hypnagogic images when falling asleep, 21% hypnopompic images when walking, and other experiences found in 30% of people included various forms of synaesthesia*.

---

*Deja vu. 'We have all some experience of a feeling which comes over us occasionally of what we are saying and doing having been said or done before, in a remote time — of our having been surrounded, dim ages ago, by the same faces, objects, and circumstances — of our knowing perfectly what will be said next, as if we suddenly remembered it'. Charles Dickens. *'David Copperfield'*.

To explore hallucinations further is to enter the realm of metaphysics — the science of the primary principles of human knowledge and that which determines the ultimate meanings, foundations and limits of our beliefs. It is necessary to discuss the reality of perception and the nature of matter. Higher forms of life make use of a variety of biological sensors in order to extract information from their surroundings and to communicate among themselves. The most commonly used sensors are visual, acoustic, tactile and olfactory; and our knowledge of the world about us depends entirely upon the perceptions gleaned through these mechanisms. These perceptions are so important to us that without them there would be no concept of 'self' or of substance — to quote David Hume (1711-76):

'There is no impression of self and therefore no idea of self. For my part, when I enter most intimately into what I call myself, I always stumble on some particular perception or other, of heat or cold, light or shade, love or hatred, pain or pleasure. I never catch myself at any time without a perception and never observe anything but the perception'.

Our world is a visual, auditory, tactile, olfactory world and little else. However, other animals can use alternative biological systems to gain perceptions of their surroundings: bats by sonar techniques, certain fish by electric field scanning and sensing, some snakes by temperature scanning and silkworms by chemical sensing. As Franc Marc said in relation to art: 'How does a horse see the world?' Can a bat be hallucinated by a spontaneous or disturbed sonar perception or an electric eel by an illusory current?

It is necessary to apply metaphysics to avoid the assumption that all our perceptions are exact and what we see, hear or touch has the substantive or concrete attribute we suppose. Take a diagram of a brick:

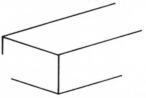

Hypnagogic hallucinations. Classically take the form of a feeling that someone is in the room beside the sleeper. The sensation may be one of movement, sound or shape. Hypnagogic images are often geometrical forms, nature scenes, noises, all experienced when going off to sleep. Hypnopompic applies to similar sensations at the time of waking, though the term has also been used to describe the perseveration of images as can happen after driving through fog all day so that one may see oneself passing along foggy roads as one tries to sleep. Both hypnagogic and hypnopompic imagery are similar in type and take the form of microdreams like a rapidly flickering lantern show, rather than as a continuous cine film.

Synaesthesia. Usually applies to the mixing of different modalities of sensation. Colour associations may link numbers subconsciously with different colours, the days of the week may be seen as a pattern with a trough on Monday and high spots on other days (diagram forms), modalities of sensation may merge into one another and two images appear from one sensory stimulus, e.g. colour hearing as with Scriabin's orchestral composition *Prometheus,* complete with a keyboard of coloured lights.

Here the brick is illustrated as an illusion because when we look at an object not everything is in focus and we add subconsciously to the incomplete image. We know it is a brick because we can perceive its shape with our eyes and we have an impression of its feel, solidity and weight without touching it by the application of past experience of similar objects. We assume that it is solid but we cannot perceive the inner part of it. That space is metetherial. We can assume that the brick is physically there; but the image may appear just as plain and substantive if it were reflected in a mirror. What are we then assuming? In that case it is no more than an apparition, occupying metetherial space. What then is Matter?

Bertrand Russell supplied the answer:

'For ought we know an atom may consist entirely of the radiations which come out of it. It is useless to argue that radiations cannot come out of nothing . . . The idea that there is a little hard lump there, which is the electron or proton, is an illegitimate intrusion of common sense notions derived from touch . . . "Matter" is a convenient formula for describing what happens where it isn't.'

That scientists should contemplate the insubstantiality of matter recalls the Pneumatistic concepts of primitive people worldwide. In primitive mysticism and in the art of primitive peoples the term 'pneuma', or its equivalent*, is used repeatedly to represent a psychophysically undifferentiated spirit or soul, a breath or bodily exhalation. Do we therefore exist upon waves? Koestler, in his book the *The Sleepwalkers, a History of Man's changing Vision of the Universe,* sees 'waves' as the ultimate answer which modern physics has to offer:

'These waves, on which I sit, coming out of nothing, travelling through a non-medium of multidimensional non-space, are the ultimate answer modern physics has to offer to man's question after the nature of reality. The waves that seem to constitute matter are interpreted by some physicists as completely immaterial "waves of probability" marking out "disturbed area" where an electron is likely to "occur". (They are as immaterial as the waves of depression, loyalty, suicide, and so on, that sweep over a country.) From here there is only one step to calling them abstract, mental or brainwaves in the Universal Mind — without irony'. The irony of the 'nonsense of the universe' was very much the basis of the tentative philosophy upon which Giorgio de Chirico developed his metaphysical art *(pittura metafisica)* which relied upon unusual ambiguities of objects and strange architectural perspectives to create an atmosphere of mystery

---

*Pneuma.

Atua — Polynesia
Bali — Bornea
Bukura — Costa Rica
gnama — Africa
ndjaka — Bantu
nikissi — Fiort
Orenda, maniton, wakanda — American Indian
nirvana — Sanskrit

and hallucination:

> 'A work of art must stand completely outside human limitations; logic and commonsense are detrimental to it. Thus it approximates to dream and infantile mentality . . . One of the strongest sensations left to us by prehistory is that of presage. It will always be with us. It is as it were an eternal proof of the nonsense of the universe'.

Yet more metaphysical would appear to be the writing of the scientist Eddington:

> 'The stuff of the world is mind-stuff. The mind-stuff is not spread in space and time; these are part of the cyclic scheme ultimately derived out of it. But we must presume that in some other way or aspect it can be differentiated into parts. Only here and there does it rise to the level of consciousness but from such islands proceeds all knowledge. Besides the direct knowledge contained in each self-knowing unit, there is inferential knowledge. The latter includes our knowledge of the physical world'.

Most scientists and most artists are less abstract but the concept of the neutrino which can pass through any form of matter still exists. Whilst accepting that there may be 'lumps of matter', the scientific writer, Lyall Watson, states that even so, there is proportionally as much empty space inside the atom as there is in the universe. We are hollow men' (as might be represented by Henry Moore or Barbara Hepworth) 'and our insubstantial bodies are strung together with electromagnetic and nuclear forces that do no more than create the illusion of matter'. Is it by reminding us of our insubstantiality that Moore is able to produce objects of art 'with a vitality of their own, a pent-up energy and an intense life', or Hepworth 'project into a plastic medium renewal of our sense of mystery and our imagination in the contemplation of Nature'?

Any attempt to explain hallucinatory phenomena would be incomplete without a brief reference to Mass Hallucinations, about which very little has been written. The Royal Psychic Society (some 70 years ago) reported that out of 1,087 visual experiences, 9% or 95 were collective hallucinations, i.e. seen by more than one person. The data as presented does not allow for the chance factor that other people were present at the time. The possibility of a collective experience in fact arose on only 283 occasions; so that the 95 collective experiences represent about one-third of the occasions where this was possible. For auditory experiences a similar state of affairs appertained. Out of 493 auditory hallucinations, others were present on 94 occasions and the hallucinations were collective on 34 occasions, i.e. a third of those possible and 7% of the total. Very often, a collective hallucination is later found to have a simple physical explanation such as a mirage or illusion and theologians have long since come to terms with the fact that many so-called miracles were due to physical events which have added to the their authenticity by enabling them to be historically dated (e.g. the crossing of the Red Sea). Magicians may spell-bind an audience into accepting that the seemingly impossible is occurring. A good example is the Indian Rope Trick where the audience is collectively persuaded, as if by hypnosis, to accept the illusion that there is a boy climbing a rope. The Royal Psychic Society believed that the most likely explanation for collective apparitions is that there are sensory hallucinations which can be telepathically induced and are akin to hypnosis. Certain manifestations are common to most forms of collective experience. The presentation may be spatial, with the apparition behaving as though aware of their surroundings, coming and going without leaving a physical trace and inhibiting the normally perceived background behind them as though fading into it as it re-emerges again. Each perceiving individual is left with a sense of cold or chill, suggesting a possible hypothalamic disturbance. So little is known that it is perhaps best to allow this explanation to stand until otherwise accounted for. The experience of individuals who have had complex scenic hallucinations has often indicated a coexistent physical event which has left them stultified, requiring a prolonged convalesence. No artist has laid claim to quite such a dramatic experience as that of St. Paul. Was Schopenhauer right to describe 'dreams as brief madness and madness as a long dream'?

A summary of the essence of this chapter, setting forth the relationship between normality and abnormality of imaginative experiences, is well provided for by De Chirico (1919) on Metaphysical Art:

'A continuous control is needed of our thoughts and of all those images which come to our minds when we are awake but which have, nonetheless, a close relationship to those we encounter in dreams. It is a curious fact that no dream image, strange as it may seem, strikes us with metaphysical force. We therefore refrain from seeking the source of our creation in dreams. Although the dream is a very strange phenomenon and an inexplicable mystery; far more inexplicable is the mystery and aspect our minds confer on certain objects and aspects of life. Psychologically speaking, to discover something mysterious in objects is a symptom of cerebral abnormality related to certain kinds of insanity. I believe, however, that such abnormal moments can be found in everyone, and it is all the more fortunate that they occur in individuals with creative talents or with clairvoyant powers. Art is the fatal net which catches these strange moments on the wing like mysterious butterflies, fleeing the innocence and distraction of common man'.

Chapter Four

The Experiences of Sensory Deprivation

SENSORY deprivation, to many people, is an enigma, something they feel they should know about, a phrase increasingly bandied over the media and in conversation, but something imperfectly understood. Stimulation reaching the brain comes from our sense organs and from our skin, feet, hands, mouth, bladder and intestines. These and other afferent stimuli are selected and filtered so that a particular stimulus may arouse or guide a specific response, but both selected and unselected stimuli have a collective function in maintaining the normal waking organisation of brain function. Sensory deprivation is an unnatural situation and causes an almost total perceptual void which may be clouded by poorly selected thoughts and perceptions. Most of the anomalous experiences related to sensory deprivation come into the realm of pseudohallucinations. Some are clearly illusional and dependent on the few remaining stimuli. This type of hallucinatory experience can be manipulated if suggestibility, stress, fear or wish-fulfilment are added in situations where normal stimuli are decreased or become distorted. Accidents and errors by long distance night truck drivers (highway hypnosis), jet pilots, and radar sentinels become more understandable when it is realised that they are caused by perceptual distortions and impaired attention and concentration that result from altered sensory stimulation (Ziskind, 1964).

During enforced sensory deprivation, normal human beings not suffering from any mental illness may report experiences akin to or identical with hallucinations. Whilst the level of sensation allows contact to be maintained, their unreality is recognisable; but when the state of partial or total deprivation is prolonged, the hold on reality is lost and the personality itself becomes disjointed. Finally, a frank psychosis can develop. Those concerned in brain-washing soon learned that the stages of disjointed personality and psychosis are reached more rapidly if, in addition to withdrawal of natural stimulation, the victim is hounded by artificial stimuli. Examples, modern and historical, include the use of continual monotonous whining sounds, water dripping on to the forehead of the prisoner as he is chained in a dungeon or blazing white light in the face as the interrogator drones on hour after hour destroying sleep. The term sensory deprivation, in these circumstances, is clearly a misnomer: sensory distortion or manipulation would be more correct. What is torture but the application of abnormal stimuli? The application of sensory deprivation is but an horrific sophistication.

An allusion was made to the paradox whereby true hallucinations provide pure representational art yet fantasy requires all possible technique and artifice to heighten its sensationalism. More so even than the nightmare, the experiences of sensory deprivation are depicted without artistic embellishment unless an artist has borrowed his subject matter from others, as did Jean-Louis Géricault in the Raft of the Medusa (1816).

Starving artists know that hunger* and sleeplessness can heighten their visual perceptions, illness and fever superadded more so, and intoxication after abstinence from food can have fearsome effects. The visions induced by fasting as an instrument of divination and purification have inspired St. John the Baptist, primitive and early religious painters, and acted as portents for the fledgeling warriors of the Blackfeet Indians. However, only one modern artist has sought to explore sensory deprivation as a conscious stimulus to his art. Peter Lanyon (1918-64), one of the St. Ives painters who quell the ravages of storms along the Cornish coast in lyrical oil painting, turned to the Constructivist techniques of Ben Nicholson and Naum Gabo showing the interface of sea and land in flatter juxtaposition. He then investigated the play of spatial volumes in intricate constructions and joined a gliding club (later dying in a gliding accident) to explore the sensations of flight and movement, the nature of air and the elements, combining them in abstract compositions such as 'Thermal' (Tate Gallery, 1960).

Christopher Nevinson (1889-1946), the First World War artist, tried to express in his pictures the sensation of flight, and the Italian Futurists, notably the painter and poet Filipino Murinetti, produced a Manifesto of Seropittura in 1929, attempting to describe on canvas and in poetry, r.g. 'Le Démon de la vitesse', the sensations induced by the technical phenomena of modern life, especially flying. The Futurists sought to portray the simultaneous representation of different phases of movement, the lines of force which expose the dynamic features of a given object, the combination of kinetic images and the interpretation of different levels of reality.

Explorer and artist share the search for new perceptions but hitherto solitude has rarely inspired art and, though we are all haunted by dread situations in illness, rape, robbery, kidnapping, terrorism, brain-washing and the mass experiences of war, we are inhibited by the psychic trauma they induce and too little art has penetrated these inhibitions. Prophets have emerged from the desert with new visions and new creeds. Is the Yeti, known to Everest explorers, a figment of the imagination, or, as Sherpa Tensing declares, a reality? Peoples of all lands have been possessed with Jinn, Latah, so that they run Amok. Kayakangst comes to the Arctic hunter out alone in his kayak on a featureless sea; there is a trance-like

---

*When painting Le Carnaval d'Arlequin, Miro was producing drawings in which he recorded hallucinations brought on by hunger.

lowering of consciousness from a kind of hypnosis along with curious kinaesthetic shifts in body image and ego. Such disorientation produces a deep fright; panic ensues with phobic and conversion symptoms. In the folklore of the high altitude Algonquin Indians wintering in the Rocky Mountain range, the unsuccessful hunter, afflicted with Windigo, returns without game, his mind commandeered by the spirit of a cannibal giant whose bones are made of ice, and, on entering the camp, gnaws chunks of flesh from the sleeping limbs of his mates. In past times the fear and power of the visionary guided the destiny of simpler souls. When threatened by persecution, Peter the Hermit subjected himself to isolation and fasting. His vision of Christ eventually inspired the First Crusade. Shamanism throughout the centuries used archaic techniques: isolation in caves, binding, beatings, burnings, amputation and surgical ordeals to promote hallucinatory visions among the mystical, primitive and insane. Hostage hallucinations is the modern phrase used to describe visual imagery induced by isolation and life threatening states today (Siegel, 1984). The 'Stockholm Syndrome' refers to the alliance that may form between terrorist and victim whereby both express a fear, distrust or anger towards authority outside the hostage situation. Hostage hallucinations may take a positive form as new visual perceptions or negative hallucinations with lapses of awareness.

The drama of the occasion may heighten the situation as with hi-jackings at sea, in buses, trains or in the air. A man, aged 52, and his 24 year old son were driving across the Arizona desert. It was noon when they heard a strange 'mechanical' noise in the full glare of the sun. They were blinded and paralysed by a brilliant flashing white light. As they left their car, they appeared to levitate into the air and independently described floating down a long tunnel-like corridor constructed of gleaming metallic lattice work. They perceived a bright light at the end of the corridor and entered a gleaming, illuminated room where they saw the vague outlines of humanoid creatures behind the lights. They experienced a flashback in their past lives and, convinced that they had been abducted by a UFO, came to, sitting on the bonnet of their car, seven hours later, in the dark of night. Was this an isolated event, a 'folie à deux', related to the father's earlier mental illness? It is but one of at least six 'authenticated' reports of UFO abductions, supported by abundant literature. Grinspoon and Persky (1972) suggest that under severe stress individuals can regress to primal modes of magical/mythical thinking, including the perception of archetypal geometrical forms which then become the observed UFO. C. G. Jung (1958) also suggests that flying saucers are just such archetypal images. Historically, UFO abduction is no new phenomenon. The earliest account of a hostage experience was given in 593 B.C. by the Babylonian priest, Ezekiel. The Book of Ezekiel reports several journeys which Ezekiel made in an authentic space ship of ideal shape and type, passing the scrutiny of space mission engineer at Cape Kennedy, J. F. Blumrich (1974). Menzel and Taves (1977) regard Ezekiel's experience, if other than allegorical, as the result of hallucinations induced by staring at solar haloes.

Sensory deprivation became a scientific study in order to understand and counter life-threatening situations, brain-washing, terrorism and weightlessness in space. Following the Korean War, when brain-washing of prisoners became a major issue, McGill University in Canada became the main centre for research; and, as with all good scientific endeavour, the study commenced with an historical survey of the recognisable effects of isolation.

Among genetic phenomena is that of balanced polymorphism whereby the homozygous sufferers of a disease are balanced by the advantageous survival of the heterozygous carriers of that trait. Thus in West Africa, sickle cell anaemia may lead to early death but the sickle cell trait increased resistance to the malarial parasite. Likewise, it has been suggested that the schizoid trait (as opposed to schizophrenia) enables people to exist in the remote parts of the world and there are many instances of such people accepting psychotic experiences and hallucinations as a fact of life. Brownfield (1965) cites several examples. Norwegians living north of the arctic circle more or less accept psychotic experiences so long as the person does not destroy himself or someone else. Eskimo fishermen may hallucinate or lapse into a trance without hope of getting back if they venture out to sea alone. Skin divers can be overcome by 'the rapture of the deep' if working alone. And the Truk Islanders of the Western Pacific rather expect to see ghosts if they go out alone at night.

Many historical accounts of lone voyagers and explorers have provided evidence of hallucinatory experiences; thus Jean Merrian, The Solitary Navigator (1954), collected 185 instances of psychotic episodes — one of the earliest and best known being that of Captain Joshua Slocum (1900) who became ill whilst sailing from the Azores to Gibraltar:

'I set sail from Horta early on July 24th . . . Passing the island of Pico, after the rigging was mended, the 'Spray' stretched across to leeward of the island of St. Michael's, the wind blowing hard.

Since reaching the islands I had lived most luxuriously on fresh bread, butter, vegetables and fruits of all kinds. Plums seemed the most plentiful on the Spray, and these I ate without stint. I had also a Pico white cheese that General Manning, the American consul-general, had given me, which I supposed was to be eaten, and of this I partook with the plums. Alas, by night-time I was doubled up with cramps. The wind, which was already a smart breeze, was increasing somewhat, with a heavy sky to the south west. Between cramps I got the mainsail down, hauled up the earrings as best I could, and tied away point by point, in the double reef. I am a careful man at sea, but this night, in the coming storm, I swayed up my sails, which, reefed though they were, were still too much in such heavy weather; and I saw to it that the sheets were securely belayed. In a word, I should have laid to, but did not. I gave her the double-reefed mainsail and the whole jib instead, and set her on her course. Then I went below, and threw myself upon the cabin floor in great pain. How long I lay there I could not tell, for I became delirious. When I came to, as I thought, from my swoon, I realised that the sloop was plunging into a heavy sea, and looking out of the companionway, to my amazement I saw a tall man at the helm. His rigid hand, grasping the spokes of the wheel, held them as in a vice. One may imagine my astonishment. His wig was that of a foreign sailor, and the large red cap he wore was corkbilled over his left ear, and all was set off with shaggy black whiskers. He would have been taken for a pirate in any part of the world. While I gazed upon his threatening aspect I forgot the storm and wondered if he had come to cut my throat.

This he seemed to divine, "Señor," said he, doffing his cap, "I have come to do you no harm". And a smile, the faintest in the world, but still a smile, played on his face which seemed not unkind when he spoke. "I have come to do you no harm, I have sailed free" he said, "but was never worse than a contrabandista. I am one of Columbus's crew" he continued. "I am the pilot of the Pinta come to aid you. Lie quiet, señor captain," he added, "and I will guide your ship tonight. You have a calentura, but you will be all right tomorrow." I thought what a very devil he was to carry sail. Again as if he read my mind, he exclaimed: "Yonder is the Pinta ahead; we must overtake her. Give her sail, give her sail, Vale, vale, my vale!" Biting off a large quid of black twist, he said: "You did wrong, captain to mix cheese with plums. White cheese is never safe unless you know whence it comes. Quiensabe, it may have been from leche de Capra, and becoming capricious."

"Avast, there!" I cried. "I have no mind for moralising."

I made shift to spread a mattress and lie on that instead of the hard floor, my eyes all the while fastened on my strange guest, who, remarking again that I would have "only pains and calentura", chuckled as he chanted a wild song:

> *High are the waves, fierce, gleaming,*
> *High is the tempest roar!*
> *High the sea-bird screaming!*
> *High the Azore.*

I suppose I was now on the mend, for I was peevish, and complained: "I detest your jingle, Your Azore should best roost, and would have been were it a respectable bird!"

Great seas were boarding the Spray, but in my fevered brain I thought they were boats falling on deck, that careless draymen were throwing from wagons on the pier to which I imagined the Spray was now moored, and without fenders to breast her off. "You'll smash your boats" I called out again and again as the seas crashed on the cabin over my head.

I found then my pains and calentura had gone, that the deck, now as white as a shark's tooth from seas washing over it, had been swept of everything moveable. To my astonishment, I saw now at broad day that the Spray was still heading as I had left her, and going like a race horse. Columbus himself could not have held her more exactly on course. The sloop had made 90 miles in a night through rough seas. I felt grateful to the old pilot, but I marvelled some that he had not taken in the jib.

I was getting much better now, but was very weak, and did not turn out reef that day or the night following although the wind fell light; but I just put my wet clothes out in the sun when it was shining, and lying down there myself, fell asleep. Then who should visit me again but my old friend of the night before, this time, of course, in a dream. "You did well last night to take my advice", said he, "and if you would, I should like to be with you often on the voyage, for the love of adventure alone". Finishing what he had to say, he again doffed his cap and disappeared as mysteriously as he came, returning, I suppose, to the Phantom Pinta.'

Admiral Richard Byrd, *Alone, A Classic of Endurance* (1938), isolated for six months in a small hut in Antarctica, developed psychotic obsessions and hallucinations until he realised that they were triggered by carbon monoxide poisoning from the tunnel vent of his shelter. Christine Ritter (1954), *A Woman in the Polar Night,* describes how on Spitzbergen at various times she saw a monster and heard ski strokes in the snow when no one was evident. She felt a monomania to get out over the snow and expose herself, describing feelings 'as though her imprisoned senses circled in the past in scenes without spatial dimensions'. Once depersonalised, she and her companions 'were dissolving in moonlight as though it were eating us up. The light seemed to follow us everywhere . . . Neither the walls of the hut nor the roof of snow could dispel my fancy that I am moonlight itself'. And Walter Gibson (1953) in relating the story of survivors after their boat had been torpedoed in the Indian Ocean in World War II, states that almost everyone hallucinated scenes of rescue and drank sea water thinking it were fresh. We began to dream — fierce, vivid dreams — of food and drink and friendly gatherings. We would compare these dreams and nearly all of them had points in common.

A very different approach to these complex phenomena is provided by Albert Heim (1892) who accumulated accounts of more than 30 survivors of falls in the Alps. He claimed that in every instance a similar mental state developed — calm seriousness, profound acceptance, mental quickness and a sense of surety. The survey, with its laid-back title, 'Remarks on Fatal Falls' was published in the Yearbook of the Swiss Alpine Club.

According to Francis Galton (1883), some leaders experience an isolation in their solitary position, and in Napoleon's case it took on an hallucinatory form: General Rapp recalled an occasion when he entered Napoleon's hut whilst he was working. Napoleon seemed to be staring but, noticing the General, spoke excitedly: 'Look up there, what do you see? It is my star, it is before you, brilliant. It has never abandoned me. I see it on all great occasions, it commands me to go forward, and it is a constant sign of good fortune to me''.

The concept of sensory deprivation, as often partial as complete, with unusual stimuli which are misconstrued, has been found to apply widely in the modern world. Thus Bridgeman *(The Lonely Sky,* 1955) describes his feelings when flying at altitude:

'Fifty nine thousand, sixty thousand, reeling off sixty one thousand. I have left the world. There is only the ship to identify myself with, her vibrations are my own, I feel them as intensely as those of my body. Here is a kind of unreality mixed with reality that I cannot explain to myself. And with this adrenalin-inflicted states floats the feelings of detachment.'

According to Clark and Graybird (1957) this experience 'the break off phenomenon' affects up to 35% of jet pilots causing sensations of remoteness, loneliness, anxiety or elation, but above all a feeling of separation from earth.

What Galton called the 'maddening effect of solitude' is a cause of hallucinatory phenomena in patients with medical conditions, for example following surgery upon their eyes. One doctor provides a vivid description of his own experience of an ascending paralysis:

'The next few weeks were unpleasant. I had an indwelling catheter and no knowledge of bowel action. The severe pain continued. Several times I experienced a disturbed body image: I was convinced that my left leg was sticking up at an angle of about 45°. I could see my paralysed leg lying on the bed, but the sensation was so clear and so painful that more than once I asked nurses to pull my leg down for me. One vivid and distorted sensation occurred when I felt I was lying across two commodes. I could even "see" the pattern on the lid of one and "feel" the edge of each. My arms were too ataxic to try to feel the edge with my fingers and anyway I had no sensory perception so had to ask the nurse what I was lying on, which brought the response, "Nothing but the water bed". These distortions of body image, bizarre sensory disturbances, and repeated vivid memories made night especially long and unpleasant. Like a drowning man I saw the events of my life pass before me.'

Mendelson and Foley in 1956 described sensory deprivation as a particular hazard affecting nine patients with poliomyelitis treated in tank respirators (iron lungs). Well organised delusions and hallucinations occurred in overt forms after two to seven days and continued for 10 to 15 days. Recovery was independent of both motor function and continued existence in the respirator. Fear was not a factor, no drugs were given, and no metabolic aberrations could be demonstrated. Disorientation, particularly at night, was the common substrate. Psychomotor agitation rarely occurred and the content of the experiences could be pleasant or horrendous. The patients were able to recall their experiences vividly many weeks after the symptoms ceased although many were unable to recall events of their more lucid intervals in the respirators.

The major role of the McGill group has been to collate and structure the assessment of these phenomena. Student volunteers lay in a cubicle on a comfortable bed, wearing frosted goggles to exclude patterned vision, sponge rubber over their ears to reduce sound, and gloves and cuffs to allow free movement yet limiting tactile stimulation. Microphones and speakers permitted communication with the subjects. Most subjects found the experience unpleasant; they had difficulty in concentration and directional thought, and some reported visual imagery ranging from simple lines and figures through more complex wallpaper like patterns of integrated action three dimensional scenes. The majority recorded visual surface distortions, metamorpheses, and loss of constancy effects, and there were sometimes persistent after images. In a few cases these changes lasted for an hour or so beyond the experimental period. Other scientists, not confined to McGill, enlarged on this work. Dement found that the same effects could be induced by dream deprivation, producing not only hallucinatory effects, but also disrupting the personality. If random forms of visual stimulation were given to an otherwise sensory deprived individual, hallucinations would still develop, suggesting that the brain requires a continuous and meaningful contact with the outside world. And in a third study, a shorter period of sensory deprivation was needed to produce hallucinatory experiences provided that an element of suggestibility was added to the atmosphere of the test. Curiously, they reported that the number of visual sensory reactions was higher when there was a diffuse input of stimulation than when stimulation was totally restricted. Normal individuals reacted with more discomfort to the isolation procedure than did psychotic and schizophrenic patients.

With modern emphasis centred upon the hostage situation, the old work of Heim was revived by Noyes and Kletti in 1976. They collected 114 accounts of near death experiences from 104 persons and noted a strikingly similar pattern throughout. External time appeared slowed whilst inner time gathered increasing momentum, streams of thoughts and images passed through the mind within seconds. About half the total number involved experienced a lack of emotionality. Fear settled into calm as though a wall existed between their feelings and themselves until a state almost of elation was reached. They, the world, everything felt strange and unreal 'as if', 'as though'. In the words of a 19 year old mountaineer who had survived a fall he expected to be fatal: 'not only were my thought processes speeded up, but I was aware of a definite and intense deviation from normal consciousness. The intense fear and subconscious hope of survival instinctively forced a concentration of my thoughts on rescue efforts and a redirection of my whole mind on to whatever might be necessary to prevent the potential plunge. For example, if I had been cold, I would not have felt it. If I had been hurting myself, I would have felt no pain . . . My vision was very active and alert'. And a soldier whose jeep was blown up by a mine recalls: 'Almost immediately after the explosion, I was certain that death had occurred. I experienced no physical sensations, no sense perception. Rather I seemed to have entered a state in which only my thoughts or mind existed. I felt total serenity and peace. I had no remembrance of anything, only the realisation of time passing, only of one moment which never altered. Neither did I have any concept of space, since my existence seemed only mental. I cannot stress strongly enough the feeling of total peace of mind and of total blissful acceptance of my new status, which I knew would be never-ending'.

These experiences seem to us unreal. We are inured to them and to such thoughts as the hackneyed phrase, 'nothing concentrates the mind like the threat of execution'. The trauma of the children following the Chowchilla School Bus kidnapping has an altogether different effect upon us. A school bus containing 26 children from five to 14 years of age was halted at a road block by three masked men who took over the bus at gun point transfering the children to two blackened, boarded over vans in which they were driven about for 11 hours. They were then transferred to a 'hole' (actually a buried truck-trailer), and the kidnappers covered the truck-trailer with earth. The children were buried in the hole for 16 hours until two of the oldest and strongest boys (ages 10 and 14 years) dug them out. By then the kidnappers had left the vicinity. Over the succeeding year the parents of the children became increasingly alarmed by the personality changes and emotional turmoil of their children and a child psychiatrist undertook to examine them in detail. The children suffered from repetitive dreams, fears that a mundane situation would develop suddenly into something horrendous, and fears of future kidnappings. Their sleep continued to be disturbed by dreams. They would wake in terror with no recollection of the content of their disquietude. Some dreams had disguised themes with clear psychotological implications often incorporating a sense of dying, yet others were exact repetitions of the kidnapping events or modified repetitions with different kidnappers, victims, outcomes or settings.

The aftermath for both children and adults in such situations can be psychiatric sequelae including nightmares, recurrent unbidden images, startle reactions, inability to concentrate, uncontrolled anxiety, depression, hopelessness, apathy, anhedonia, and paranoia. Siegel (1984) examined the phenomenology of hostage situations, involving prisoners of war and victims of rape, kidnapping, terrorism and robbery. Although all suffered from stress, isolation and life-threatening situations, only 25 per cent experienced visual hallucinations. In the first place the hostage victims experienced a mixture of reactions to their environmental conditions. Isolation was not always complete and some hostages were able to create their own world and insulate themselves from surrounding pressures. Where entoptic phenomena appeared they could begin after as little as 15 minutes blindfolded as flashes of white lights in the corners of their visual fields. These flashes had amorphous configurations, appeared to pulsate or vibrate, and varied in duration from fractions of seconds to several seconds. Also in the periphery of their vision geometric patterns might appear moving in a horizontal plane. As they became more definite they were seen to include tunnels, lattices, symmetrical kaleidoscopic patterns, webs, and curved lines. Most patterns were located aproximately two feet in front of the eyes and were characterised by saturated colours, intense brightness and varied in apparent size. Complex visual hallucinations of recognisable objects, people and scenes appeared during the later stages after several hours or days. These images included small animals, insects, monsters, devils, police, mountain scenes, buildings, family members, friends and childhood memories. While the images were generally vivid, concrete and three dimensional, only two of the eight victims confused the images with reality.

On further analysis, it became clear that all the hostages who experienced hallucinations also reported sleep difficulties and felt continually fatigued yet aroused during their captivity. These are just those conditions most liable to conjure forth hypnagogic imagery and, indeed, all the described imagery could fit such a supposition.

Hallucinations in the Course of Battle

The major concern of hostages is survival. From a state of total well-being the victim in seconds finds himself in mortal peril. At first he cannot believe what is happening; he is stunned, disoriented, often paralysed with fear — but then he may also reflexly try to defend himself or escape. In situations of stress in war as the tension mounts the senses are alerted and the mind races. In retrospect, the children of the Chowchilla kidnapping searched for omens which might have saved them. As the circumstances become more impending the superstitions of the Armed Forces become more acute. The destroyer, H.M.S. Plymouth, was regarded as one of the luckiest ships of the Falklands war. As soon as she arrived in the South Atlantic a white dove flew out from land and perched on her superstructure. From then on, despite being in the thick of battle, the ship escaped serious harm, although she had many near misses and was 'hit' by bombs which failed to explode. Several Naval officers at Dunkirk gave firm assurance that while waiting to take troops from the beachhead they clearly heard what they knew as Drake's Drum:

> *'Drake he was a Devon man, an' ruled the Devon seas*
> *(Capten art tha sleepin' there below?),*
> *Rovin' tho' his death fell, he went wi' heart at ease,*
> *An' dreamin' arl the time o' Plymouth Hoe,*
> *"Take my drum to England, hand et by the shore,*
> *Strike it when your powder's runnin' low;*
> *If the Dons sight Devon, I'll quit the port o' Heaven,*
> *An' drum them up the Channel as we drummed them long ago".'*

Many accounts describe the hallucinatory or delusional episodes of the First World War. Most renowned are the appearance of the 'Angels of Mons' in late August 1914 and the 'White Cavalry' in July 1918. These quickly passed into fiction, e.g. Arthur Machen, *The Bowmen'*, substituded the bowmen of Agincourt for the Heavenly Host against the Prussian hordes, but there are many accounts which substantiate the original incidents.

Towards the end of August 1914 the German Army, sweeping all resistance aside, had advanced on a wide front into the heart of Belgium and France. The heaviest attacks were launched against the British; and the troops, greatly outnumbered, had been fighting continuously for several days, with little or no rest, and men were almost dropping from fatigue after a prolonged rearguard action during which men and guns had been lost. Serious defeat appeared inevitable.

A detachment of troops was retiring through Mons under heavy German artillery and machine gun fire and knelt behind a hastily erected barricade. The firing on both sides was very intense, and the air reverberated with deafening crashes of exploding shells.

Suddenly, firing on both sides stopped dead and a silence fell. Looking over the barrier, the astonished British saw four or five wonderful beings much bigger than men, between themselves and the halted Germans. They were white robed and bare headed, and seemed rather to float than stand. Their backs were towards the British, and they faced the enemy with outstretched arms and hands, as if to say: 'Stop, thus far and no further'. The sun was shining quite brightly at the time. Next thing the British knew was that the Germans were retreating in great disorder.

On another occasion the sky opened with a bright shining light and figures of 'luminous beings' appeared. They seemed to float between the opposing lines to prevent a further advance of the enemy.

In July 1918, a pocket of British troops were trapped near the area of La Bassée. Talk was of the German troops getting through to Paris. The enemy gun fire, largely directed at the town of Bethune, suddenly lifted and began to burst over a slight rise beyond the outskirts. This open ground was absolutely bare of trees, houses or human beings, yet the enemy gunfire broke on it with increasing fury, and was augmented by heavy bursts of massed machine guns which raked it backward and forward with a hail of lead. The enemy's fire suddenly ceased and a lark arose from the remains of a meadow and soared up, singing. A dense line of German troops, who a short time before had commenced a forward movement to victory, in mass formation, suddenly halted and broke into retreat. Shortly afterwards several prisoners were captured who testified to a brigade of cavalry coming up through the smoke towards them. They were described as colonial or Egyptian because of their white uniforms. As they surged forward, remorselessly, the Prussians had fled, panic striken.

There have been various explanations for these phenomena such as the effect of searchlight from both sides playing upon the dust and clouds.

Sensory Adjustment in Space

There are few hallucinary effects associated with man's venture into space. The brain and sense organs function well and there is actually an improvement in the acuity of vision. The sleep patterns of Skylab astronauts remained virtually unchanged and in the early American missions — Mercury and Gemini — motion sickness did not occur. The original astronauts were restrained in their couches, wore helmets which prevented quick head movements and the visual clues were adequate and plentiful. Only when freer movement was permitted as in the early Russian and later Apollo flights did the phenomenon of motion sickness appear in association with a sensation of twisting or tilting. The symptoms of motion sickness were clearly due to neural conflict between visual and vestibular stimuli but adapted and abated after about three days. A feeling of postural stability then occurred despite continued exposure to weightlessness as in Skylab.

The paradoxical improvement in visual acuity, so much so that astonauts at 100 km could see individual cars or count the ships in San Francisco harbour, remains a mystery. One hypothesis that the fine fixating movements of the eye are speeded in weightlessness because of reduced friction was not confirmed but there was evidence of a 25 per cent decrease in the chromatic perception for blue-green and purple, while that for red and other colours remained unaltered. Phosphenes in the form of flashes of light were experienced by a few astronauts, in most instances when passing through a belt of trapped cosmic radiation known as the South Atlantic Anomaly. To observe these light flashes, the astronaut had to be relaxed and dark adapted for at least ten minutes. Whitish flashes would appear when heavy ions or neutrons pass through a dielectric field at a speed greater than that of light to excite the retina directly or to produce a fluorescence within the vitreous humour (Cerenkov's effect).

The cosmonaut on the Moon sees a black sky set against zones of brilliance, 25 per cent brighter than any on earth. These lighting effects make the appreciation of the lunar landscape and distances difficult. To look at the sun, special phototropic goggles are necessary and the earth appears four times as big and eighty times as bright as the appearance of the Moon from Earth.

Chapter Five

Altered States of Consciousness

'Le Rêve est une seconde vie'.
Gerard de Nerval

We have some awareness of the neurophysiological functions of the mantle of cortex which covers the brain but little of the inner working of the brain. When we latch on to the psephismata of tabulated information, there is the ever present danger that we do so at the expense of an understanding of the broader perspectives of the function of the integrated nervous system. For in looking at the cortex — 'our roof-brain, the latest and crowning organ of our nervous system' (Sherrington, 1906) — we are, in all probability, being mesmerised by the complexity of the dashboard and ignoring the powerhouse under the bonnet. Thus, if we use dementia as an example, the disintegration of the intellect (dementia) has been defined in the past in terms of progressive loss of function of cortical cells. In actuality, loss of brain cells is extremely well compensated for socially; and dementia only becomes manifest where there are pathological changes affecting the co-ordinating fibres subserving behaviour, emotional responses and sleep patterns.

Similarly, the midbrain activating system is regarded as a small generator regulating the sleep/wake cycle. Consciousness, which implies an experience or 'concept' of self and depends upon perception, involves three active processes — arousal, intentionality and maintenance of attention. The specific functions which are connected with arousal, such as sleep, hunger and thirst, are represented as very small areas on the cortex but are decisively controlled by much more definite regions of the basal forebrain and midbrain, i.e. by phylogenetically older parts of the brain common to all vertebrates. Structures within these phylogenetically older areas such as the hypothalamus, thalamus, reticular formation and their cortical connections and association pathways excite or inhibit, chemically and electrically, the rest of the nervous system and open or close the gates to sensory stimulation whether from the body or from the sensory organs.

The older parts of the brain are also concerned with governing the rhythmicity of the body. Within the midbrain, the nucleus coeruleus controls the serotoninergic neurotransmitters involved in the sleep/wake cycle. The orchestrated control of hormones from the hypothalamic-pituitary axis produced a fluctuating release of chemicals to the blood stream, brain and elsewhere, which are only mildly influenced by extraneous forces such as daylight and darkness. There is an innate stability of these circadian rhythms. It matters not whether they are diurnal, monthly or of longer duration. The phases of growth, particularly puberty, set the patterns of the reticulo-hypothalamic activating system which is rarely seriously disturbed. Similarly the continuous process of filtering and selecting sensory information develops and matures from early infancy.

The patterning of these basic mechanisms, becoming more fixed as the individual adapts to the demands of adolescence and adult life, means that the nightmares of childhood become less frightening, lapses of vigilance become rarer, and aberrations leading to dissociated functioning of sensory processing, with dreams and hallucinations, are fewer and of shorter duration. Normal individuals may still experience falling or floating feelings and *deja vu,* but such phenomena are characterised by their brevity. Apart from brief *deja vu* or vestibular illusions the hallucinatory experiences of adults are commonly related to confusion, somnolence or altered consciousness. Sir John Walton (1977) summarises the aetiology of most hallucinations in one concise sentence: 'Psycho-physiologically' though hallucinations manifest themselves as changes in the content of consciousness, there is considerable evidence that they are often the result of disordered function of the reticulo-hypothalamic and associated pathways concerned with the state of consciousness as a whole'.

Examples of mild confusional states with hallucinosis may be seen in dementia, with space occupying tumours of the brain, blood clots, and abscesses, with or without involvement or the cortex, and with chemical changes either metabolically or drug induced. Even with states of stupor and coma, the brain remains remarkably resistant to illusory intrusions. Relaxation of vigilance is rarely total and we should regard sleep and even delirium not as passive but as active processes in which the nervous system responds to physiological or pathological changes of the body's microcosmic interior *(milieu interieur).*

Freud in *The Interpretation of Dreams* (1900) was one of the first to envisage sleep as an active, not as an inert, state. Sleep itself has a protective value, preventing exhaustion, conserving and replenishing energy stores. All vertebrates sleep. Only sharks (elasmobranchs) are denied sleep! Sleep deprivation leads to impaired coherence and performance. Silly mistakes, lapses of concentration and even of consciousness develop. It has been shown that astronauts and divers who need to work for prolonged periods in conditions that are not ideal for sleep, benefit psychologically and physically from brief periods of napping. The restorative value of deep or slow wave sleep (SWS) is readily understood, but that of REM (rapid eye movement), or paradoxical, sleep is less readily appreciated. REM sleep recurs 5 or 6 times per night, occupying 20% of the average total sleep duration. This is the segment of the complex heterogenous sleep process when sleep arrhythmias provoke fits, migraines, night terrors, enuresis and somnambulism. The body stirs and changes position. Spontaneous noctural emission and penile erections may develop. Dreaming occurs during REM sleep with the release of thought images that are visual and auditory in the proportion of 3:2. On average people dream for 2 hours nightly (Jung, 1954), and the rapid eye movements, like the less usual sleep talking (somniloquy), may indicate active participation in the world of dreams. Dement (1960) concludes from his experimental studies that dream suppression if carried on long enough could cause a serious disruption of the personality.

The vicariousness of dreams — moving, fleeting, shadowy — makes their recall particularly difficult and repeated awakenings are required for their scientific study. Reasonable recital occurs immediately after wakening but most dreams, unless the emotional content is strong, quickly fade from our minds. It is quite possible that an artist might train his mind to concentrate upon the dream imagery, thus Oskar Kokoschka, writing on the nature of visions (1912), advises that we must harken closely to our inner voice:

'The state of awareness of visions is not one in which we are either remembering or perceiving. It is rather a level of consciousness at which we experience visions within ourselves. This experience cannot be fixed for the vision is moving, an impression growing and becoming visual, imparting a power to the mind. It can be evoked but never defined. Yet the awareness of such imagery is a part of life. It is life selecting from the forms which flow towards it.'

There are reports in scientific journals which suggest that concentration upon dream imagery and attention to detail may augment the presence of colour in dreams. Kahn *et al* (1962) found that 70% of people had definitely coloured dreams and a further 17% vaguely coloured dreams whilst Schachter *et al* (1965) reported that 50% of art students, 16% of science students and 0% of engineering students experienced coloured dreams. Linn (1954) and Calef (1954) both connect colour in dreams with the super ego; but an Argentinian psychologist, Angel Garma (1961), attributes coloured dreams to repressed anal excremental contents, adding that this particular memory of coloured dreams can be connected with that of painting, which is also an expression of anal excremental instincts!

Pathological Disorders of Sleep

The study of pathological disorders of sleep is a relatively new science which has gained momentum in the past decade.

Encephalitis Lethargica

The epidemic of encephalitis lethargica which struck Europe between 1915 and 1921 had a major impact on the art scene. Egon Schiele (1890-1918) the distinctive Austrian expressionist painter of erotic and agitated figures, Harold Gilman (1876-1919), exponent of Synthetism and founder of the Camden Town Group, and Guillaime Appollinaire (1880-1918), champion of the Cubists and influential art critic who supported Orphism, the Futurists and the early Surrealists, all died of it; Giorgio Chirico (1888-1978) was mildly affected and Edvard Munch (1863-1944) painted his self portrait suffering from its effects and entitled 'Spanish Flu'. Many of that generation who were to develop Parkinson's disease in later life were undoubtedly its victims. The encephalitis could last days or years. According to Lord Brain (1955), the three most constant symptoms of the acute stage were headache, disturbances of sleep rhythm and visual abnormalities — usually blurred or double vision. The characteristic disturbance of sleep rhythm is lethargy by day with insomnia or restlessness at night. The lethargy has been sufficiently constant, especially in the early cases, to contribute the epithet 'lethargica' to the name of the disease. The patient can always be roused except when lethargy passes into coma. Neither lethargy by day nor insomnia by night are present in all cases. Either may dominate the diurnal picture throughout the twenty-four hours. Delirium and fever occur in the more severe cases.

Other wild fluctuations include alterations in behaviour and bodily habitas with variable changes in muscle tone so that a patient may pass from a statute-like catatonic rigidity or universal stiffness to complete freedom of movement within the 24 hour cycle. A patient with 'soldered' attitudes and inability to perform simple movements on request may get out of bed in the evening and do a few steps of a dance with ease and celerity, then relapse into her 'frozen' posture (Wilson, 1933). This variability may mark different periods of the day or night, or be induced by sundry intrinsic or extrinsic stimuli (emotion, agitation, commanding orders, etc.) whose mode of working is not clearly understood. Spasms and fluctuations may affect speech, breathing, eye movements, writing — sometimes with inertia, sometimes with hyperkinesia. The nightmares and hallucinations may show similar violent changes which are perhaps better understood when we examine the other sleep disorders of narcolepsy and sleep apnoea.

Narcolepsy

Uncontrollable episodes of day time sleep were first described by Westphal in 1877 but the full blooded narcoleptic syndrome where the patient may experience each or all of four cardinal symptoms — narcolepsy, sleep paralysis, cataplexy and hypnagogic hallucinations — is usually ascribed to Gelineau (1880). Narcolepsy was depicted by Melville in *Moby Dick;* a character with a 'species of exaggerated lethargy without ability to stir' almost certainly had sleep paralysis in Edgar Allan Poe's *The Premature Burial,* and David Livingstone, paralysed by fright as he was mauled by a lion, experienced profound cataplexy. The syndrome and its variations are relatively rare, probably involving 10,000 people in the United Kingdom and a proportionate number elsewhere. Episodes of sleep, rather than somnolence, may recur from 2 to 20 times a day, aften at inappropriate times and frequently as a result of monotony as when listening to a lecture. The sufferer may fall asleep whilst standing, eating or talking, can be roused easily, as from natural sleep, or may waken spontaneously, feeling refreshed after 10 to 20 minutes.

Cataplexy is a momentary inhibition of postural muscle tone — 'I felt weak at the knees with laughter' — caused by emotional stimuli. For some, the trigger can be slapstick, banana skin humour; for others it may be a subtle, wry joke. From the Sleep Disorder Clinic at Stanford University comes observations on longer lasting cataplectic episodes. If prolonged for a minute or more the immobility may be combined with a 'dream type of perception' integrated curiously into the reality of the surroundings. Common among the sensations experienced are those of weightlessness, floating in the air, and changes in size (the Gulliver syndrome). In the mesh of reality and hallucinatory dreams the patient may hear or try to obey the observer, appearing to be in a dream situation that he knows is unreal but which is intense enough to make him call out a name or try to run away from a frightening scene.

As with cataplexy, the recovery from a sleep paralysis which immobilises voluntary movement on waking is usually spontaneous after a few seconds but can just occasionally last for up to 30 minutes. All these symptoms, including hypnagogic hallucinations, can be experienced by normal individuals but are exaggerated in Gelineau's syndrome. Hallucinatory experiences in the daytime, not accompanying sleep, are not uncommon. Roth and Brukovà (1967) describing the dreams of 451 patients with a number of sleep disorders found that in the narcoleptic syndromes the dreams were particularly terrifying but Marsden and Parkes (1974) are equally insistent that the dreams of narcolepsy are most commonly mundane and some may be intensely pleasurable, bordering on ecstacy. A few patients can also develop obsessional rituals to avoid the least pleasant experiences.

Narcolepsy during the daytime is inevitably associated with night sleep which is deranged and disordered. The phases of REM and deep sleep fluctuate rapidly with frequent wakenings and REM periods marked by muscle twitchings, irregularities of breathing and of the heart. A chemical imbalance at the nucleus coeruleus probably determines both the sleep disturbance of narcolepsy and the loss of muscle tone of cataplexy.

Sleep Apnoea and Daytime Drowsiness

Those who venture up mountains are aware of mountain sickness as the atmosphere becomes thinner and the lack of oxygen and carbon dioxide lessens their respiratory drive. Once this occurs, their sleep at altitude is punctuated by frequent awakenings. Hypnagogic and other hallucinations are common and have entered into the mythology of the mountains.

That people choke in their sleep — a frequent subject of nightmares — can certainly happen. Obstructive sleep apnoea, where the tongue falls back in the mouth, or where the air passages become deformed and lax, or the sheer bulk of the person makes adequate respiration difficult, as the breathing rate drops in sleep, are all well recognised. The fat boy in Pickwick is just such an example. In addition to a disturbed sleep at night, he also suffered from hypersomnia with daytime somnolence such that he would fall asleep whilst holding a fist full of aces during a game of poker. His sleep problems could have been eased by losing two or three stones in weight. Partial obstruction, often more evident when the muscles are made more lax by alcohol, produces snoring. The dreams and sudden awakenings of the alcoholic may resemble the night terrors of childhood. Agitated slaps and kicks may endanger their spouse. Sometimes a patient may try to get out of bed, stand up, try to walk and fall to the floor, spending the rest of the night on the carpet, bruised and in a very abnormal position. Children and even adults may have repetitive enuretic episodes (bedwetting), and in the morning appear in a dazed foggy state, putting the butter into the tea pot and pouring the tea into the sugar basin.

The hypnagogic hallucinations of children often reflect their fantasy world of monsters such as King King and Frankenstein and can be so frightening that they fear falling asleep, fight against sleep or waken in the middle of the night with night terrors. Hallucinations in the sleep deprived and hypersomniac can persist after wakening. Their effect can be dramatic and may lead some of them to question their own sanity as the continued interaction of the altered state of consciousness with the surrounding world can eventually lead to marked secondary psychological disorganisation (Guilleminault *et al,* 1975).

The syndrome of daytime drowsiness or hypersomnia can affect automatic behaviour. In the first place they feel not as 'awake' as before, and usually fight against the feelings of drowsiness. Later they become less aware of their actions and performance deteriorates often with incoherence. Periods of forgetfulness, of unexplained actions and silly or dangerous happenings punctuate the day.

However, the most dangerous situation is that when respiration fails. The continuous respiratory drive, derived from the brainstem respiratory regulatory centres, imparts a rhythmicity as important as that of the heart, but occasionally stop to give apnoea. Any form of disturbed sleep may be interrupted by apnoeic episodes with cessation of breathing through the nostrils and mouth for at least 10 seconds at a time. Central apnoea is the Curse of Ondine — the mythical water nymph whose human suitor was cursed to lose control of such autonomic functions whilst asleep. Frequent and severe non-breathing episodes are always potentially lethal and may account for many of the cot deaths of infancy or necessitate emergency treatment in older children and adults.

The Interpretation of Dreams

The scientific exploration of dreams began with Freud's *The Interpretation of Dreams* (1900). This work was a godsend to the Surrealist movement pledged to inventing a new art embracing the abnormal, the illogical and the accidental; so opening up the superreality of fantasy, dream and imagination. Surrealists believed that only when we reach out beyond the limits of habitual experience, circumscribed by reason, can we fulfil ourselves and hence know ourselves. Many years later Klee wrote of the right of the painter to excite the imagination and to consider dreams, as well as still life, as material for his art.

Pictorial communication from the private world of dream experience will always possess an element of chance: to some the picture so drawn will appeal either by its strangeness, its intrinsic value or its correspondence with their own prepossessions, but to others this idiosyncratic art form will not appeal and the talent will be denied.

In the Surrealist Manifesto, *La Revolution Surrealiste* (1924), Boiffard, Eluard and Vtrac claim that 'surrealism is the crossroads of the enchantments of sleep, alcohol, tobacco, ether, opium, cocaine, morphine . . . we dream, and the speed of the lamp's needles introduces to our minds the marvellous deflowered sponge of gold'. Freud was a hero, establishing a direct contact between the dream and the unconscious mind and at the same time through the new science of dream symbolism 'emancipating' sex. They greedily accepted his dictum that we are inclined 'greatly to overestimate the conscious character of intellectual and artistic production'. They wished to release experience from its cage of immediate utility and commonsense, where it was governed by logic and rationalism. All too often their zeal outstripped Freud's sage caution.

Freud stressed the personal aspect of the dream and thereby its essential link with reality. A dream is a product of the dreamer's own mental life; its contents derive from selection by his own motives from his own past experiences. Rather than indiscriminate speculation concerning the symbolism of dreams, he stated that it is essential to have the presence of the dreamer to obtain from him his associations with the various ideas of the dream's contents. A mere collection of dreams without the dreamer's associations, without knowledge of the circumstances in which they occurred, tells nothing — but their purpose is clear: the maintenance of our sanity relies on the dynamic balance between the forces of the conscious mind, the preconscious and unconscious. The active categorisation, sorting and pigeon-holing of the various events and emotions of the day leaves the mind clear for the next. Dreaming may thus help the encoding of cyclic memory traces. Problem solving, particularly of codes and mathematics, almost seems to be facilitated by dreaming. Who has not got up in the middle of the night to write down a thought before it is lost for ever?

Of the classical psychologists, C. G. Jung is closer to the surrealists than Freud, believing that the dream is a 'little hidden door into the innermost and most secret recesses. of the psyche' which needs to be disentangled and presented, 'infantile, grotesque and immoral as it may be'. Although Breton eulogises on 'the remarkable images and perfectly correct syntax (which) appear to the first rate poetic material', not all dreaming, whether reality or psyche based, represents a logical sequence. There is more than a suggestion of an analogy with the thought processes and language of schizophrenics. 'While we are asleep in this world, we are awake in another one; in this way every man is two men' (Jorge Luis Borges), and Oswald (1962, Professor of Psychiatry and Sleep Research in Edinburgh) emphasises the frequency in sleep of semi-schizophrenic, dereistic thinking — broken, unreal and replete with neologisms.

In the Surrealist pack of cards the honours of the Dream Suit are represented by Lautrèamont — Genius, Alice — Syren and Freud — Magnus but there are earlier sources of dream mythology which appealed especially to the Surrealists. Edgar Allan Poe wrote that 'the pure imagination choses from either beauty or deformity only the most combinable things hitherto uncombined' and Horace Walpole (1764) wrote his novel *The Castle of Otranto* under the influence of a dream in which he found himself on the great staircase of an ancient castle and saw on the topmost banister a gigantic hand in armour. 'In the evening I sat down and began to write, without knowing in the least what I wanted to say or relate'. Thus Walpole by combining automatism and dreams can be said to be the first Surrealist.

According to Dali the utilisation of dreams by the Surrealists can be considered in three separate phases. He conceives the early surrealist experiments — automatic writing, accounts of dreams, etc. — as a nocturnal phase, characterised by a descent into the subterranean labyrinths of the psyche. Real and imaginary objects appeared to have a life of their own but 'dreams, hallucinations, automatisms taken as ends in themselves with no communication with the real, are doomed to stereotypy and consequently to failure'. In the next phase, characterised by Breton's dream objects, the object assumes a tangibility and a power to displace the limits of the real, its existence already dependent upon the experimenter. There followed a more active phase indulged in by Dali, Miro and Margritte who did not wait on the passivity of the dream but used the gift of clairvoyance to appraise the objects of every day and release from within them a mysterious and ominous element which normally passes unnoticed (de Chirico). Elsewhere de Chirico distinguished sharply between the climate of the dream and the dream itself. An essential problem, already alluded to, is the difficulty with all but the immediate recall of dreams. Foulkes *et al* (1967) obtained a 72% dream recall when children were wakened during episodes of REM sleep. The recall of dreams (récits de rêves) as practised by the Surrealists often proved to be attenuated versions of the original dreams since they are in fact reconstructions from memory. Furthermore, they were soon to realise that the 'récit' deals mainly with the surface of a dream and, for the most part, this is all we can retain (Breton).

Although dream imagery is repeatedly used by the Surrealists there are few examples of what appear to be true dreams. Max Ernst 'Two Children Threatened by a Nightingale' starts from one of those instances of irrational panic which we suppress in our waking lives. Only in dreams can a diminutive songbird scare the daylights out of us; only in dreams can the button of a door bell swell to the size of a beach ball and yet remain just out of our reach. One can imagine Ernst still half alseep fantasising on his original dream to complete the construction. He also describes hypnagogic fantasies of his father provoked by an imitation mahogany panel opposite his bed. By contrast Tanguy's paintings could not strictly be called dream images because they do not, particularly as depicted in his later paintings, deal with objects of the real world which dreams always do. Only when one has seen a Tanguy painting would one dream of such objects.

The Primitive painter, Henri Rousseau (Douanier Rousseau), places an inscription below his painting of a Dream (1914) which adds to the reality of his experience in a way which we can all accept:

'In a beautiful dream
Yadwigha gently sleeping
Heard the sounds of a pipe
Played by a sympathetic charmer
While the moon reflects
On the river and verdant trees
The serpents attend
The gay tunes of the instrument.'

The adjective 'oneiric' is constantly used to describe the imaginative works of this artist, often synonymously with dreaming, but this is not the exact use of the word.

Normal and auto-erotic Perceptual Phenomena

Piaget (1974), *The Child and Reality*, states that until 7-8 years of age dreams are still systematically considered as objective reality, 'as a sort of ethereal picture floating in the air and fixed before the eyes'. It is not possible to recognise hallucinations in childhood as such until after this age as a certain degree of maturity is needed before children are able to experience and communicate their hallucination to others. Even after this age hallucinations among psychotic (usually neurotic) children have been recorded in a mere 1.1% of those examined. When they do occur, they occur in a setting of mood changes and perceptuo-cognitive abnormalities, most often precipitated by illness, occasionally with actual or threatened separation from their parents, changes of school, loss of friends or death of a close relative. In contrast to the difficulty in differentiating between dreams and other subjective phenomena like hallucinations, is the fact that young children have no apparent difficulty in distinguishing self-induced fantasies or 'pretend' activities from reality. But the topic of 'true' hallucinations in childhood cannot be dismissed without injecting a note of scepticism. Garralda (1982, 1984) states that in the case of non-psychotic children with hallucinations, auditory hallucinations were present most frequently (in 85%); visual hallucinations were present in 40%, olfactory in 15% and mixed modalities in 30% of those affected. If we define an hallucination as something which an adult knows 'is not real', it is quite possible that the preponderence of 'auditory' hallucinations is an artefact due to the fact that the hearing range for children is higher than that for adults. A child may hear a wolf-whistle, the rustle of mice in grass, the noise of telegraph wires transmitting, and left alone in a quiet house, especially an old one (*vide* John Masefield, *The Midnight Folk,* or Mary Norton, *The Borrowers),* may hear sounds, often quite loud sounds, and misinterpret noises which adults will deny exist.

Foukes *et al* (1967) in a study of dreams of the male child in which 32 boys, aged 6-12, were wakened a total of 249 times during episodes of REM sleep found some item of substantive mental content in 72% of these awakenings. The majority of reported dreams were predominantly 'good' or effectively neutral and 'their manifest content often dealt in a relatively direct manner with major foci of juvenile and preadolescent social adjustment: parents, siblings, male peers, recreational or play settings and activities'. Bad dreams (20%) with unfriendly or escape social themes were more prominent among the younger boys. The same authors reported the presleep viewing of a 'blood and thunder' film appeared to reduce dream intensity in general and any hostile or unpleasant content in particular. Bad dreams among children are liable to occur with disturbed sleep either in the same setting as that in which hallucinations are reported — fever, separation, bereavement or deprivation — but also with overindulgence in food, e.g. cake and unripe fruit, leading to stomach upsets and gastro-intestinal disturbances; threats, punishments and abnormal behavioural attitudes. Abnormal behaviours seeking unhealthy ecstatic experiences can occur in children often with a disastrous or fatal outcome. Breath-holding episodes in infancy and early childhood may be attention seeking. A masochistic sexual satisfaction may be sought by provoking photic of hyperventilation epilepsy or causing an 'anoxic high' apnoeic state by glue-sniffing or self-induced smothering or strangulation.

Children with the most creative imaginations readily indulge in a wealth of normal perceptual phenomena (Edgell and Kolwin, 1972). The majority of psychologists believe that most fantasies, day dreams and fairy tales have a positive and constructive value, 'their content is really nothing more than the disguised realisation of wishes'. Furthermore the creation of imaginary companions (companions in fantasy) is a positive and healthful mechanism. Their experiences may be heightened by eidetic imagery and hypnagogic phenomena which may allow them an occasion to escape into a make belief world or, alternatively, to act out imaginary situations which may have a real preparatory value — playing with dolls, keeping house, exploring. Parahallucinatory imaginary companions are no longer considered purely as an escape for the lonely and rejected child.

The healthy child identifies in a unique and personal way with its genitalia, learns their physiological functions and increasingly associates the genitalia with auto-erotic fantasies, love objects and imaginary sexual partners as a prelude to sexual maturity. In the past, throughout the Western World, auto-erotic fantasies have been swathed and stigmatised by guilt complexes. However, if we accept the universal nature of the normal sex drive, that penile erections and emissions may occur in REM sleep, that coitus has a healthy amative as well as reproductive function and that early masturbatory activity particularly occurs in a hypnagogic setting, then it is possible to discuss sexual fantasies in a serious manner, to recognise their universality and not to deny, for example, that handicapped people also have a need for sexual fulfilment. We recognise that there is a perverted aspect which Salvador Dali, among others, has sought, as in the Great Masturbator, to convert into an art form replete with phobic-anxiety states, castration complexes and intra-uterine retreat; but such endeavours are nothing to the multiplicity of erotic art built upon normal sexual fantasies. Sexually based fantasies are a major stimulus to image building, fashion, design and pornography. 'Non, non, la pornographie n'a jamais été et ne sera jamais révolutionaire, pas plus que l'immoralité'' (Jaques Duclos, *Les Droits de l'Intelligence,* 1938). Much of society is built upon basically immature sexual activities such as visual masturbatory fantasies and erotic day dreams which are enriched by psychic elements and genuinely erotic stimuli. The impact of these fantasies upon art in enormous.

Art, in every age, has overtly or surreptitiously escaped from the puritanical promulgations affecting the rest of society. Edward Lucie-Smith's monograph on *Eroticism in Western Art* (1972) — dedicated (without permission) to Lord Longford — begins with a chapter on the 'erotic and the sacred'. Montgomery Hyde (1964) on his book *A History of Pornography* cites the case of a Mr. Wise from Kansas who was found guilty in 1895 of sending obscene and pornographic matter through the U.S. Mail. It so happened that the material in question consisted of quotations from the Bible (Ezekiel ch. 16 and 23, and Samuel II ch 13 vv 1-17). In 1957 the British Customs seized a book on soil erosion entitled *Rape Round Our Coast!* But painters renowned for their religious morality and fervour such as Hieronymous Bosch 'The Garden of Earthly Delights' and Albrecht Dürer 'Imperial Bath' and 'Woman's Bath' have depicted scenes which were clearly auto-erotic in their origin. The nude has flourished in art. Pagan and Classical scenes, allegories and rapes, and the works of such artists as Boticelli, Michelangelo, Raphael, Correggio, Tintoretto, Carravagio, Rembrandt, Géricault, Delacroix, Ingrès and Manet, are no less obvious than the erotic fantasies of Fuseli 'A Sleeping Woman and the Furies', the bold eroticism of Aubrey Beardsley or the brothel scenes of Dégas and Toulouse-Lautrec. It has been left to much modern art in the name of sexual explicitness to root around the garbage of sado-masochism, scophilia and fetishism. Such artists have yet to emulate psychologists such as Fenichel (1946) who have related kleptomania (doing a forbidden thing secretly), pyromania (sexual excitement at the sight of fire is a normal occurrence in children), gambling (displaced expression of conflicts around infantile sexuality) and drug addition to masturbatory fantasies.

Twilight States

Maury (1848) regarded hypnagogic hallucinations as errors of cerebration during the intermediate stage between wakefulness and sleep, arising as products of a mind far from its optimum efficiency in which attention is ill-directed because of healthy physiological change. In sleep there is an alteration of consciousness: in pathological delirium and confusional states there is a dissolution of consciousness; and just as sleep contains dreams, so the state of confusion contains oneirism, hallucinatory twilight states and various forms of depersonalisation (Ey, 1969). In psychotic states the subject may be distressed by imaginary happenings, fight snakes under the bed, turn pictures face to the wall to stop the portraits watching and ordering his actions, break mirrors, bolt doors against imaginary assailants. Oneirism is a prolonged psychotic experience persisting for days or months. Although oneirism is often drug induced, e.g. from amphetamine abuse, there may be a confluence of a schizophrenic psychosis and a recognisable genetic tendency. Consciousness is deeply disorganised. The dream is all the more vivid because the subject participates (sometimes with considerable motor activity), living through multiple scenic hallucinations, intense emotions and disordered perceptions. He is held prisoner by his dream as if hypnotised and unable to free himself by waking.

In twilight states (dämmerzustände, états crépusculaires) the subject appears passive with marked psychomotor retardation, although often experiencing the liveliest emotional involvement as he witnesses scenes frequently of an apocalyptic, literary or historical nature enacted as florid visual apparitions entering the objective world which he continues to perceive. The episode may last 1-2 hours and terminate in a generalised convulsion. Biblical scenes, a Western movie, a horror story or a magic display may form the basis for such a cosmic dream or ecstasy, e.g. the Crucifixion or Stanley Spencer's The Resurrection. A recent example is related in the *Ghost Book of York,* and anyone who joined the Ghost tour of the city (alas now discontinued) would have had the privilege of listening to the subject of the experience as guide. I quote from his adventure with his express approval:

'The most remarkable story of hauntings in York in recent years must surely be the events which were recorded by Harry Martindale in the early nineteen fifties. At that time alterations to the Treasurer's House were going on. Harry, an apprentice aged about 17, had been working in one of the cellars, installing piping for central heating. He was standing on a short ladder when he first heard the sound of a trumpet. He paid little attention to this, other than feeling the slight surprise that the sound of a brass band should have reached him where he was working, but the sound drew nearer and nearer, and suddenly the figure of a horse came through the wall. It was large and lumbering — its fetlocks heavy and shaggy. Harry fell from his ladder to the earth floor in a state of confusion and shock. More was to come. On the back of the horse was a man dressed in Roman costume, and behind him came a group of soldiers, not marching in formation, but shuffling in a dispirited way, with their heads down. They took no notice of Harry as he lay on the floor, but the details of their appearance were to remain with him.

He was surprised by their small stature, and shabby appearance. He describes with great detail the rough, home-made clothes they were wearing. The sandals, cross-gartered to the knees, were very badly made, and their kilted skirts, green in colour, gave the impression that they had been roughly dyed. They carried round shields (an unusual feature in the Roman army), long spears and short swords. He cannot remember any banner or standard, but the trumpet was very clear, a long, straight instrument, mush used and battered. The finest part of their equipment appeared to be the helmets, with fine plumes of undyed feathers.

The portion of the cellar they were in is low and narrow, and is below the level of the old Roman road which the archaeologists had recently uncovered, together with a fallen column from the HQ building. At one stage, when the horse was first coming through the wall, the group appeared to be in mid-air, that is, on the original level of the Roman road itself. Still with the air of utter dejection, the group crossed the cellar and silently disappeared through the opposite wall.

Shocked and trembling, he rushed up the cellar steps to the ground floor. Here he stumbled against the curator who said, noticing his agitation, "You've seen the Romans, haven't you?" This remark was of great comfort, as Harry then realised that he had neither been seeing things nor was going out of his mind. At the suggestion of the curator he wrote down what he had seen, and was later astonished to find two other people had also left accounts, giving identical details.

For twenty years he kept quiet about this strange experience. A few close friends had been told and some details had been given, but it was not until 1974 that he could be persuaded to make public what had happended to him. Harry is now P.C. Martindale, an honest and discriminating citizen who would scorn to add anything to his story that didn't actually happen. He has been questioned by experts in Roman history, who have been impressed by the details he has given. Throughout he had assured them that his previous ideas of Roman soldiers were derived only from Hollywood epics and do not fit in with what he actually saw in the cellars. And through it all comes his puzzled cry. "Why me? I wasn't interested either in ghosts or in Romans?".'

Pathological dream states have provided themes for literature and drama, none more so than the appearance of phantom mirror-images of oneself — the döppelganger of German folklore, traditionally interpreted as a foreboding of death during a toxic infective illness. Guy de Maupassant was visited by the apparition of his double, was subject to persecution and hallucinations, and finally became insane. The same thing happens to the hero of Kafka's *The Trial*. In primitive communities, those affected by such states may run 'amok' (Malaysia). Brief episodes of depersonalisation are recognised in normal people but the more graphic states are associated with temporal lobe lesions and De Clerembuet (1942) described a 'split personality hallucinatory state with subjective and objective experiences intermingled', which he described as syndrome d'automatisme mental. In Korsakoff's psychoses, usually but not inevitably related to recovery from alcoholism, time relationships are lost, hallucinations common and the patient will readily confabulate a story and explanation; e.g. "I came to this place (a hospital) on my number one elephant. You can hear those bells. They are to let us know that the other elephants are following."

The Nightmare

The nightmare deserves separate consideration from the dream, often being associated with periods of melancholy. 'The whole mind is wrought up to a pitch of unutterable despair; a spell is laid upon the faculties which freezes them into inaction; the wretched victim feels as if pent alive in his coffin or overpowered by resistless and unmitigable pressures' (Macnish, 1834). Ernest Jones in 1931 defined a nightmare in similar terms as an agonising dread, a sense of oppression or weight at the chest which alarmingly interferes with a respiration and a conviction of hopeless paralysis.

The symbolism of Bosch strikes many as possessing a nightmarish quality and we know that Dürer was haunted by apparitions and dreams which came to him from the depths of a soul torn by religious experience. 'How often', he wrote, 'do I see great art in my sleep, but waking cannot recall it; so soon as I awake, my memory forgets it'. Nonetheless, his Dream wherein a winged devil with a pair of bellows is blowing into the ear of man seated before a stove, The Apocalypse, Melancholia, Agony in the Garden, and The Flood could only emanate as products of a disturbed, melancholic sleep.

Fuseli's The Nightmare is the most quoted. The symbolism — a horse's head, a goblin, the distorted pose of the sleeper — are all too obvious, yet disturbing. There is an artificiality: the picture is meant to have been painted as a parody of one by his friend Sir Joshua Reynolds entitled The Dream. Fuseli had already become a national institution shocking all with his sarcasm, profanity and pugnacity. His acclaim earned his elevation to Professor of Painting and Keeper of the Royal Academy. Born in Switzerland (1747-1825), renouncing holy orders, he lead a Bohemian life as a literary personage until his deeds forced him into exile from his native land. In London he befriended Reynolds who encouraged him to draw. After a period in Italy, studying the works of Michelangelo, he returned to England and proceeded to satisfy the popular demand for the horrific, grotesque, imaginative and sublime. They gloried in the more bloodthirsty plays of Shakespeare — murders, ghosts and witches. He painted Lady Macbeth seizing the Daggers, The Witches' Cauldron and others of similar ilk: 'Fear', 'The Blinding of Prometheus'. A book had been published in 1775 on the pleasures derived from objects of terror, an enquiry into the kinds of distress which excite agreeable sensations. This was the age of the Marquis de Sade, of Goya, of Piranesi's prison scenes. If, in his nightmare, Fuseli was more interested in eroticism than in the unnatural, he could draw upon a recent medical opinion 'For nightmares in young girls are often induced by a copious eruption of the menses. Such dreams are usually about violent sexual assault, as from a devil or incubus' (Dr. J. Bond, 1753). Fuseli remained the Bohemian masked by respectability. His visions of sleeping women stirring uneasily under the influence of disturbing dreams reflects real imaginative need. Kenneth Clark, in his analysis of Fuseli, supposed that Fuseli's dreams like the many hundreds of erotic drawings incinerated by his wife after his death were ferociously obscene, more frightening than provocative, far less innocuous than the flying maidens — a recognised symbol of sexual desire — in Puvis de Chavannes, The Dream (1883).

The Dream, by the novelist Victor Hugo (1802-85), is simpler but just as haunting. A hand rises frighteningly in a storm. His penchant for vague, gloomy ink drawings, the use of unusual media such as cigar ash and coffee grounds, and his dramatic, surreal lighting effects earned him the epiphet, the Gothic Piranesi. The Gothic imagination thrived on the flux of art between Romanticism and Symbolism of the 18th and 19th centuries. Natural disasters provided the subject matter for Friedrich, Turner and many others but particularly for Vernet (1714-84), about whom Diderot wrote: 'he has his own peculiar obsession, it is a kind of sacred horror. His caverns are deep and gloomy; precipitous rocks threaten the sky . . . man passes through the domain of demons and gods'. The Black pictures of Goya must be considered separately; but Géricault, Delacroix, Chasseriau and others painted imaginative and grisly topics with all the fury at their command. To paint the Raft of the Medusa (1817) medical students supplied Géricault with bits of cadavers. He himself painted and studied the heads of persons who had been guillotined, and the emaciated torso and jaundiced face of a friend suffering from a disease of the liver. 'Even the waves', comments Aldous Huxley, 'are corpse-coloured. It is as though the entire universe had become a dissecting room'. As a prelude to the 20th-century horror movie, Eugene Delacroix very successfully articulated the sexual-sadistic plunge of consciousness in a way that captivated the taste of his time. The Massacre at Chios (1824) and Death at Sarapalus (1827) provide a seige of writhing bodies, a sensual feast in which the tradition of the female nude reaches a new pitch of sadistically provocative poses. When painting, Delacroix described himself as spellbound like the serpent in the hand of the snake charmer. Having chosen the subject, he would make all the necessary preparations most carefully and perhaps paint many preliminary studies; but when it came to the final picture, all of these would be cast side, and he would paint, as he said, with his imagination only (Sir. H. Reed, 1931).

The development of the black and white lithograph popularised the appeal of art and book illustration, presenting the macabre with a new force. Rodolphe Bresdin's best known print, the Comedy of Death (1854), depicts, as described by Huysmans (A Rebours) 'In an unlikely-looking landscape, bristling with trees, coppices and clumps of vegetation, all taking the forms of demons and phantoms, and covered with birds with the heads of rats and tails of bean-pods, upon a terrain scattered with vertebrae, rib-bones and skulls, some willows rise, surrounded by skeletons who are waving a bouquet with thin arms in the air, while Christ flees away through a dappled sky, and a hermit with his head in his hands, meditates in the depths of a grotto, and an unfortunate lies dying, worn out by privations, with his feet before a pond.'

Another artist to attract Huysmans' attention, Odilon Redon (1840-1916) received universal applause for the macabre fantasy and hallucinatory states of mind applied to black and white lithographs 'with the sole aim of producing in the spectator a sort of diffuse and dominating attraction in the dark world of the indeterminate', being variously described as the 'subtle lithographer of suffering' and 'discovering the new realm of nightmare vision in the revelation of modern science'. Redon's 'Noirs' incorporated all the standard symbols of the time-masks, snaky monsters, severed heads, femmes fatales, and new interpretations of classical mythology. Amoebae and other creatures seen down the microscope provided a new range of horrors, Collections of lithographs were sold in book form: the Dream, To Edgar Allan Poe, Homage to Goya, Origins, and Night, often anticipating Wagnerian themes. A series of lithographs would be loosely strung together by a prose-poem, devoid of definite meaning:

'In my dream I saw in the sky a face of mystery,
the Marsh flower, a human and sad head,
a madman in a bleak landscape.
There were also embryonic beings,
A strange juggler. On waking, I saw the
Goddess of the Intelligble
with her severe and hard profile'.

The prose-poem as an independent literary form enjoyed a real vogue in the early 1880s.

Redon had a solitary and melancholy childhood, beset by illness and he achieved fame only about his fortieth year. He described dreams and fiction as the stuff of art and claimed that his works are based entirely on a 'docile submission to the upsurge of the unconscious'. 'Secret laws which have somehow allowed me to create within the limitations of my imagination and my abilities, objects into which I have put my whole being'. Others described him in even more colourful and metaphysical terms; thus Aurier called him a thinker whose work was hermetic and baffling but nonetheless contained themes of philosophical and metaphysical proportions. 'It was', he wrote, 'terrible, vertiginous work, the work of a poet and philosopher, distressing work of both dreams and terror, and also of metaphysical magnetism and despair'. He was later to confound his critics by entering on a later highly productive colour period, softer and more sublime than his earlier work. The deep and dark visions were cast aside in his more mellow art. He always denied any analytical spirit in his works. Thus it was never possible to distinguish, even in his own lifetime, between nightmare and technical brilliance.

Of all artists, Edvard Munch (1863-1944) could produce in a single picture an image that 'pierced the whole of Nature' with a sudden, vast and quite irresistable sense of panic and despair. Every element of a given composition somehow contributed to the mood, purpose and emotion of the scene, adding to its realistic but psychic intensity. His mother died of tuberculosis when he was five. Thereafter his father's religious anxieties, puritanism and difficult temper dominated his upbringing, with the constant threat of punishment in Hell hanging over his head. Munch said of his childhood that 'disease and insanity were the black angels of his cradle'. His eldest sister died when he was fourteen years old. He himself was often ill — rheumatic, feverish and sleepless — but his aunt who ran the household discovered and encouraged his artistic talents. Many of his early and most typical portraits were of members of his close family; even they did not escape the abject and repressed sexuality with which he mostly depicted the female sex. As a struggling artist he trod a lonely path from Christiania (Oslo) to Berlin and thence to Paris. The philosophy of Nietzsche deepened his inner remorse and, though outwardly charming, handsome and affable, he became embroiled in the most lurid and melodramatic of private entanglements. When he was 40, for example, he was involved with a girl who had herself laid out, as if on her death bed, in an attempt to prevent him leaving her; and when she threatened to shoot herself and Munch tried to restrain her, the gun went off accidentally and he lost one of his fingers in the struggle. Two or three years later he had to leave Norway after a public brawl with another man. His brooding nature, by turns morbid, sadistic and anxiety provoking, led to a number of illnesses both mental and physical in the 1890s and in 1908 to a nervous breakdown. As late as 1930, he was still reliving the day of the brawl, still picturing the look of his bloodied antagonist as he staggered along the narrow lane towards Munch's house, and still recalling the reflex instinct with which he himself had picked up a gun as if to ward off a second attack. As with Ensor, the years of psychoanalysis diminished his powers as an artist, feeding the myth that creative originality is necessarily tied to neurotic behaviour. In one significant picture of 1930, Munch made a drawing of himself as a corpse lying with an open chest on a dissecting table in front of the physician. The Czech critic, F.X. Salde in 1905 described Munch as 'a dispeller of dreams, a painter in terror-inspiring colours ravaged by all the sufferings of life, a man possessed by ashen horror and gloom, a coarse barbarian and a subtle decadent in whose work both the old world and the new inferno play their parts, in whose pictures objects literally shed the blood of their colours and shriek out their sufferings and the mystery of their being; a painter whose colours are no objective manifestation but a lyrical fate . . . While this man is obsessed by vampire-like dreams, he is not only a painter of creative power with purely and simply a painter's vision and sense of values, but also an artist with a melancholy understanding insight that caresses and enchants.'

The cry of suffering pervades the German schools: Die Brücke (the Bridge) before World War I and Neue Sachlichkeit (New Objectivity) in the 1920s and 30s. The neurotic energy unleashed in the paintings and woodcuts of Die Brücke, founded in 1905, was deeply rooted in the Gothic tradition, the philosophy of Nietzsche and revolutionary forebodings of tremendous social upheavals. They probed and parodied megalopolitan fashion as a scene of artificial anti-nature. Klee described Emil Nolde (1867-1956) as the demon of the lower realm with his presentation of the twilight zone of chthonic legend. The most brilliant and restless of the group, E. L. Kirchner (1880-1938), until his nervous breakdown after enlistment in 1914, depicted in his woodcuts (e.g. Mountain Melancholia: self-portrait) and in caustic, gaudy colour contrasts (e.g. Women in the Street), an horrific vision of the individual battered by society then left destitute to fend alone. Grosz and Dix brought to the Neue Sachlichkeit a satirical and bizarre violence but the group's artistic merit rested upon the development of Max Beckmann's (1884-1950) brutal talent founded upon traumatic experiences in World War I. He began his military service as a healthy, untroubled youth in the medical corps on the Russian front and then in Flanders. After barely a year, he went to pieces and had to be discharged, a hopeless neurasthenic, unfit for further duties. When he began to paint again it was, as he said in 1917, 'to reproach God for his errors'. His paintings from 1917-1920 present terrifying visions of monstrous human figures with great simplicity of expression, crowded and crushed within a vertical format into a collective scene.

Chapter Six

Hallucinations At The Periphery: End-Organ Dysfunction

'Every creative art involves a new innocence of perception, liberated from a cataract of accepted belief'.
Arthur Koestler. The Sleepwalker.

The majority of hallucinations arise from an impaired state of arousal of the sensorium, affecting the filtering, selection and recognition of stimuli centrally. The next most frequent origin of hallucinatory phenomena, less readily separable from illusions, is disturbance of function of the sensors — those parts of the body adapted to receive stimuli directly as with visceral, vibration and tactile sensations or indirectly via an interposed medium as with the special senses of sight, hearing and smell. From aviation and space research, we now know that man does not possess a prolonged 'spatial memory' providing an unimpaired representation of our orientation within the environment; in conditions of weightlessness a sense of motion is lost and skydivers report that, after they reach constant velocity in a jump, they feel as though stationary unless they can see the ground or other visual 'landmarks' such as clouds (Lackner and Graybiel, 1983). Intersensory mismatching can be such that early in space flight some crew members have perceptual defects with resultant delusions of flying upside down, tilting or turning that subside with adaptation (Goode, 1981). We are dependent upon a constant flow of recognisable and recognised images from our sensory end-organs to maintain our inner equilibrium; but the flow of images may be subject to unusual or unnatural stimuli, physiological distortion or pathological impairment. In-built faults affecting the end-organs and their connections provide illusory features which the sensorium is mostly able to exclude from interpretation or otherwise compensate for. However, in abnormal circumstances, these phosphenes and photisms may impinge upon the conscious mind. In short, hallucinations may be derived from abnormalities in sites away from the analytical parts of the brain, triggered by the interaction of one or more factors including the absence of normal stimuli from the periphery, distortion of information as a result of the deranged or degenerate state of the end-organ, spontaneous irritability of the end-organ, alterations in the state of alertness and coexistent disturbances of cerebral function.

Phantom Limbs

Among the sensory end-organs, the eye is arguably the most complex and the distortions that arise from its impairment are the most varied and extraordinary. It is simpler, therefore, to start with an appraisal of the phenomenon which may arise when a limb is amputated. An almost ubiquitous consequence of amputation is the persistent sensation of the missing limb, first called 'phantom limb' by Dr. Weir Mitchell in his study of 90 amputees among American Civil War veterans in 1871. Phantom limbs are not encountered in infants born limbless nor in young children who lose limbs; but where the body schema has been unnaturally altered in teenagers or adults they appear within days of the trauma and persist for months or years. Occasionally they are abruptly abolished when a stroke, damaging the brain, obliterates the central image of the limb. Stimulation of the severed nerves in the stump produces distorted sensations as though the limb were moving, tingling, falling asleep, vibrating, gripping, clenching or clutching. The shape of the phantom does not follow the boundaries of the missing member: areas of greatest representation in the brain, such as the thumb, index finger or big toe, feature more prominently than supporting structures such as the calf or forearm and there are usually gaps in the phantom that cannot be felt.

The most comprehensive studies of phantom limbs have tended to follow wartime experiences, as with the excellent study of 73 Israeli male soldiers injured in the Yom Kippur of War of October 1973. All experienced an illusory awareness of the missing part. With time the phantom tended to weaken in intensity and the limb telescope in towards the stump until the digits of the phantom merge into its substance. A painful phantom is less likely to shrink in size with time and may remain, continuing to cripple and oppress. Thus 5 to 10 percent of patients suffered disagreeable sensations, variously described as cramp, shooting, burning and crushing. These burns generally follow irritant wounds and emergency amputation, sometimes 'freezing' the phantom in distorted attitudes such as that which it occupied at the time of the accident. Pain emanates from pressure on specially sensitive areas, trigger zones which are situated initially in the injured part but gradually spread to other areas of the body which are healthy and unrelated to the injury; so much so that urination, defaecation and ejaculation may be accompanied by a burning sensation in both the phantom and the stump end.

Intersensory and auditory hallucinations

Sensory end-organs, no less than the mutilated limb, may give rise to abnormal sensory signals from severed or degenerate nerve endings. Irritation of the severed optic nerve commonly causes flashes of light. Occasionally, as after surgical enucleation (Uhthoff, 1899), more vivid hallucinations are produced, with visions of clouds, birds and angels - an experienced shared with St. Lucy. Other forms of organic hallucinosis such as central or thalamic pain, tinnitus (hisses, whistles or other sounds from the ears) and vertigo (from the organ of balance) are presumed to be generated spontaneously by damaged end-organs or their pathways.

Healthy people are often disturbed, notably during quiet periods of the day, by noises or ringing in their ears. Such tinnitus can be more persistent in the presence of wax or if induced by certain drugs. These abnormal sensations, called 'acuphenes' in the Continental literature, may develop a buzzing, hammering, hissing or sibilant quality, particularly as accompaniments to progressive hearing loss and often reach a painful intensity which prohibits the use of hearing aids. Just occasionally, after an antecedent tinnitus of several years duration, a deaf person may start to hear a constant, vivid perception of music reflecting past memories, typically consisting of previously forgotten lyrics (Miller and Crosby, 1978). Songs of a religious nature are common, as are other types of instrumental and vocal music. The hallucinations are disturbing only by virtue of their monotony and persistence and there is no evidence of psychosis. In a second part of musical hallucinations accompanying deafness, Hammeke *et al* (1983) describe a combination of unformed irregular sounds of varying pitch and timbre, and musical passages or voices first heard in childhood. Generally the experience was constant but intensified during periods of inactivity and under conditions of reduced ambient noise levels. Their patients indicated that they could replace ongoing hallucinations wilfully with songs or prose of their own choosing by concentrating their thoughts or by subvocalisation.

Intersensory and multifactorial hallucinations are well illustrated by black-patch delirium following cataract extraction or corneal grafting. Hallucinations occur most readily in the presence of sensory deprivation and mild senile brain changes. Delirium is especially common if hearing is also impaired and, despite the fact that both eyes are covered, is apt to be more severe at night. Some normal individuals see flashes of light if aroused from a dreamy state by a sharp noise. Such sound-induced hypnagogic photisms are called Schreckblitz and Weckblitz in the German literature where they were first described. Bender used the term 'visual synaesthesiae' when these phosphenes occur in the presence of disease — usually to the optic nerve — and described a patient with optic neuritis who saw a blue light whenever he heard a loud noise or experienced sudden pain. Lessell and Cohen (1979) suggest the possible mechanisms to explain such hallucinatory phenomena. Ephaptic transmission between adjacent neural axons or the convergence of visual and auditory signals on the same post-synaptic elements in the brain — a feature well recognised at certain cerebral loci.

Visions from within the eye

The tautological statement that entoptic visions can and do arise within the eye is undoubtedly true. Pressure, sudden movement or traction on the globe of the eye can produce flashes of light. A sudden saccadic, or flick, movement to the healthy, dark-adapted, closed eye may transmit pressure waves through the semifluid contents of the eye to the vitreous attachments of the retina, inducing a phosphene in the shape of a narrow streak of bright light pointing towards the temporal field of vision from the fovea (Nebel, 1957). The phenomenon may fatigue, changing from a brilliant white light to a desaturated purple or orange colour. Temporary obscurations of vision in an otherwise healthy eye, produced by vascular spasms as with retinal migraine, by embolic blockage of an artery, or with raised intracranial pressure transmitted to the optic nerve head, may be associated with positive visual phenomena or photisms. Similar phosphenes may result from disease affecting the optic nerve; thus sudden movement of the eyes may be accompanied by a shower of sparks lasting for a few seconds in patients with retrobulbar neuritis or with multiple sclerosis. They represent the ocular equivalent of the better known L'Hermitte's (or barber's chair) sign, due to demyelination (loss of insulation) between nerve fibres in the spinal cord, whereby a nod or flexion of the neck provokes electric tinglings down the back or into the legs and arms.

With ageing, sensecent changes produce liquefaction, cavitation and subsequent collapse and detachment of the posterior vitreous with the production of opacities, or floaters, within the vitreous. In disease states, these changes may occur a decade or so earlier, and myopic individuals run the additional risk of vitreous haemorrhage and retinal tears. As is well known, floaters are sensitive to gravitational effects whereas obscurations secondary to a retinal defect remain constant in location. A frequent accompaniment of floaters and other vitreous disturbances are recurrent stereotyped vertical flashes of light perceived periodically for a few weeks or a month or two in the temporal visual field after eye movement. These 'lightning streaks of Moore' (1935) are most frequently seen in the dark and tend to be followed by 'spots' before the eyes. Verhoeff (1942) described them as 'vertically curved streaks of brilliant white or sluggish bluish light, sometimes slightly zig-zag, appearing to flash predominantly into the temporal visual field'. Their harmless nature has been repeatedly emphasised (Zaret, 1985).

As a result of concussion, disease of the choroid membrane or opacities within the vitreous humour, the retina may be irritated with the production of impressions of luminous spectra, thus an early sign of haemorrhage may be visual symptoms of 'rising smoke'. In 1930, Edvard Munch, at the age of 69, developed a small haemorrhage within the vitreous of one eye causing a small clot shaped like a bird with a long beak. This shape was consequently to intrude into several of his paintings. Earl Grey, noted for 'The lights are going out all over Europe' before the First World War, was troubled by a peculiar spectral illusion of a gory head, which, however, he could banish temporarily be a strong effort of the will. Dazzling photopsia, caused by movements of a detached retina, may excite visions of green forests or seas of colour. With retinal haemorrhage, startlingly clear visions of people and animals may occur. And one patient who was blind with cataract complained so bitterly of incessant golden rain pouring before her sightless gaze that she submitted to two leukotomies in a vain quest for relief (Macdonald Critchley, 1966).

Klein (1917), Horowitz (1964) and others have abstracted the entoptic visions into a series of simple elements and argued that the images from anatomical structures such as the retinal ganglionic network and from 'luminous dust' which are normally filtered out from conscious perception impinge upon the deranged mind and are misconstrued. Horowitz noted when observing schizophrenic patients' paintings that they would stop and stare with an expression of abstract, perplexed intensity that seemed to be associated with hallucinatory phenomena and then resume, constructing simple figures which were different from the previous pictorial forms. The supreme example of such intrusion is provided by the cat drawings of Louis Wain. During exacerbations of his schizophrenia the cats would disintegrate into mosaics of reduplicated entoptic material.

With incipient blindness, visual phenomena may occur, invoking dreams of intense visual imagery. In many respects they are the equivalent of the tinnitus of deafness or the sensations of a phantom limb. A 19th-century physician, Dr. Abell (1845), gave a personal account of blindness developing over four years. Blindness in one eye was associated with smoke-like visions during the day and beautifully coloured patterns on the walls at night. Total blindness brought dramatic landscapes, cities filled with people and animals, parades of gorgeously caparisoned soldiers, and many other wonderful and strange sights. Indeed, his greatest suffering was that these never ending luminous apparitions prevented him from sleeping.

Philosopher's visions

A curious condition occurring in the elderly with preserved intellectual function takes the form of vivid, elaborate and dynamic recurrent visual pseudo-hallucinations of a pleasant nature. The first description comes from the pen of the Swiss philosopher, Charles Bonnet (1720-1793), who in an *Essai Analytique sur les Facultés de l'Ame* (1769) relates the experiences of his grandfather, Charles Lullin, an 89 year old magistrate from Geneva. At an advanced age he underwent cataract operations and in 1758 for three months saw 'without any external stimuli the images of men, women, birds, buildings that change in shape, size and place but which he never accepted as real'. The visions came only when standing or sitting but never in the recumbent position and were clearer in his left visual field, disappearing when turning his eyes to the right. 'He still had a remarkably good memory for his age. He read a great deal, retained most of it and loved entertaining his friends with lectures. He particularly enjoyed history and politics. I was among those who often attended his lectures and I frequently saw him interrupting the description of some historical event to pay attention to a vision that he experienced at that particular moment. "There it is" he would say to me, "the tapestry is covered with paintings, the frames are gilded, etc.." Immediately after, he would describe in detail another decoration or some other vision; and, after having jested over these fictions in his brain, he would calmly resume his discourse.'

Later in life, Bonnet himself had similar experiences and saw, according to his biographer, Leveque de Pouilly (1794), 'a number of fantastic objects which he recognised as illusory'. It is known that Bonnet suffered from a marked reduction in his visual acuity at the age of 25, to the extent that he was forced to forfeit the use of a microscope. Another philosopher,

Pierre Jean George Cabanis (1757-1808), remembered today by Carlyle's epigrammatic caricature of his system 'the brain secretes thoughts as the liver secretes bile' — (in actuality, he argued that to understand the operations resulting in thought, the brain must be considered as an organ appropriated to the production of thoughts) — had visions when he would clearly see people walking on the pathway at a distance'. The physiologist, Johannes Muller (1826) and the philosopher and psychologist, Ernest Neville (1908) were similarly affected. Their experiences are described by Morsier (1936) who proposed including visual hallucinatory phenomena in the elderly with preserved intellectual functions under the label of the Charles Bonnet Syndrome, the principal features of which are that they occur in clear consciousness, do not deceive the subject, can be combined with normal perceptions, are exclusively visual, do not produce bizarre sensations, appear and disappear without obvious cause, and are amusing rather than worrying to the subject.

Is it possible that similar phenomena have led to greater creativity in certain artists in the senescence of their lives? Possible examples are Monet (1840-1926), Renoir (1841-1919) and Bissière (1886)-1964). Of these Bissière is the most probable.

Claude Monet (1840-1926)

The word Impressionism was derived from the title of Monet's painting, ''Impression : Soleil levant'', exhibited in 1874. Claude Monet was the first Impressionist, the first deliberate painter of light in its endless transformations, and the first to understand that shadows actually are combinations of colour in which any tone may predominate under given conditions. Cézanne said of Monet that he was 'only an eye, but my God what an eye'. He lived in poverty from 1865, when his family cut off his allowance, until 1883 when he settled at Giverny. In 1900, he temporarily lost his sight of one eye. In 1911, his second wife died. By 1912 his sight was deteriorating. His son Jean died in 1914. Between 1908 and 1917 he painted very few works. Over 70 years of age, with diminishing eyesight, he was reluctant to tackle another seemingly impossible task. However, encouraged by Clemenceau, from 1914-6, Monet started to plan his most famous paintings — a large scale mural cycle of water-lilies from his elaborate garden at Giverny to decorate the Orangerie in Paris. He had a large new studio built to accommodate them and started work. In 1918 he offered two of these canvasses to the state to commemorate the Armistice; this became in 1920 a plan to complete 12 enormous canvasses, despite the fact that he was half deaf and half blind. The plan was formalised in 1921 with the reconstruction of the Orangerie at the Palais de Louvre. He pushed forward his art, desirous to paint 'everything before I can no longer see anything at all', tortured even in his dreams by his compulsive imaginations and drive (Seitz, 1960). In 1920, almost blind from double cataracts, everything appeared yellow and he abandoned work. An operation in 1923 restored partial sight to one eye and he continued working despite extreme depressioin and anxiety until his death in December 1926. Despite his 'compulsive imagination' in old age, I feel that the coexistent depression renders the possibility of pseudo-hallucinations of the Charles Bonnet type unlikely.

Pierre Auguste Renoir (1841-1919).

Before studying at the École des Beaux Arts he had served a three year apprenticeship as a porcelain painter for which his myopic vision was especially suited. He remained the most individualistic of the Impressionists, developing the use of pure tones at maximum intensity with the elimination of black, combining colours optically by their juxtaposition and subordinating outlines. During the 1880s he drew away somewhat from Impressionism and began to paint in a more classical manner, with hard outlines, as though impelled by a new creative urge towards the magnificent maturity of his final years.

He achieved fame and recognition in his middle period but from the age of 63 until his death when aged 78 he lived in the south of France and although crippled with arthritis, at times paralysed and confined to a wheelchair, he painted ceaselessly and achieved the most original of his masterpieces, the linearity of his middle years giving way to a more plastic sense of painting. As if the output of his later years was not enough, he modelled sculptures, often using direct transformations of painted motifs with the aid of assistants, usually Richard Guino, a pupil of Maillot, as his own hands were crippled with arthritis. His myopic vision was such that even in his sixties he did not need glasses for painting or reading. Unfortunately his biographers, including his own son (Jean Renoir, *Renoir My Father,* 1962), give insufficient insight into his thoughts and feelings to provide a convincing explanation of what drove him to an ever increasing output in old age.

Roger Bissière (1888-1964).

From the Academy of Art in Bordeaux Bissière went to Paris ostensibly to work as a journalist whilst continuing to paint landscapes of his native 'Lot et Garonne' which were notable for their strange fascination of expression. He produced equally sensitive Cubist works but from 1925-38 he was best known as a teacher of abstract art at the Academie Ransom. His own work remained highly individualistic but almost unknown. In 1939 the development of glaucoma diminished his sight to one-third normal vision and he retired to a farm near Boissierette. Whilst on the farm he carved several totemistic wooden sculptures and collaborated with his wife on a number of beautiful tapestries. His vision was partly restored by an operation in 1948. He began to paint once more and in 1957 also produced stained glass windows for Metz Cathedral. His new paintings achieved considerable fame, so much so that he was able to command some of the highest prices of any living artist for the creation of large tapestry-like compositions in warm, rich shades of gold, brown, purple and pale green. Their abstract designs were the result of a careful and sensitive reduction of natural appearances to scintillating patterns of interacting colours.

In considering the works of elderly painters, we should heed the writings of Hokusai in the preface to his *Hundred Views of Fuji:*

'All I have produced before the age of 70 is not worth taking into account. At 73 I have learned a little about the real structure of nature, of animals, plants, trees, birds, fishes and insects. In consequence, when I am 80 I shall have made still more progress. At 90 I shall penetrate the mystery of things, at 100 I shall certainly have reached a marvellous stage. I beg those who live as long as I to see if I do not keep my word. Written at the age of 75 by me, once Hokusi, today Gwakio Rojin, the old man mad about drawing.'

Visual Defects and Art

Perfect vision is not a prerequisite for an artist. Refractive errors leading to astigmatism, short-sightedness (myopia) or long-sightedness (hypermetropia), increased pressure within the eyes (glaucoma), damage to the retina or the cornea, opacities within the chambers of the globe or within the lens (cataracts), even red-green colour blindness, can affect artists as they may anyone else. Myopic sight places the emphasis on detail as seen near to and it has even been argued that peripheral, as opposed to central, vision adds to the imagery and inspired Impressionism, Constructivism and other movements in Modern Art. Lloyd Mills (1936), whose paper on *Peripheral Vision in Art* is central to this theme, had his attention drawn to the problem in the 1920s when he examined opthalmologically an artist who had a sprightly sense of colour and contour but who created curious distortions of detail, such as too long hands and enlarged knuckles, which suggested the likelihood of imperfect sight. He proved to be myopic and astigmatic and corrective glasses were supplied. The new spectacles made him aware of the distortions of his painting and led him to complain that the unaccustomed clarity of detail and colour made him lose the effects of masses of colour and of the essential lines of contours and form which are more marked when the vision is blurred. He was never able to paint in his established style when using glasses.

Lloyd Mills also claims that the myopia of Cézanne and the forced use of his distorted peripheral vision created the pattern for neo-impressionism. 'His work, except for a few self portraits, is out of focus and follows no optical laws, and his interpretation of colour, form and mass, so far as his pictures exhibit these qualities, is wholly that of distorted side-vision, with many of the secondary colour defects resulting from the myopia'. Huysmans prophetically called Cézanne 'an artist with diseased retinae who, exasperated by faulty vision, has discovered the prodromes of a new art'. In confirmation of this, Cézanne painted a portrait of his biographer, Ambroise Vollard (1865-1939) and after 115 sittings Cézanne told him 'I hope to make some progress. You understand, Monsieur Vollard, the contour keeps slipping away from me'.

Short-sightedness has a prismatic effect on light and it is scarcely surprising that many artists such as Kandinsky who were myopic were also especially interested in colour theory. Cataracts will exclude all but the red end of the spectrum and following cataract extraction a person's sight becomes bathed in a surplus of blue light. Such changes are seen in Monet's art and there are many similar examples, as with a painting of a boy in reds and yellows by the Lancashire artist, Tom Bradley. Cézanne had poor eye-sight made worse by diabetes. El Greco, Gainsborough, Modigiliani, John Singer Sergeant and Francis Bacon were astigmatic. Rembrandt and Titian in later life became hypermetropic. Monet, Matisse, Vlaminck,

Derain and Braque were myopic. Degas was extremely so and wore heavy lenses throughout his adult life. In his last years he was observed climbing the windy streets of old Montmartre, half-blind, tapping the ground with his stick like a latter day Homer. George Grosz, whose *tour de force* was representing Christ on the Cross in a gas-mask and wellies, overcame his myopia by the constant use of a pair of binoculars and Pissarro suffered from repeated ulceration of the cornea from the age of eight. Other examples will suffice to show the impact of imperfect vision upon various artists:

Sir Joshua Reynolds (1732-92) initially lost the sight in his left eye and then developed cataracts in his right eye, becoming blind in 1789. He wrote:

> 'Whilst there was yet some remainder of sight, I no sooner lay down in my bed, and turned my side, but a copious light dazzled out of my shut eyes, and, as my sight diminished, everyday colours gradually more obscure flashed out with vehemence; but now that the lucid is wholly extinct, a direct blackness, or else spotted, as it were spotted with ash-colour, is used to pour itself in, nearer to whitish than black; and the eye rolling itself a little, admits a little swallow of light, as though a chink'.

Sir Matthew Smith (1879-1959) developed cataracts. Until 1952 he showed a preoccupation with greens and yellows, browns — earthy and sunny, cool and warm — as against his reds, though these reappeared suddenly as he stretched his palette to bold, brilliant extremes, for a spate of floribunda, still life and highly decorative panels. After cataract operations his old colouration with its purples, puces, and violets returned, reflected in the clarity and effluence of his canvasses. Thereafter, his work sounds a quieter, serener strain with white and even blacks more evident.

Wyndham Lewis (1884-1957) developed a pituitary tumour. He began to lose the outer fields of vision in each eye just before the Second World War. He was just able to complete the painting of T. S. Eliot by sitting about six inches away from the canvas before the 'sea-mist' that had been closing in on both sides reached across the island of sight that remained and his days of painting were done.

The American romanticist painter, Albert Pinkham Ryder (1847-1917), suffered from myopic, damaged eyes to the detriment of his education but this did not prevent his artistic development as seen in highly imaginative, deeply religious paintings 'dwelling in dreams' and in mystical landscapes and seascapes. His methods and approach were largely self-taught and he lived and worked most of his life as a recluse and dreamer in New York, dressed like a tramp. His aphorisms reflect the visionary nature of his art which was often based upon heroic themes from opera and literature:

> The artist should fear to become the slave of detail. He should strive to express his thoughts and not the surface of it. What avails a storm cloud accurate in form and colour if the storm is not therein;
>
> An artist must feel free to create something that was 'better than nature' for it was vibrating with the thrill of new creation;

Imitation is not inspiration, and inspiration only can give birth to a work of art. The least of a man's original emanation is better than the best of a borrowed thought;

I've carried the idea for some of my pictures around in my mind for five years before I began to put them on canvas;

Have you ever seen an inch worm crawl up a leaf or twig, and then clinging to the very end, revolve in the air, feeling for something to reach? That's like me. I am trying to find something out there beyond the place on which I have a footing.

> *Who knows what God knows.*
> *His hand he never shows*
> *Yet miracles with less are wrought*
> *Even with a thought.*

Ryder's paintings reflect the limitation of his sight with a predilection for broody, nocturnal moonlit scenes and the components of his later seascapes are limited to the basic elements of boat, sky, moon, cloud and sea. The ships do not move. Their shapes are imprinted on and becalmed in stillness. He ceased painting two decades before his death, presumably because of a further impairment of his vision. The haunting quality of his expressive scenes and sombre colours have been justly praised. Unfortunately he was ignorant of many technical problems, painted over wet surfaces and used bitumen that discoloured. Many of his paintings thus cracked and decayed, so much so that another American artist, Morris Graves, deliberately cracked his paper surfaces to give a sense of age as did many forgers anxious to cash in on Ryder's national appeal.

Luminism was a characteristic of the Hudson River Group of American painters who included Washington Allston, Thomas Cole, J. F. Kensett, George Caleb Bingham, Lane, Mount and Homer. They produced paintings of a phantom-like lightness and coldness of touch and tint which gives them a somewhat unreal aspect but nonetheless they possess lyrical qualities with allegorical and dream like visions. Thus the New York Graphic Society's *Visual Dictionary of Art* (1974) decries Allston's picturesque, mysterious visions as limited by 'puritanical moral myopia'. One is left wondering how he should have corrected this mental astigmatism!

Chapter Seven

Focal Hallucinations

The image formed at the retina is transmitted along the optic nerves to the optic chiasma where a partial decussation of fibres occurs so that the inner fibres, derived from the outer fields of vision, cross to provide two binocular images which continue backwards along the optic tracts to the lateral geniculate bodies and thence are relayed via the optic radiations within the substance of the brain to the calcarine region at the tip of the occipital cortex. The occipital cortex functions as a 'screen' upon which the illuminated perceptions, derived from the eyes, optic tracts, lateral geniculate bodies and from other parts of the brain, impinge. In the course of transmission other fibres derived from the retina will be diverted elsewhere to aid such involuntary acts, connected with vision, as alerting, following and focussing. At each stage in the progression we must assume that some modification, and possibly some distortion, of the image may occur. We know, for example, that the retinal image is inverted on the cortex, and we presume that our dreams and thought images are also projected on to the same cortical fields. The further analysis of the information received by the primary visual cortex occurs in cortical and subcortical areas anterior to the occipital lobe; and, by and large, the further from the occipital pole the more the image is elaborated and integrated with other functions including body image and language in the parietal lobe; hearing, bodily sensations and the emotions in the temporal lobe; but ultimately all parts of the brain have a role in thought, perception and the intergrated functions that stem from their elaboration.

True hallucinations may arise from focal irritation to nerve cells or neural pathways within the nervous system or from 'release' of inhibiting influences upon these cells even in states of clear consciousness from metabolic or drug induced disturbances. The type of insults provoking the hallucination — tumors, degenerative states, vascular disorders, trauma

— in no way determine the form of the hallucination. The ease with which hallucinations may be released by irritative stimuli, e.g. electrical stimulation to cortical cells, has suggested that these phenomena have a physical, that in non-physcial, basis in keeping with the definition of a true hallucination as fundamentally a percept of memory abnormally released, or excited, by an unusual stimulus.

The focal nature of this instability was clearly recognised in 1888 by Dr. Hughlings-Jackson, the doyen of British neurology, with respect to epilepsy. Epilepsy has been known since time immemorial and can arise as a symptom of many forms of disordered cerebral function. The word implies no more than a paroxysmal and transitory disturbance of the functions of the brain which develops suddenly, ceases spontaneously, and exhibits a conspicuous tendency to recur. The epileptic disturbance can take many forms: with localised or generalised involuntary movements, or loss or alterations of consciousness, or spontaneous sensations, i.e. hallucinations. There is initially a localised hypersynchronised discharge (shorting) of groups of brain cells. Provided the spread of abnormal activity does not occur too rapidly with early impairment of consciousness, an aura or warning phase is recognisable and directly relates to the localisation of the initial cellular disturbance. Thus there can be many forms of aura or primary sensation. In Dostoyevsky's case his aura took on a non-visual form with a brief experience of an altered emotional state of pleasure:

'There are moments, and it is only a matter of five or six seconds, when you feel the presence of the eternal harmony . . . a terrible thing is the frightful clearness with which it manifests itself and the rapture with which it fills you. If this state were to last more than five seconds, the soul could not ´endure it and would have to disappear. During these five seconds, I live a whole human existence and for what I would give my whole life and not think that I was paying it too dearly . . . remember Mohammed's water jug; for the space of time it took to empty it, the prophet was rapt into Paradise. Your five seconds are the jar . . . Paradise is your harmony . . . the Mohammed was epileptic!'

In the poem, *Mazeppa,* Byron describes his own elaborate visual aura:

'The sky spun like a mighty wheel;
I saw the trees like drunkards reel,
And a light flash sprang o'er my eyes,
Which saw no farther. He who dies,
Can die no more than I died'.

It is not always possible, even after death, to determine in anatomical terms from whence an epileptic aura arose; but the Canadian neurosurgeon, Dr. Wilder Penfield, and his co-workers took advantage of the insensitivity of the surface of the brain to examine at operation the effect of focal electrical stimulation and the nature of the hallucinations which can be provoked at different sites of stimulation. Thus when stimulating near the occipital pole he was able to report that his patients described: 'flickering lights, dancing lights, colours, bright lights, stars, wheels, blue, green and red coloured discs, fawn and blue lights, coloured whirling balls, radiating grey spots, becoming pink and blue and a long white mark'.

These findings are relatively unexciting compared to the more varied findings when the temporal lobe is stimulated. One patient heard an orchestra playing a certain song when a point on the superior surface of the right temporal lobe was stimulated after removal of the anterior half of the lobe. The hearing seemed to her so realistic that she thought a gramaphone had been turned on. The same spot was restimulated many times and each time she heard the same orchestra which seemed to begin playing at the same place in the same piece. When she was warned falsely, and the stimulation was withheld, she heard nothing; when stimulated, with or without warning, she heard it. When she hummed, accompanying the music in her mind, the tempo was about what might have been expected of an orchestra. The continued repetition seemed to facilitate this particular response rather than other possible responses. It was not a song that she knew very well and she could not recall when it was that she had 'heard it that way before'.

Another person responded to stimulation of the right temporal lobe: 'I hear people coming in — I hear music now, a funny little piece'. Stimulation was continued and she went on to explain that the music she was hearing was the theme song of a children's programme. Among those with visual experiences, one saw a man fighting but when the point was restimulated he saw a man and a dog walking along a road. Another patient exclaimed, 'Oh I had the same very, very familiar memory — in an office somewhere, I could see the desks. I was there and someone was calling to me, a man leaning on a desk with a pencil in his hand'.

Penfield (1955) comments that these are all 'strips' of experience. Sometimes the patient can recall the event, more often it has faded from recollective memory. But always it is familiar and he seems to be present and acknowledges it as part of his own past. When music is heard, he may not be aware of its source or he may seem to be present in the theatre or church or cafe. He may re-experience the sense of enjoyment that came to him that moment. Because such phenomena can occasionally be produced by stimulation of the cortex of the temporal lobe, Penfield suggested that the electrical current follows a pathway of facilitation that was formed during the original experience while other pathways remain closed to it. However, it may well be that direct stimulation of the brain produced a purely artefactive effect but comparison with naturally sustained insults to the brain is difficult for the reason that most forms of insult, e.g. infections, tumors, abscesses and vascular accidents, although capable of producing hallucinations, invariably involve many parts of the brain and produce diffuse effects upon it. In future, we may be able to be more scientific as we are now entering an era when refined techniques of brain scanning at last enable us to recognise much smaller areas of brain damage, as from localised vascular disease; but the most accurate localising information to date has been that derived from the study of traumatic injury, particularly that sustained in combat.

Traumatic epilepsy resulting from war wounds has proved a valuable aid to cerebral localisation. Patients can survive such injury provided certain central structures have not been destroyed, and it is possible to hypothesize a schema of cerebral localisation which has a theoretical and imprecise value with considerable overlap. What is evident is that the facility with which hallucinations are produced is proportional to the wealth of interconnections from cells at various sites. If we ignore this clinical fact and assume that a cell at a particular locus has a specific function, we can dogmatically suppose that cells at the occipital pole of the calcarine cortex produce static light and stars, that stimulation of cells in their neighbourhood may either cause negative phenomena in the form of a grey or black fog, or positive lights which appear at the periphery and move towards the centre, and from the parieto-occipital cortex (including parastriate areas 19) the hallucinations are stereotyped but have the appearance of formed objects, people and animals (zoonoses). While these apparitions are one degree more complex than the flashes, zig zags and whorls of colour obtained from the primary receptive cortex, they fall short of an integrated visual memory.

The parietal, occipital and temporal association areas are ontogenetically the last parts of the brain to reach the adult state of maturity. Myelination of nerve fibres can be delayed until late adolescence and this presumably permits some plasticity of functional development. Delayed or impaired myelination may account for certain specific learning dysfunctions. On the other hand the especial developments of these areas may account for the most highly developed talents of artists, musicians and others. From these same association areas other phenomena may occur along with visual hallucinations. These include perseveration of a visual impression, either in time (palinopsia) or in space (visual illusory spread), impaired visual recognition (visual agnosia), failure to recognise faces — usually of humans, but a farmer may fail to recognise his animals (prosopagnosia),*— defective visual localisation, errors in naming colours (anomia), and defective preception of colours (achromatopsia).

Hallucinations from the temporal cortex are more complex, thus scenes recalled from previous experience, e.g. a stereotyped scenario of a train crash, may recur or follow stimulation of the posterior part of the temporal lobe. Visual hallucinations alone may result from stimulation of a large area of the lateral surface of the non-dominant temporal lobe. Elsewhere, they may be combined with auditory hallucinations, may involve distortion of the size of objects (macropsia or micropsia), or be associated with sensations of familiarity *(deja vu)* or unfamiliarity *(jamias vu),* with depersonalisation or personalisation of the image (autoscopy). The Doppelgänger phenomenon (heutoscopy) where a person sees a phantom image of himself is most commonly attributed to lesions too complex to be represented on a body schema.

---

* A syndrome with poor anatomical localisation is that of Capgras — the delusions of doubles — the patient appears to preceive changes in familiar faces and there follows a delusional elaboration as to the cause of this, i.e. the reason for the replacement in the patient's mind of a spouse, relative or friend by a double or imposter. The syndrome may follow either neurological or psychiatric disease.

Other areas of the brain appear to produce particular forms of apparition. Parietel lobe lesions may be associated with visual extinction of part of the field of vision or a somatosensory neglect of one half of the body; thus the individual may eat from food on one side of a plate only or put on one trouser leg but not the other. Even rarer he may have a feeling of actual reduplication of a limb. Hallucinations from the uncinate area of the temporal lobe commonly give rise to rancid burning smells and abnormal tastes, but this hallucination may be accompanied by a visual image of a little dark woman cooking or carrying sticks. Kaleidoscopic, Lilliputian, penduncular hallucinations are usually ascribed to release of dream imagery but can arise from tumours and other organic disturbances of the mid brain and brain stem. Minute, vividly coloured visual images of people, animals, plants, scenes or geometric patterns are usually pleasurably received but may rarely occasion a sense of fear.

Although individual case reports do describe visual hallucinations arising elsewhere in the brain or along the optic tracts, their rarity is in sharp contrast to the frequency with which tactile sensations can arise from almost anywhere within the nervous system. In practice, as stated, the complexity of the hallucinations does not provide accurate localisation; thus a patient described by Putnam with an occipital tumour experienced unformed hallucinations — spots, circles, flashes of light — prior to surgery but following the craniotomy saw a variety of formed images — Dante's profile, Theodore Roosevelt, a white punchinello who kept bowing, dogs, goats, lions, a Japenese warrior in a tortoise shell armour, and a fat man blowing his nose. This is by no means as isolated example: where blindness affects part of the field of vision, as from a thrombosis in the territory of the posterior cerebral artery, there is often a latent period before hallucinations appear. The earlier hallucinations tend to be simple — rows of dots, patterns or mosaics — but later give way to more complex scenery, people and bizarre architectural features.

In most instances, hallucinations arising from the brain in clear consciousness are confined to one part of the field of vision and appear consistently in that direction; thus a lady was frightened by tripping over white cats which ran in front of her left leg. Another patient of mine aged 73 had had several strokes affecting his field of vision to his right and had hallucinations of people. These were quite fascinating in their complexity. He would sense that there was a man with a donkey fringe sitting on his right, a little man who his wife had to tell to go away and eventually he disappeared. Sometimes when people entered the room from his right he would see them wearing a different dress and carrying a babe on their lap or something of that sort. The wall in front of him appeared to have a picture of a very attractive Indian lady complete with a cast mark on her forehead. He would also see on the wall to his right a picture of the Last Supper or of Roman soldiers and when his wife left the room she would appear to walk through the wall.

Just as failing vision within the eye may be associated with hallucinations, so failing vision caused by disorder of the primary receptive cortex can be a source of hallucinations. Cortical blindness can be complete (total) or partial, either involving islands of vision (scotomata) or part of the field of vision, e.g. one quadrant or a hemianopic loss, or, alternatively, isolation of the cortex may occur due to disruption of the connecting fibres. Cortical blindness may at first be denied (Anton's syndrome), perhaps because the visual image is replaced by a grey mist or other phosphenes. Most frequently patients are unaware of partial loss of vision, apparently ignoring what cannot be seen; alternatively the defective hemianopic field may be occupied by phosphenes of heterogenous colours or shapes, or even by patterned phosphenes in the four major colours — red, green, blue and yellow — as reported by Kölmel (1984). There is an increased likelihood that organised hallucinations will occupy part of the blind field; thus, in dementia a blind hemianopic field may be colonised by imaginary strangers who remorselessly gesticulate and from whom there is no escape. Freakish and mischievous intruders may plague the aged arterio-sclerotic especially if his conscience is unclear (Savin, 1958).

Split brain operations have been performed for the relief of otherwise intractable epilepsy and for some tumours. The operation involves a longitudinal separation of the connecting fibres between the two hemispheres. Thereafter the visions which fall upon two occipital cortices are processed differently. On one side objects may be seen but cannot be described: on the other the patient may be able to describe what is seen but not copy it. Other forms of 'blind vision' also exist whereby people may appear to respond to objects which theoretically they do not see. The defect is presumably not so much that of the visual cortex but of a partial disruption of certain connecting fibres emanating from it. Thus one patient of mine who had had a stroke would react violently and suddenly to approaching traffic on his blind side when seated in the front passenger seat of a car.

Lilliputian Hallucinations

A curious feature of several 17th-century artists was the manner in which they peppered their scenes with hundreds of small, elongated tatter-dermalion figures whilst skilfully avoiding the effect of overcrowding by masterly grouping and perspective. In the works of Jacques Callot (1592-1635), Pieter van Laer, known as Il Bamboccio, (1592-1642), and Allessandro Magnasco, known as Il Lissandrino, (1667-1749), monks, nuns, gipsies, mercenaries, witches, beggars, hunchbacks and inquisitors were presented in grotesque manneristic style. If there was an hallucinatory inspiration for such diminutive figures, several sources are possible. Micropsia (small sight) occurs with temporal lobe involvement; drugs such as modern barbiturates and damage to the occipital cortex with impairment of the fields of vision can all be associated with reduced size of hallucinatory objects; thus the Australian neurologist, James Lance (1976), when recording hallucinations arising from the occipital cortex, notes that whereas most apparitions from this region of the brain appeared lifelike, full-sized and clear in detail, two of his patients experienced visions that were smaller than lifesize, one patient a quarter life-size and two others tiny visions of giraffes and hippopotamuses sitting on the right side of a pillow, and a little man crawling on the foot of the bed respectively.Migraine attacks involving either the occipital or temporal lobes are the most likely inspiration for Swift's *Gulliver's Travels in Lilliput,* illustrated by Arthur Rackham and others, and for the 1864 *Childrens Book of Verse, Lilliput Levée* by W.B. Rands, illustrated by Sir John Everett Millais and G. J. Pinwall.

However, a tantalising group of hallucinations in search of an anatomical localisation are the peduncular of Lilliputian hallucinations, first recognised in France in the 1920s. The novelist, Alfred de Musset, experienced visions which passed before his eyes, so much so that he would question his brother Paul as to whether they were real or imaginary. 'Un petit homme haut de trois pouces et portant sur son dos une fontaine de marchand de coco ambulant. Ce Lilliputien se promena sur l'écritoire et sur les livres'. Leroy (1921) associated 'd'hallucinations visuelles, miniscules, colorées, avec un état affectif généralement agréeable' with toxic states, in alcoholism and in fever. Flourney in 1923 considered that they represented a regression to an infantile state with sexual and phallic connotations*; but their localisation to the brainstem and midbrain was suggested by L'Hermitte (1922) when he described a 72 year old lady with vascular disease of the midbrain. She had vivid hallucinations of cats, chickens and children and, as L'Hermitte noted, these would present when drowsy or mildly confused, representing a release of dream activity normally suppressed during wakefulness. Patients with these hallucinations tend to be sleepy but can be wakened and the onset of visions most readily occurs in the dark when silent, mobile figures in bright colours flit past the eyes like scenes in a motion picture, usually appearing mildly amusing but occasionally evoking a sense of fear and anxiety. The anatomical localisation and reality of L'Hermitte's syndrome has been disputed. Few modern neurologists have first-hand experience of this syndrome which can be mimicked in hypnagogic states and with drug intoxication but there is a report wherein angiography of the vertebral artery, supplying the brainstem, induced in several patients elaborate peduncular hallucinations and even Pick's visions in which the patient claims that he can see through walls into adjacent rooms.

Image Persistence

Experimental psychologists and artists of the Op Art and Kinetic Art schools are especially aware that the brain and eye may be tricked by the illusory spread or continuation of certain colours, shapes or patterns. If a series of objects is flashed on a screen at high speed, a normal person may have difficulty in attending to any one particular aspect of the fleeting impressions. He will be helped in his selection of detail where the image

---

*Flourney (1923)

'Il semble bien y avoir dans cette action du lancement une régression à une stade infantile. Il s'agit, dans cette dernière image, de la vision désexualisée d'une naissance, au moyen du serpent, le symbole bien connu d'organe generateur. La fantasie de la naissance peut se manifester sous une forme plus crue, lorsque l'être humain sort d'un autre être humanin. Mais ici encore l'image primitivement sexuelle est travestie, en ce sens que c'est en général le front on l'oeil sont le seige de cette mise au mode.

of a particular object appears to stick or remain, lingering in the mind's eye after others in the sequence have passed, and will find the task easier if the sequence of objects is repeated a second or a third time. He may be helped or hindered in his selection of detail by any emotional associations he may have with the objects exhibited.

Normal after images have well recognised characteristics:

the intensity and duration of the initial visual stimulus determines the intensity and duration of subsequent after images; a high intensity stimulus can even elicit a flight of coloured after images;

the apparent size of the after image may increase when seen against a far surface as compared with a near surface;

against a dark background the image is the same colour as the stimulus but with a light background the colours may be compliment-ary (e.g green after red);

after images may be prolonged or reappear after a blink or a wave of the hand in front of the eyes;

the after image of a stimulus seen by one eye is perceived binocularly;

several after images may be seen concurrently; and the after image may appear to move with movement of the eyes.

Eidetic images (discussed earlier) are similar in many respects to after images. However, they are usually richer in detail and are evoked more readily and persist longer than normal after images.

Under the influence of drugs or with evolving lesions of the brain other, more abnormal phenomena may occur. An illusory extension of the visual perception over an area greater than that which the stimulus object would be expected to excite (visual illusory spread) may occur so that 'if a person were wearing a striped or chequered garment, the pattern would seem to extend over the person's face; the pattern of cretonne curtains would often seem to extend along the adjacent wall; or iron railings round a park would appear to extend across the road and the taxi, bringing the patient to hospital, appear to be charging through this barrier'. One artist who appears to use visual illusory spread is the Fauve painter, Henri Matisse (1869-1954) in Madame Matisse: the Green Line, where a vertical green line is central to the portrait, and in Woman with the Hat, where one side of her hair appears red, the other green and the face is streaked with lilac, green and blue.

The other term, palinopsia (palin = again) was also coined by Macdonald Critchley (1951) to describe episodic illusory after images which reappear as hallucinations, i.e. the reoccurrence of visual perceptions after the stimulus object has been removed. Once again those affected have either taken drugs or have evolving cerebral lesions. At half-hour intervals the image of a Dresden china dog, an alarm clock, camels from a circus, or a zebra would recur. The images could be of subject matter seen anywhere from seconds to many years before. The appearance may not be disturbing; one patient appeared to enjoy placing the palinoptic image of a doctor's beard on the faces of the nurses as they entered the ward. Palinoptic images may be multiple, thus Teuber (1961) tells of a patient, who after the real image of a motorcycle had formed across his bad visual field, saw a string of motorcycles standing still. Use of repeated objects, anticipating cinephotography, was developed as an art form by Man Ray and Art Warhol.

An additional, but rare phenomenon, in most cases associated with migraine where temporary impairment of circulation to the occipital cortex can lead to displacement of the image, is optic alloaesthesia whereby the optical image is inverted so that people may appear to be walking on the ceiling. It is in a way surprising that visual phenomena as described above are exceedingly rare when compared to the frequency with which sounds may linger, recur or spread; repeated pin pricks lose their precise localisation or an itch persist long after the stimulus is removed.

The Visual Hallucinations of Migraine

Millions of people will have experienced in the course of their lives many of the phenomena associated with migraine. Migraine can afflict healthy people at the height of their powers and, after a few hours or days of torment, leave them fully restored to health and their powers undiminished.

'Inside my brain a dull tom-tom begins
Absurdly hammering a prelude of its own,
Capricious monotone
That is at least one definite 'false note'.'

T.S. Eliot.

One in 10 of the population is prone to common migraine, 1 in 50 liable to classical migraine and 1 in 200 experience attacks of focal migraine. Shakespeare, Dryden, Cervantes, Pope, Swift, Trollope, Chesterton, Kipling, Emerson, W. S. Gilbert, Mary Stewart, Pamela Hansford Johnson and Arthur Ransome have all utilised their own experiences of migraine in their writings. The teichopsia of classical migraine is one of the most commonly experienced forms of visual hallucinations; what remains surprising is that, although such forms closely resemble the imagery of Op and Kinetic art as exemplified by Victor Vasarely and Bridget Riley, the connection between art and migraine is so rarely drawn. Perhaps people search for more colourful explanations, e.g. that the imagery was induced by drugs or derived from a study of primitive art.

To illustrate the sheer complexity of visual experiences which can occur with migraine I propose to do no more than quote from a standard book of advice for patients with headaches and migraines (1980).

'Classical migraine is the term used when the symptoms of unilateral headache are preceded by warning signs such as disturbed vision, taking such forms as zig-zags, brightly coloured spots or islands of visual loss. Occasionally, when the visual scintillation phenomena are severe, there may be photophobia, scotomata and fortification spectra. These symptoms occur with constriction of blood vessels and often last for 10 to 30 minutes before the onset of headache.

Focal migraine is the term used when focal symptoms overshadow the actual headache attacks. The visual symptoms may be quite dramatic with brightly scintillating, shimmering or coloured blobs causing patches of visual loss. Visions may be lost to one side, at the sides, or altitudinally. The disturbances may appear hallucinatory with objects appearing larger, smaller, or, as a mosaic, like broken coloured pebbles. Colours may be heightened or objects appear strange or unduly familiar. Double vision or drooping of the eyelid can occur. With retinal migraine the loss of vision in one eye may be followed by a headache localised to the affected eye. With other types of focal attacks, speech may be affected with words slurred or jumbled. One half of the body may go numb or weak.' Critchley (1980).

There is a rare form, seen mainly in children, consisting of hallucinations in which the size or shape of the body is distorted — the Alice in Wonderland, or Alice and the Mushroom disorder. I can quote the experiences of an adult, a lady of 20 who, whilst sitting having tea, stretched out her right hand and thought it seemed to have grown. She could not see to her right or see her children on the settee. Then the arm, from the elbow to the finger tips, appeared numb and her speech became garbled. The right side of her mouth went dead. The whole episode lasted 20-30 minutes.

The Swiss neurologist, Professor Baumgartner (1977), provides a more scientific account of the visual symptoms:

'Of 84 patients with disturbances of vision in connection with headaches, 52 reported as a first sign only 'defective vision'. No one was able to describe clearly the kind of defect, or to relate it to one eye or to one half of the visual field. "Something is different in my eyes. I can't tell you what, but I know I shall have another migraine in a few minutes". Following these changes, or without this preceding warning, 48 patients reported scintillations in the entire visual field, sometimes with a preponderance in one half. These scintillations often were compared with the interference on a television screen. In 23 patients, the scintillation was followed by dysopsias, i.e. perceptions of translucent, sometimes moving spots, mostly in one half or one quarter of the visual field. Scintillating scotomas were reported following the entopic scintillations and spot perceptions in 26 cases: the scotomas were always binocular and corresponded to the characteristic fortification spectra of the literature. Bright zig-zag line elements were commonly described, consisting of either one or two stripes slowly spreading across the field. The single line elements were magnified when the fortification band was propagating to the periphery of the visual field. At the same time, the speed of the spread seemed to accelerate. The fortification lines were followed by scotoma, in which occasionally filling-in processes were described. In only 7 patients were fortification illusions with scotoma reported without preceding simple, uncharacteristic visual defects, scintillations or translucent spots. Different phases of this process could occur simultaneously in different regions of the visual field so that it is often very difficult to obtain an unambiguous description. Colour phenomena within the zig-zag lines of the fortification spectra, and motion illusions of the spots were frequent but irregular.'

No wonder Lewis Carroll (Charles Lutwidge Dodgson), who suffered from classical migraine, which in his diary he called 'bilious headaches' and which were preceded by the eye disturbances we now recognise as 'fortification spectra', was able to draw upon the whole experience of migrainous phenomena to provide the fantasy which gave the world *Alice in Wonderland* and *Alice through the Looking Glass*. *Alice in Wonderland* starts and ends with a vertiginous aura, speech is jumbled to produce the Jabberwocky poem, islands of scotomatous vision appear and recede as the Cheshire Cat, the baby metamorpheses into a pig, splitting of images produces Tweedledum and Tweedledee — ' "I'm very brave generally", he went on in a low voice, "only today I happen to have a headache" '— Alice grows and diminishes in size — the same illusion that Swift used in *Gulliver's Travels* — all these have been immortalised in Linnell's illustrations.

Victor Hugo, *Le Rêve,* pen and ink drawing, *Cliché: musées de la Ville de Paris.* © by Spadem, 1987.

Giorgio de Chirico (1888-1978), *The Melancholy of Departure,* oil on canvas, The Tate Gallery. © DACS, 1987.

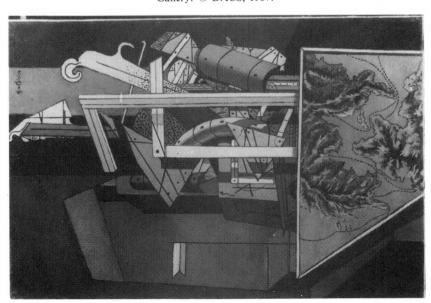

Tanguy, *The Invisibles,* The Tate Gallery. © ADAGP, 1987.

Goya, *The Colossus,* Museo del Prado.

Henry Fuseli (1741-1825), *Lady Macbeth Seizing the Daggers,* oil on canvas, The Tate Gallery.

Michaux, *Unititled Chinese Ink,* The Tate Gallery. His drawings under the influence of mescaline became stereotyped and uninteresting.

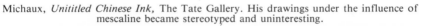

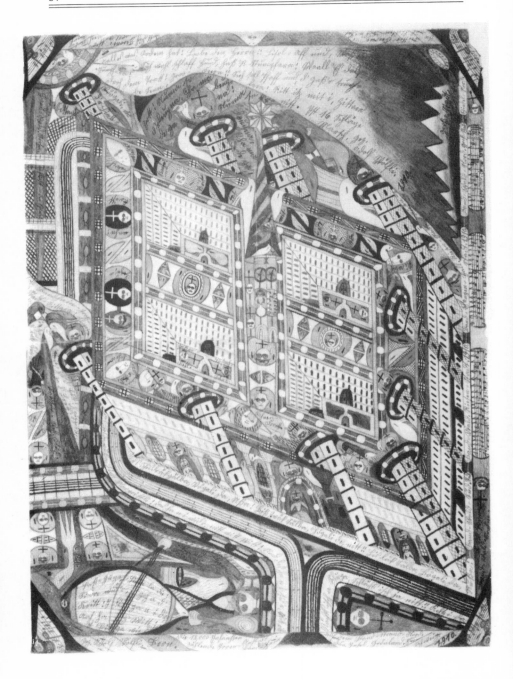

(Above): Edvard Munch, *The Scream,* © Oslo Kommunes Kunstsamlinger.

(Opposite): Adolf Wölfli (1864-1930), *Mental Asylum Band = Hain,* 1910, pencil and colourpencil on newsprint. Wölfli spent most of his life in a mental asylum and signed his pictures 'St Adolf II'.

Tête Bêche Error - a similar inversion of images can occur during an attack of migraine.

Richard Dadd (1817-1866), *The Fairy Feller's Master-Stroke,* oil on canvas, The Tate Gallery. Dadd murdered his father and spent most of his life in an asylum.

(Left): Peter Lanyon (1918-1964), *Thermal,* oil on canvas, The Tate Gallery.

(Below): John Martin (1789-1854), *The Fallen Angels Entering Pandemonium* from *Paradise Lost,* Bk 1, oil on canvas, The Tate Gallery. 'Mad' John Martin's work is perhaps typified in this apocalyptic picture.

(Above): Dante Gabriel Rossetti (1828-1882), *The Beloved ('The Bride'),* oil on canvas, The Tate Gallery. A Pre-Raphaelite fantasy picture.

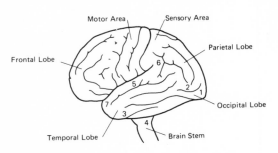

(Left): A lateral view of the brain to illustrate areas involved in hallucinations.

1. Unforced visual hallucinations: flashes, cones, bright lights
2. Partially formed visual hallucinations identifiable shapes
3. Zoonoses: small animals
4. Lilliputian hallucinations: small people
5. Auditory hallucinations
6. Complex hallucinations: battle scenes and noises
7. Smells

Chapter Eight

Childhood and Primitive Art

'Genius is childhood found again at will'.
Baudelaire

IF we search the animal kingdom for nascent thought processes and imaginative experiences from which human creativity could be said to have arisen, we turn from laborious tool-using attempts, to exciting courtship displays and finally settle on the lively fantasy of the play routines of young animals. In abstract preparedness, the manoeuvres of the attack — stalking, waiting, the spring to action, the fight and the joys of success — are acted out. The more timorous cub will play along with its bolder companion until it too acquires courage to emulate its peer. In the absence of a playmate, imaginary objects or harmless insects may be treated as though they represented live game to be captured and despatched triumphantly.

In our society, children are given similar disinhibited but sheltered opportunities to act out anticipatory struggles of later years. They perform with a freedom to act, explore and fantasise — to see visions and to dream dreams — which becomes stultified by inhibitions as they approach puberty. The rich capacity of each child to derive pleasure, and horror, from dreams and to fantasise — bringing their dolls to life, giving them separate personalities or adopting imaginary companions who can even be shared among their close friends — would suggest that the potential would exist for children's art to embody all the romanticised claims made about it. Unfortunately, this is not so. There seems little wonder that mature artists try to place themselves in the positions of children and with the wit, technical skill and humour of Paul Klee try to bring to life the 'wasted dreams of childhood'. In commercial life, the whole enterprise involved in selling children's toys, 'love-objects' and games has been adapted to tap the same potential. Strangely, only in the use of computers and computer games do most children far surpass most adults. Why so?

Children differ from the young of animals in the prolongation of the period of helplessness, dependence, and learning. Once an animal ceases to suckle or a bird leaves its nest it is mature in its motor skills. The foal is no longer clumsy after the first week of life. The human evolutionary success story, by contrast, depends not on innate genetic preconditioning but upon the prolongation of childhood — prolonged foetalisation in the continued growth of the brain after birth, the unsophisticated development of the hands allowing later flexible, skilled development, and the prolongation of the period for learning, acquiring knowledge and developing skills.

The romantic notion that the newborn somehow represent a purity of perfection takes various forms. King James I believed in a *lingua adamaica* — that all children left to their own devices would speak perfect Hebrew or perfect Latin. The birth cry of a male child to the untutored ear may sound very like 'o-ah' but if listened to carefully was 'O Adam cur peccacisti' (Oh, Adam why has thou sinned?). In like manner, many people even today assume that the newborn child is a thinking individual even from or before birth, though there is little reason to believe that thought is possible before language and gesture provide the vehicles for thought. A similar claim is made that childhood drawing represents an uncontaminated view of the body image as seen by a child. What is the actuality about language, thought and body image?

Firstly, language develops from very limited beginnings but its development is aided by an emerging framework of syntax and grammar (Lenneberg, 1967). The progression from babbling to speech is dependent upon a variety of reflex mechanisms, environmental, organic and psychological factors. The capacity to listen develops before the capacity to speak. Secondly, the initial comprehension of the environment into which a babe is born is very limited. At first the babe, its mouth, the source or warmth and the source of milk is a continuum. Its next focus is the mother's face, her voice and her touch in lifting and holding. Everything else is strange and resisted. Gradually the little world of the play pen and the family takes shape. Starting school, several years later, is the first occasion when the average child begins to make relationships outside its immediate family. It has yet to learn to play with or even alongside other children. The barriers of total ego-centricity are beginning to be breeched. Thirdly, we know very little about a child's concept of its body image. Drawing is a highly artificial mode of expression: the moulding of malleable and flexible materials is more likely to be helpful. The early depiction of a man as a head with two legs is highly stylised and bears little relation to what the child sees of its own image. Boaz (Primitive Art, 1955) tells the story of an Eskimo asked to draw the picture of a hunt, failed miserably, but when given a piece of ivory and allowed to carve the scene did so beautifully.

The adult world is stigmatised as stultified and inhibited but the number of possiole symbols is vastly greater than that of the child's world. Adults find that the capacity for abstract art is not innate in all of us. It is not from lack of confidence that each of us is not a potential Grandma Moses. If the truth were tested, most of our attempts would be crude, dull and stylised. The best abstract art is born of a profound knowledge of Universal Art: just as the best of all kinds of pictorial art is inspired by the appreciation of earlier masters. How then does a child's art develop?

Give a two year old a pencil and it will scribble; a set of crayons and it will crayon, often preferring the more garish colours. Given a brush it will paint. But the scribbling, the crayonning and the painting will be indecipherable. Such a child is not preoccupied by meaning, form or colour, but with the materials it is using and the physical manipulation of the brush. It may be distracted by using brushes of different sizes. Interest lies in the 'act' of painting. The child would prefer to paint with its finger tips but, told to hold and use a brush, a less certain thrust of the paints upon the paper is achieved. The essence of the Montessori school of teaching recognises the need of a child to explore the environment using water, sand, clay, paint and plasticine. By such means the child not only develops motor skills but is using its visual and tactile sensations to explore the environment mentally. With greater control the direction of scribble becomes less haphazard, chance forms appear, single arcs may be made using the dominant hand, vertical marks appear easier to accomplish than horizontal, dots and blots occur in addition to lines.

The next stage in development would suggest that the child is handicapped by the comparatively slow rate of development of its motor skills. As with speech development in which action words come before concrete nouns, the four year old moves from play with materials to the attempt to display action. His effort may amount to no more than something that looks like a crude three sided box, but when asked what he has painted he will produce an involved dramatic story with non-sequitors so that one may hunt in vain to connect the account with what appears on his paper. He strives after communication and the parallel with the confabulatory drawing of adult schizoprenics who will add, for example, snakes from every orifice to explain certain forms of possession, will be seen in the manner whereby a drawn object makes free a stream of disconnected thoughts.

Between five and seven years stylized and symbolic painting first appears. The scribble of a five year old is more controlled and the more distinct marks take on basic forms and simple formulae start to appear. Thus for all animals a body, head, four legs or an eye are presented in juxtaposition. Symbols are at first disjointed but the component parts are realised and placed adjacent to one another. A car or train is a box with four wheels in proximity. Men appear face on as a circle for head with vertical lines representing the legs. Later the head remains a circle situated above a round or elongated trunk, arms stick out with sausage like fingers, five per hand, and the legs are similarly represented. In the succeeding stage each part is jointed together, the head is smaller and more in proportion to the rest of the body, but a part such as an arm may appear relatively enlarged if some action, such as carrying a sword, requires its emphasis. This is, curiously, the only way in which an awareness of body schema may be said to affect the stylism of the picture.

With development, stylisation becomes more and more obsessional. The picture tells a story. The child may step into the picture: 'Me' driving a car, an aeroplane, train or boat. Fantasy may dictate the choice of subjects

— rockets, speed, machines. This schematic stage is of greatest interest to adult imitators. Animals are drawn in profile, a schematic house appears with a garden path to the door, smoke comes from the chimney and other additions decorate the picture. If a bridge is drawn, a train will cross it or a ship sail beneath. The sun will overshadow the picture of a house. All these suggest that the child between 7 and 10 years is becoming inventive but the sad aspect is that children left to themselves at this stage without guidance of their proclivities seldom improve their drawing skill relative to their mental prowess (Lindstrom, 1957).

Most teaching of art from 9 years upwards is through art classes selecting those keenest to continue. The stage from 9 to 12 is described as that of 'dawning realism' (Lowenfeld, 1970). Interest can be sustained but there is a tendency to draw from memory or imagination — usually with over-elaborate faces, ships, buildings and people in profile. At the same time, there is an increasing awareness of natural surroundings and the budding artist begins to worry about such things as proportion and depth in drawing and differences and gradations of colour. Progress may appear to be held up because of the degree of self-criticism which the child imposes on its efforts. Beyond 12 years, children become aware of the need to show expression in their portraits, to copy nature as something beautiful and to show a real interest in visual art but inhibitions may limit the imaginative scope of their product.

Artists in search of childhood imagery have another cause to talk of 'wasted dream'. Few will have possessed the early strength of their art to produce a strong visual memory, as did Blake, from the eidetic imagery of early childhood. The most persistent eidetic imagery is found in low IQ children or others who have difficulty in converting their thoughts from reproductions of actual scenes into a more flexible form. Various forms of pubescent fantasy life do emerge in art: hero worship of sporting types, fashion models, explorers, pop stars, astronauts; obsession with sports cars, motor boats or horses may transmit their enthusiasm into art. Lukianowicz (1960) describes the strength of visual sexual and masturbatory fantasies but these are rarely allowed to be expressed in teenage art; they surface in various forms of adult anti-establishment art, in Dada, Surrealism, and particularly in the works of Salvador Dali who employed every conceivable academic technique to convey infantile obsessions and masturbatory affective imagery, many of which were lifted from Krafft-Ebing's *Psychopathia Sexualis* (1899), a treatise recording an enormous variety of psycho-pathological manifestations of sexual life, laying special stress on the symbolism of sexual aberrations such as sadism, masochism and fetishism.

Ever since the beginning of the century when Picasso, Matisse and others started to collect and study African art and Picasso, for one, used the newly discovered dimensional relationships as the basis for his epoch making picture Les Desmoiselles d'Avignon, interest has centred upon what precisely we may learn from Primitive Art. It was soon realised that such art does not represent an innocent childlike depiction of people, creatures and objects emphasising a less developed, or less civilised, body image of the structure created. It is neither a spontaneous, emotional outpouring nor a mystical, intuitive creation. Primitive peoples of today do not think in a totally different, less evolved way from civilised man, nor is their art at a distinctly lower stage of evolution.

Primitive Art is best described as 'high art of low cultures' (Fraser, 1962). Such art may appear as an extension of folk art or crafts and, like a craft, is something produced for a purpose: the function is often ritualistic or social. The aims of the artist are essentially those of his group. He is rarely employed just as an artist but will be selected for the production of a prestige object. His selection may be natural or highly ritualistic: perhaps chosen from a clan within a tribe noted for particular craft skill for which he has been trained from puberty or shown a capacity for enjoying carving. Just occasionally the basis of selection may be that he has been shown to possess proven magical powers since infancy. Once selected, he will be ordered to produce an object for an express purpose. Like the icon producer, he may have to make himself fit for the task. He may need to produce, adapt or invent the tools for the purpose or learn the method to be used by rote from an elder. The dyes may be ceremoniously produced, the wood specially cut and seasoned. The whole tribe may participate thus far in the object's preparation. Fraser described primitive art as an endless incantation given visual form. Not surprisingly even when modern methods of production are used, there will be close conformity to prevailing types. The object, for example, may replace one several generations old which has fallen into disuse. Boaz (1955) in his careful analysis of the symbols of primitive art comments that by a process of 'slurring', the symbols may take on a pattern through the degeneration of their original perspective design. The remoteness of their resemblance to the objects they symbolise may be historically determined. If the object does not conform to our image of what it is meant to depict, e.g. by the presence of heart-shaped heads or long necks, there may be a deeper significance. Each feature — a high forehead, strong jaw, wide-set eyes, ample genitalia, may have symbolic meaning. In Ethiopian art, for example, the goodies are presented full face with two eyes and the baddies in profile with one eye. Primitive art represents art of a different culture from which the artist of the Western world can draw inspiration as he would from an old master.

Chapter Nine

Art in Relation to Physical and Mental Illness

'The features of this case were plainly enough distinguishable; but the question continually presented itself — in what does this man's mind differ from sound mind?'.
Dr. J. Connoly (1830) The Indication of Insanity.

THOUGHT processes in disease can differ markedly from those of the same individual when in good health. The hypnagogic visions of disturbed sleep and prolonged stupor or delirium are but one aspect of altered cerebral activity with illness. The brain becomes hyperactive with the increase in metabolism that accompanies high fever; but, at the same time, its functions may be impaired by anoxia, ischaemia or the shunting of blood elsewhere. Areas of cerebral irritability can result in multifarious focal discharges, not necessarily epileptic in origin. The mind is not permitted to rest. As Dr. Johnson has said, 'Depend upon it, Sir, when a man knows he is to be hanged in a fortnight, it concentrates his mind wonderfully'. The near-death experiences of mountaineers and other examples of awareness of impending doom confirm the rapid succession and unusual clarity of thought that can be compressed into a few seconds of expectation. The psychological effect of illness or even the presumption of ill-health cannot be ignored. Morbid thoughts and fears may pervade a brain aware of the ultimate prognosis or racked by ill-founded neurotic anxieties. We may be tempted to apply modern psychic terminology to explain how Piranesi obtained his inspiration for his many drawings of imaginary prisons whilst suffering from a bout of malaria, but the truth is that we cannot accurately analyse all aspects of the state of mind of a person reacting to the physical and mental stresses of illness. It is sufficient to state that illness can colour a person's outlook on life. 'Colour' is the operative word. With depression, the colours are invariably sombre, as with van Gogh's black crows. With hysteria, bright, primary colours predominate, used childishly with lack of control. Tuberculosis patients have an affinity for reds: red skies, like blood vessels.

A superabundance of the colour red is not an invariable accompaniment of an artist who happens to be suffering from tuberculosis; rather the sudden appearance of splashes of red suggests a cataclysmic stage in the disease, as was the experience of a physician who described hallucinations when trying mescaline coincidentally with the development of a tuberculosis pleural effusion:

'On the horizon, a setting sun, lighting up the landscape with a dark red glow. The radiations from the sun are a beautiful combination of red and black. In the foreground are several dark figures which might be camel riders or trees. A thing like an aeroplane with a long yellow body and blue wings. Almost at once it changes so that it is obvious that the centre is really a broad path leading to a high palace. The sides of the path are light blue and consist of shrubs. Now the sides are changing into a gorgeous flower bed, the predominant colours of which are white and red. The whole effect is most beautiful. The picture is now changing and has become a bowl of heather mixed with tiger-lilies. Later still, yellow specks dotted upon a black background. They are becoming larger and more numerous, and are forming a pattern. Red is now the most prominent colour; the arrangement is like a carpet, consisting of concentric rectangles, dark red, salmon pink, blue, golden, and so on. Larger white specks dart rapidly in from the periphery on to the carpet like bright silver coins pouring into the centre — or like white streaks of lightning. Everything is now moving; the carpet design is breaking up and gives place to a mass of bright spangles dancing rapidly all over the picture'.

The lives of several artists of great ability have been cut short by tuberculosis. Amedeo Modigliani is the best known and most masterly. Born in 1884 he died aged thirty-six in 1920 of tuberculosis, drugs, alcohol and self-neglect. The tubercular infection began with pleurisy when aged eleven. He is best remembered for the linear qualities of his art, the single continuous lines, fluid curves and elongated figures, but he also possessed a very fine colour sense and, to many, his use of reds is as remarkable as the reds with which Titian — using pigments very different from today — crowned his masterpieces.

The French painter and sculptor, Roger de la Fresnay (1885-1925) was a natural colourist who followed nonetheless the concept of painting developed by Cézanne and, without losing his feeling for colour, adapted to the Cubism of Braque, bridging the gap between the subservience of colour to shape of Picasso and Braque and the later development of Orphism by Delauney. In 1917 he was discharged from the army with tuberculosis and lost much of the essential energy for sustained work. He became paralysed as a result of a TB subdural abscess of the spine in 1923. His limited output from 1918 until then was largely representational and included sculptures inspired by his friendship with Maillol and Duchamp-Villon. He was also admired for his intellectual approach to art: 'In painting there are two things, the eye and the brain. One must work for their mutual development, the eye by the vision of nature and the brain by the logic of organised sensations which afford the means of expression'.

For the Italian, Scipione (Gino Bonichi, 1904-33), phthisis hung over his whole life like a dark fate. He had a poetic feeling expressed initially in a flood of apocalyptic Baroque-like pictures obsessed by the themes of death and decay. Dark colours and brown tones portrayed and caricatured the erotic and hedonistic life of contemporary Rome. Later the formal outlines gave way to rhythmically organised and intertwined colours, an expressionism replete with restless greens, reds and violets. His active career spanned just four years.

In treating art in relation to disease we are often in the realms of highly personal, expressive artefacts which to most of us represent no more than the sick humour of Dada or various forms of *art brut*. Alberto Burri served as an Army doctor in North Africa but gave up medicine in 1946 in order to paint, his mind still rivoted by the gruesome images of war. The bitter poetry of his tragic experiences in the field hospitals of the desert is personified by his Sacchi, a group of collages consisting of charged sackcloth and blood stained cloth coarsely stitched together in a pictorial representation of blood seeping through bandages, thereby symbolising man's complete vulnerability. They are a sick development of the Cubist montages. Art is used as a means of expression often turning from aesthetic pleasure to something capable of drawing from us feelings of repugnance or threat, as in an attempt to alert the uncaring to the problems of inner cities or of the inner turmoils of sick minds. The turbulent, emotional distortions of the Russian painter, Chaim Soutine (1894-1943), who suffered from alcoholism, depression and stomach ulcers, represent this borderland between art and the horrendous. The distinction between some forms of modern art and sick art may be slim: the one based upon the reorganisation of elements, the other on disorganisation.

Many painters have overcome the revulsion of their deformities to achieve success. None has been more successful in the artistic sense than Henri de Toulouse-Lautrec (1864-1901). No artist had greater influence upon poster design. No one could have illustrated more brilliantly the theatre, musical halls, cafés and low life of Paris. His deformity resulted from compound fractures of his limbs due to *osteogenesis imperfecta* (multiple epiphyseal dysplasia). Whilst recovering from repeated falls he learnt to draw, taught by the deaf-mute sporting artist René Princeteau. (Another deaf-mute of the 16th century, Juan Fernandez de Navarrete (1526-79) was the first painter to use the dramatic lighting effects called tenebrismo which were later exploited by Caravaggio. Navarrete was appointed court painter to Philip II). Toulouse-Lautrec's downfall was his very success in being accepted by and integrating into the life-style of the cabarets and brothels of Montmartre. He succumbed to its twin vices of alcoholism and syphilis. In 1899 he suffered a complete physical and mental breakdown and was confined to a sanitorium with madness and paranoia. While he was still an inmate he resumed drawing in order to establish his sanity, producing a series of pictures drawn from memory. He died in 1901 from general paralysis of the insane.

General paralysis of the insane (G.P.I.) is a late form of neurosyphilis, developing about seven to fifteen years after the primary infection. Syphilis was particularly rife among military campaigners of the latter half of the 19th century and among soldiers of the 1914-18 war. The early symptoms of G.P.I. take the form of a simple and insidious mental deterioration not immediately distinguishable from commoner forms of presenile dementia but more characteristic symptoms can then develop. Changes in personality, judgment, moral and ethical demeanour may be intermittent and misunderstood at first. Megalomania with grandiose ideas may colour the victim's behaviour. If the person is already highly placed and extroverted, as were Lord Randolph Churchill and Jules de Goncourt, the rash promises, claims of business successes or delusions of persecution may be accepted in the early stages at their face value. Later, clear evidence of hallucinations, claims of sexual prowess, or other forms of omnipotence, and gifts to all and sundry accompanied by a euphoric happy-go-lucky attitude can no longer escape notice.

Today the victim is as likely to boast sporting exploits — squaring a round of golf with Faldo, out shouting McEnroe on the tennis court — as business or political achievements. Several artists are presumed to have suffered from the condition but the clearest evidence relates to the French naive painter Séraphine (Séraphine Louis, or de Senlis) 1864-1934. She started life as a farm hand before entering domestic service and at the age of forty took up painting. Her art was curiously limited to stylised trees with fruits, leaves and flowers worked with minute accuracy to include erotic elements such as eyes and lips hidden among the flowers of her bouquets. She was 'discovered' by the art critic, Wilhelm Uhde, for whom she became house-keeper in 1912, and he supplied her with canvasses and paints. In 1930 her reason failed, she threw money in the street and became obsessed with a vision of the end of the world. She eventually died in a home for the aged in Clermont.

Vincent van Gogh stands out among the painters who suffered from epilepsy. His life story is so complex that a special chapter is needed; but other epileptic artists include Edward Lear (1812-88) and Alfred Kubin (1877-1959).

Edward Lear, dogged by epilepsy through his life, achieved greatest fame as a comic writer of limericks and nonsense verses which he illustrated himself. However, his landscapes were notable for their accuracy and he worked for many years as a draughtsman to the Zoological Society. His ornithological drawings rival those of Audubon.

Alfred Kubin's disability was less well controlled. He is best known as an illustrator of over two hundred books and became a member of the Blaue Reiter group in 1919. He also made thousands of drawings in which he depicted his own fantastic visions using a combination of bold and spidery strokes to create a dense yet extremely delicate network of lines. His mythical dream world appears also in his one Kafkaesque novel, *Die andere Seite (The Other Side),* completed in the white heat of twelve weeks in 1908 when he found himself incapable of drawing. To the second and subsequent editions of *Die andere Seite* he attached an autobiography giving details of the many crises which permeated his life.

The circumstances of his birth are not clear. His father was a surveyor who was away from home for long periods. His mother was consumptive and nervous. His habit of running away to the homes of acquaintances in the neighbourhood and sometimes to those of strangers caused her much pain. He hated school:

> 'School and church laid inexorable restraints upon the infant brute
> . . . his childish drawings showed a natural tendency towards
> exaggeration and fantasy, teeming with magicians, comic and
> terrifying cattle, and landscapes consisting entirely of fire — in short
> the seed of the whole later Kubin was contained in them'.

He witnessed the throes of his mother's death when he was ten 'but
much stronger was the terror and confusion inspired on him by his father's
complete despair'. He was sent to the Gymnasium in Salzburg. His father
married his mother's sister but she too succumbed in childbirth within
a year. Meanwhile Kubin had been expelled from school and returned
home. 'My father lost all confidence in me. I was no longer permitted
to come into his presence and had to live completely alone'. He is next
seen at the age of nineteen attempting suicide by his mother's grave. The
following year he enlisted in the army but suffered a nervous breakdown
and was boarded out. He became a serious art student and after a further
crisis, triggered by the death of his fiancée, eventually married and settled
as a professional artist. His works revealed an obsession with the theme
of death and with female sexuality as a symbol of death. In response to
yet another crisis, Bhuddist exercises provided relief;

> '. . . but after a few days I was aware of a constant pressure in
> the neighbourhood of my heart. This I carried about me like an
> incubus. Then a moment came when the recurrent palpitations of
> the heart grew too violent; fear seized me by the throat — then and
> there I cast off the whole of Bhuddism and returned to my trusted
> and familiar way of life. This happened on 12th March, 1916. The
> crisis had lasted in all for ten days'.

Reitman (1950) describes the art of epileptics as showing great gusto
for pedantic detail. Attention to detail was certainly a feature of Edward
Lear's landscapes and ornithological studies but his skill as a caricaturist
required a different approach. Kubin's illustrations are more remarkable
for their fantasy than for their minutiae and with van Gogh the intensity
of his style and depth of feeling eliminate all features which do not share
the vitality of the central theme. It is hard to find three more different
artists. Episodes of loss of consciousness from which they all suffered can
vary from simple faints to complex aurae, after effects and even
automatisms; from absences and sensations which are only apparent to
the individual, to convulsive attacks which carry all the stigmata of the
devil-possessed epileptics of the Bible. Each type of attack may taint the
person with epilepsy to a varying degree. Those mildly affected may feel
insecure; some, such as van Gogh, become very dependent on others, e.g.
on his brother Theo; yet others can develop schizo-affective disorders.
These varied reactions are more likely to temper their art than the fact
that they have had fits at one time or another in their life. Perhaps the
only common feature to the three epileptic artists mentioned is that their
essential styles were maintained throughout their life, though Kubin at
one stage eschewed colour and van Gogh's output grew with frantic
intensity as he recovered from his attacks. Outwardly Edward Lear
remained calm, feigning disaffection with his disability.

The curiosity and interest of the populace in artists who have experienced mental illness — a form of intellectual voyeurism — is two fold. Have the events shaped the artistic experience? There is the phenomena of 'Stilwandel', whereby a radical departure in style is related to a breakdown or change of personality. And, secondly, is there inherent in that artist's output identifiable features which suggest a particular psychotic trait? An artist, especially, must be interesting, and interest so often stems from the paranormal, whether that experience be external or internal. We can indulge in generalisations.

There is a positive correlation between realistic art and extroversion, and, contrariwise, between abstract art and introversion. The artistic output of most people in the course of psychiatric illness is reduced, especially so if the illness be a depressive one, but those with schizophrenia often find it easier to use pictorial expression when language would fail them. Early visual experiences tend to break through into the patient's conscious life. They often accept the opportunity to work out their problems through the medium of drawings, paintings and sculptures.

There is an innate compulsion among certain schizophrenics to use the visual medium to express their thoughts; and this tendency also surfaces in others generally regarded as more balanced but who nonetheless possess schizoid traits. It is true to say that many artists are introverted, attracted by the abstract and possess schizoid traits: but it has also to be said that a gifted artist can use any material, likely or unlikely, and derived from whatever source he chooses, provided he can create an aesthetically convincing work of art as a whole.

Schizophrenia, or splitting of the mind, is most accurately described as a symptom-complex. Kraepelin spoke of the schizophrenias. In addition to a schizophrenic psychosis, a schizophrenic state can also arise from physical illness, drug intoxication, dementia, isolation, fever, epileptic twilight states or a post-concussional psychosis. The concept of a mental illness termed schizophrenia has burgeoned with difficulty, for the concept defies definition. The fundamental fault lies in the processing of thoughts and information. This in turn results in impaired or delusional perceptions, fragmentation of the ego-boundaries and a disorder of mentation ranging from thought-blocking to crowding of thoughts, distant thoughts (e.g. extracampine thoughts coming from a distant town), voices repeating the person's own thought out loud (thought echo), voices discussing his thoughts as a running commentary, and voices accusing or directing his own thoughts.

With a disorder of the processing of thoughts occurring coincidentally with fragmentation of the ego-boundaries, the combined effect may be inhibitory or dysinhibitory; if dysinhibitory, producing at times an extraordinary release or press of thoughts often incongruous, patterned or stereotyped, sometimes spoken, often written, maybe drawn, and characteristically in the form of heavy annotation of texts or as writing intermingled with hieroglyphic symbols surrounding, underlining or even across drawings. Delusions, illusions and pseudohallucinations readily present. Sensory experiences emanating from the body, skin, viscera and genitalia may undergo delusional blending with the boundaries of control (between his inner world and the outside) lost so that he may feel himself possessed. Concentration is affected: thus he may discuss around and around a topic unable to reach a conclusion. At times the apparently enriched content of his thoughts may appear totally unrelated to his previous intelligence. Thus ruminations frequently involve higher flights of conceptual thought, leading to a prevailing concern for the world and life in general or to religion, psychology, philosophy, art or literature. Thoughts may be attached to other people, often leading to an accusation of a paranoid type. Many, aware that interruption of their thought processes impairs communication, will shy away from other people; but others find a loosening of associations resulting in klang associations or rhymes, grotesque puns, and apparent facility of associated thought through knight's moves. Such a trait may be found in comedians. New words are coined. Nonsense poetry is produced. The resulting word-salad is not that dissimilar from the automatic verse of the Surrealists!

Translated into the visual arts, it is easy to see that certain characteristics of schizophrenic thought do occur from time to time in art. Objects are commonly depicted in colours at variance with their real perception. Meaningless abstraction, bizarre ideation, grotesque humour and incongruity of relationship are not always the result of lack of sophistication on the part of the viewer. Some distortion of the body image in art is acceptable but with excessive fragmentation, stylisation, mannerism and even perseveration the non-cognoscenti begin to wonder. About five per cent of the hallucinations of schizophrenics are visual and occasionally one sees art which is obviously the pictorial representation of such an hallucination. Most schizophrenic art is the product of non-artists. The effects of hallucinogens and of schizophrenia do not make an untalented person suddenly talented but they can provide a new and powerful experience and break down perceptual inhibitions.

Some artists are by temperament subject to wide fluctuations of mood — is this not the artistic temperament? We should be able to detect these changes. In manic states the output is high but the choice of colours and subject matter is wild, producing overall a restless, disordered and incoherent uneasiness. With a consequent endogenous depressive state the colours may remain bright but limited and reasonably appropriate. There is a poverty of output and a poverty of ideas. People are rarely represented and the objects appear mundane and commonplace. If the depression is a reactive one the colours are more subdued. Symbolic language is frequently used to express emotions, and suicidal themes can sometimes be recognised.

Symbolism is often a feature of the art of the psychopath. The draughtsmanship may be skilled but there is invariably a subconscious identification of the self with the subject matter. The hysteric by contrast often chooses childish subjects with simple patterns, poor control and bright, primary colours. Careful organisation, so much so that symmetry may dictate the choice of subject, over-meticulous detail, and a clear and exact production that is decidedly mediocre, may be the mark of an obsessional neurosis.

In so far as these generalisations are accurate we can follow an artist through elated and depressed moods, where the boundaries of sanity are all but breached, and also as his work deteriorates. With general paralysis of the insane the work is clumsy, vulgar and more and more childish. With more common forms of dementia it is patchy, confused, with unrealistic colours, and profound spatial difficulties arise so that important features end up in corners. Psychotic art has been used diagnostically, as therapy, and in the attempted understanding of primitive art forms. The generalisations are most true to form when the artist whose work is analysed is an amateur provided with a palette and paint brush after many years of neglect. The professional artist is less restrained by his feelings unless they provide the prime motive for his art. Thus there is a detective element in the search for the phenomenon of 'Stilwandel'.

We can become blasé about madness and treat psychotic art as though it were no more than a development of Surrealism or Existentialism — so clinical has the diagnosis and treatment of mental illness become and so isolated and protected are we from its effects. Drugs can now calm the fevered brow. Patients can be treated, if not cured, after the most threatening dénouement. We laugh at people possessed by the devil or the Wizard of Oz or who become were-wolves. Lycantropy is mythology. We little realise that there is a generation who develop erotomania over Boy George, are possessed by the Tardis, or controlled by the Daleks. Some aspects of psychiatry are unchanging; pictures by schizophrenics of devils and reptiles attached to every bodily appendage and orifice are still drawn, painted and scribbled upon.

The psychiatric journals of 1984 were enlivened by a description of the self-shooting of a Phantom Head — an Australian patient with schizophrenia described a second head on his shoulder supposedly belonging to his wife's gynaecologist whom he believed had had an affair with her prior to her death. 'The other head kept trying to dominate my normal head, and I would not let it. It kept trying to say to me I would lose'. He fired six shots, the first two at the second head, which he then decided was hanging by a thread, and then through the roof of his mouth. Three others missed. He said he felt good at that stage, and the other head was not felt any more. Then he passed out. Prior to shooting himself, he had considered using an axe to remove the phantom head (Ames, 1984).

The best known contemporary English schizophrenic artist is undoubtedly Louis Wain. Before succumbing to schizophrenia in middle age, he was recognised as an extremely talented illustrator, noteworthy for his faithful, if sentimental, portrayal of cats whom he preferred to the company of his fellow men. With the onset of his illness his cats became stylised. The early paintings show a rainbow-like halo illuminating the cat's figure with an heraldic appearance. They are later transformed into a Byzantine mosaic of colours, presenting a rich aesthetic creation and conveying a mysterious, unearthly quality. With increasing confusion and fragmentation, the mosaic cats finally disintegrate into a kaleidoscopic mass. In the white heat of the disease the distraught psyche has somehow transformed the mundane, tame products of orthodoxy into more exotic and artistic, if compulsive, designs.

The intricate patterning of the Fairy-Feller's Master-Stroke, more delicate and far more ubiquitous than in his other works of art exemplified the best remembered oeuvre of the mad Victorian artist, Richard Dadd (1819-87). Long grasses slant from either side across the picture plane, their tips touching exactly to form a series of overlapping triangles framing the scenes beyond by means of the recognised Renaissance device of tipped perspective. The slight flattening, though in no way destroying the naturalness of the scene, gives equal emphasis to all parts of the picture and stresses the embroidered effect and the embossed, almost enameled quality to the paint (Greysmith, 1973). There is a trance-like, waxen imagery to this work, which took nine years to complete.

Retreat into childish whims is a frequent attribute of schizophrenia but Dadd's fairy themes preceded the acute onset of his illness and only one other fairy painting, Contradiction — Oberon and Titania, 1854-8, was completed from Bethlem Asylum. Dadd's early paintings were conventional enough — portraits, historical settings and seascapes, but as a highly successful enrolled student at the Royal Academy he proposed to devote himself to works of the imagination. His particular interest in fairy characters reflected the growing 19th-century obsession with the spirit world *(vide* Rossetti) and his greatest masterpiece, Titania Sleeping (1841) was not only firmly based on the conventions of the time but surpassed similar works of the period by the Irish painter and caricaturist, Daniel Maclise (1806-70). Before his illness Dadd had been an outstanding pupil. Recognised as the leading talent among the 'Clique', a group of young painters including Augustus Egg, William Powell Frith and John Phillip, a great future was predicted for him.

He possessed other recorded attributes: 'a man of strong common sense, the reverse of flighty or excitable', popular, attractive, affectionate and highly intelligent. His father, Robert Dadd of Chatham, was a chemist, lecturer in geology and curator of the museum. Richard was the fourth of seven children by his first marriage and there were two step brothers. The family moved to London in 1836 ostensibly for two reasons: recognition of Richard's special talents and Robert's desire to take over a bronze, silver and water-gilding business in Suffolk Street, Pall Mall East. His father's friendship with David Roberts R.A. enabled Richard to study at the British Museum and subsequently at the Royal Academy. By the age of twenty six he had exhibited three major works, completed a hundred decorative panels illustrating Byron's *Manfred* and Tosso's *Jerusalem Delivered* for Lord Foley and designed wood engravings for the *Ballad of Robin Goodfellow*. He then received a golden opportunity to accompany a wealthy solicitor on a sketching tour of Europe and the Middle East.

Dadd's patron and companion, the forty-two year old Sir Thomas Phillips, had achieved fame as Mayor of Newport when wounded by shots from his own side whilst reading the Riot Act to 7,000 Chartists. The journey began well enough and Dadd compiled several sketch-books; but on the return leg he began to show signs of insanity. In Rome he felt a strong inclination to attack the Pope. By Paris his faculties were yet more deranged with the fixed delusion that Sir Thomas was an emissary of the devil and an object of detestation. He claimed that he was subjected to the will of a superior being identifiable as the Egyptian god Osiris.

On his return in 1843 he showed his friends beautiful specimens of his work but their display was often accompanied by wild comments and actions. His behaviour was ascribed to sunstroke. But tension mounted. A colleague found him pale and streaming with blood. He had cut out a birth mark which, he explained, had been imprinted by the devil. Robert Dadd sought the opinion of Dr. Alexander Sutherland of St. Luke's Hospital but could not bring himself to put his son under restraint.

Two days later tragedy struck. On the promise that he would unburden his mind to his father, the two of them journeyed to Cobham in Kent, ate at the Ship Inn and went for a walk. The next morning Robert's body was discovered thirty yards from the road in Cobham Park, stabbed after an attempt to cut his throat with a razor. Dadd, who had plenty of money and a passport on his person, promptly left for France but was arrested near Fontainebleau after attempting to kill a complete stranger. Under restraint in France and at the nadir of his illness, his physical condition was such that for ten months he was too ill to travel. He failed to recognise the paints, canvasses and brushes sent by his family but stood, day in and day out, in the courtyard at Clarmont staring at the sun.

In July, 1844, the extradition order was served and after preliminary hearings at Rochester Magistrates Court, during which his behaviour left no doubt that he was insane, he was transferred under warrant to the Criminal Lunatic Asylum attached to Bethlem Hospital. The medical diagnosis was of dementia praecox, a form of paranoid schizophrenia, but it is interesting to note that in the same year his brother George, aged 20, also entered an asylum suffering from delusions, his sister Maria later became insane, and in latter years his brother Stephen 'had an attendant'. Whilst familial schizophrenia is well recognised, it is just possible that there may have been a rare, recessive 'inborn error of metabolism'.

For some years after his admission Dadd was considered a violent and dangerous patient. He would jump up and strike a violent blow without aggravation, or gorge himself till he actually vomited, then return to the meal. Later he became less subject to sudden and unpredictable impulses but retained fixed, immoveable delusions. Those able to ignore certain revulsions of behaviour and steer clear of contentious topics found him companionable, able to converse agreeably, and with the intellectual part of his capacity practically untouched.

What of his art? His notoriety matched his fame. To stem the publicity, the family prevented the release of his pictures and may even have destroyed several of them. However, in 1845 the magazine *Art Union* stated that they had seen some drawings recently executed by Dadd which exhibited all the power, fancy and judgment for which his works were eminent previous to his insanity. In actuality his work was decidedly uneven but the best retained all his consummate professional skill and finish.

On his arrival at Bethlem he came under the care of Sir Alexander Morison and Dr. Edward Munro. Dr. Munro's father was a noted patron of the arts, holding the friendship of Turner, Girton, de Wint, Cozens and Cotman. The portrait by Dadd of Sir Alexander Morison, the background showing his estate at Anchorfield near Leith, has recently been sold by the Royal College of Physicians of Edinburgh to the Scottish Portrait Gallery. In contrast to this polished work is a 'ghastly little invention of desert horror framed in by demons such as his distempered brain alone could desire'. Thus he painted 'with all the poetry of imagination and the frenzy of insanity — in parts eminently beautiful, but other parts, in madness, without method! (a report of 1848).

However, Dadd's most productive years in psychiatric care occurred after 1852 when Drs. Munro and Morison were pensioned off after an official inquiry and were replaced by the reformer, Dr. Hood, later Sir Charles Hood. The atmosphere of the asylum was changed, with the introduction of aviaries containing song birds and pictures decorated the walls. From 1853-55 Dadd produced some thirty sketches to illustrate the Passions. They share the common characteristic of all Dadd's work, namely the rounded faces with large, unwinking eyes; but, in contrast to the detailed miniaturism of other works, controlled washes of colour were used with a realistic style and imaginative content. They contain a degree of violence unbeknown in his other paintings. He appeared to identify with the central figure in each scene, each depicting a theme taken from literature. By 1860 another change had occurred. William Rossetti visited Dadd and reported that 'he still employs himself daily with his brush, but he is slower in completing any work he takes in hand. His mind is full of delusions'.

With the end of the Passion Sketches the sequence of pictures of fighting and murder seems exhausted. From now on Dadd's work is much calmer and more meditative though their quality and content continued to vary. When the more spacious Broadmoor Hospital was opened in 1864 he was transferred there and contributed a drop curtain for the stage, elaborately fanciful murals and even painted some of the furniture. The pictures were fewer. One of Job suffering from the plague of boils shows the boils depicted at each stage in the most microscopic manner. He seemed to delight in painting them, licking his brush over an extra-ulcerous one. Yet he could paint the Superintendent, Dr. Orange, with all the propriety required of him and all the command of his medium that he had possessed in earlier years. He died of consumption in 1887.

There are two Swedish schizophrenic artists of note: Carl Fredrik Hill (1849-1911) and Ernst Josephson (1851-1906). Hill left Stockholm for Paris in 1873 and, inspired by the Barbizon painters, including Corot, made his name as a landscape artist in paints and chalks. He evolved a highly personal, if sentimental, approach with an intense tonal range of colour. In 1876 he came under the influence of the French Impressionists but his career was cut short by schizophrenia. His departure to Sweden in 1880 was considered a great loss to art. However, his present reputation rests to an equal extent upon the many thousands of drawings and pastels produced in his years of seclusion. Although they reflect his psychotic state, they retain an amazing subtlety of colour, emotional expressiveness and keenness of design.

Josephson was a leading Expressionist painter of his day. To quote

Hodin (1972) 'Expressionism is a sombre, passionate art in which spiritual experience asserts itself against the dehumanisation and mechanisation of culture'. His paintings were characterised by their intensity and depth of colour. The emotional power and vitality of his landscapes made a considerable impact on his contemporaries but the zenith of his career lay in his penetrating female portraits, remarkable for their detail, psychological insight and the richly orchestrated colouring of the interiors. In 1888 he became schizophrenic and was obliged to return to Sweden where he produced two hundred paintings and two thousand drawings whose themes were taken from myths, fairy tales, poems and historical narratives. Gentle lyrical motifs expressing passivity alternated with motifs of volcanic ferocity. During the acute phase of the psychosis, he believed that he was guided by great artists of the past, thus two drawings from the Karolinska Institute bear the signatures of Rafael Sanzio and Velasquez through Ernst Josephson.

Another schizophrenic artist obedient to an inner voice is Augustin (Le Mineur) Le Sage (1878-1928) who exhibited at the Institut Metapsychique de Paris. This scarcely literate ex-miner began to produce enormous decorative panels including examples copied from the Orient. He claimed that he merely acted as the medium for the spirit of Leonardo da Vinci who would guide him in his choice of colour and design. His paintings were inscribed with the names of Jesus Christ, Moses, Isaiah, Krishna, Pythagoras, Plato and Tutunkamun. His first work was a nine foot 'Great Painting', displaying an amazing sense of order, balance and organic harmony (Argüelles, 1975). His later paintings were more ornamental and less spontaneous, with brilliant evocations of temples and hieratic architecture.

Prinzhorn in his *Artistry of the Mentally Ill* (1971) presents ten very capable schizophrenic artists of whom the best known is Franz Pohl (1864-). But the mentally deranged artist who attracted most attention from the surrealists, proving that even the least cultured can possess genius, once it had abandoned itself to the promptings of the unconscious mind, was a Swiss patient, Adolf Wölfli. Certainly he illustrates that a peculiar form of compulsive creativity can develop in schizophrenia. Adolf Wölfli (1864-1930) who signed his paintings St. Adolf II, is an example of a poorly educated farm labourer isolated from the world after five years total madness and, without any formal training, producing (according to the American writer and artist, Jose Argüelles, 1975) in colour, design and symmetrical formalism works reminiscent of the art of Medieval Europe and certain works from India and Tibet. In the same psychic frenzy he composed music, manufacturing crude trumpets for the purpose, and wrote a cosmically endless autobiography. His autobiography is replete with the most idiosyncratic language, subtle associations and puns, and contains as complete and integrated a psycho-cosmogony as that created by William Blake. Such a biography frequently lists 'omens' — he was born on February 29th, 'an uprooted childhood' — his mother died when he was eight and he passed from one orphanage to another, and real or imaginary 'unrequited love affairs' — as an intinerant labourer aged 16 he declared his love for a lady beyond his reach.

Thereafter Wölfli's illness began insidiously, punctuated by a downward progression of sexual perversity. In 1888 he contracted venereal disease after a love affair with a prostitute. In 1890 he attempted rape on a 14 year old child but escaped punishment by giving a false identity. In 1891 he attacked a 5 year old and was duly imprisoned for two years. He began to hallucinate. His obsessions varied from biblical declarations to paranoid delusions. After release in 1895, he assaulted a 3 year old and was incarcerated for life in Waldau Insane Asylum.

His schizophrenia reached fever pitch. From 1895-9 uncontrollable chaos reigned, marked by sexual fantasies, obsessions, hysterical outbursts, oneiristic states, catatonic depressions lasting for months and violent attacks upon the guards and other inmates. A profound metamorphosis occurred in 1900. A general calm prevailed and he suddenly became intensively creative; a state of affairs which persisted until his death. At first he painted scenes of self-punishment, where he showed himself undergoing tortures, then grandiose scenes where he appeared as a masked superman surrounded by heraldic beasts and winged angels. No space was left unfilled, his surfaces were overloaded, replete with decorations and even musical compositions. By now he was a model patient; even in 1917 he behaved inordinately gently towards two idiot boys, but whenever the suggestion of release occurred he would commit an act of violence in order to ensure his measure of psychic freedom.

Nowadays psychotic art holds a peculiar attraction, supposedly releasing the uninhibited stuff of human creativity. The traditional source of inspiration for the aspiring professional artist is an eclectic knowledge of the works of earlier generations: he indulges in mimesis. Avant-garde movements have sought the power of originality elsewhere. Dada, the anti-art movement following the First World War, developed as a violent, gimmicky reaction against traditional smugness by giving emphasis to the illogical and absurd. Surrealism sought a pure psychic automatism.

The Compagnie d'Art Brut was founded by Jean Dubuffet in 1948 to tap the unselfconscious and spontaneous images emerging from the works of children, untrained amateurs, solitaires and the fringe dwellers of society. Conventional artistic materials were disparaged to be replaced by pates or constructs of sand, glass, asphalt, rope or other junk crudely manipulated to suggest shapes. Graffiti were seriously studied and copied; and a primordial art sought among the dabblings of the mentally ill, mentally defective and maladjusted. Dubuffet (1901-) had begun his career as a gifted painter and caricaturist at the Academy Julian and in the surrealist circles of Paris but preferred the life of a wealthy dilettante, renouncing art for the prosperity of the family's wine business. He began to exhibit once more in the late 1940s, and, more than any other painter, including Klee, Ernst, de Staël, de Kooning, or even Passmore, he began to adapt with a richness and versatility these primordial art forms into an artistic movement for which Michel Tapié has coined the phrase 'art autre'.

From then on Dubuffet rose to rapid fame, initially on account of the scurrilious nature of his art but, not content with his own work, he exhibited over 5,000 collected examples of art brut. Nearly half the exhibits were the works of schizophrenics. However, Dubuffet has since repudiated the concept of psychotic art, claiming that 'there is no art of the insane any more than an art of dyspeptics or an art of people with knee complaints!'.

Chapter Ten

Drug Induced Hallucinations

'A Person who has taken Opium, sees either gay scences, or ghastly ones, according as the Opium excites pleasant or painful Vibrations in the Stomach'.
D. Hartley, 1791.

FEW drugs which enter the body fail to have influence upon the brain, affecting the mood, the state of alertness — cognition and perception — and exerting some changes upon the personality. They are foreign chemicals reacting at many sites throughout the central nervous system, interacting with other absorbed compounds and affecting the equilibrium of the body — leastwise if it is healthy, but capable of causing a powerful effect upon a body or mind already disturbed by disease. Acute intoxication may result in drowsiness, delirium or psychotic states. With chronic intoxication, where consciousness remains intact, delusional ideas and illusory phenomena often result. Thus the unsought effect of a drug may take the form of a psychotic reaction, epilepsy, behavioural disorder, depersonalisation or derealisation. By inducing drowsiness or altering a person's contact with reality, an indirect result of drug action may be to produce an hypnagogic or unreal state capable of stimulating hallucinatory phenomena. The drugs themselves or their impurities may also directly stimulate the visual areas of the brain or temporarily dampen the activities of these areas and precipitate, as their action wanes, secondary release hallucinations. Acute drug hallucinoses occur abruptly in a setting of dulled consciousness, mild disorientation, mood swings usually of anxiety, and commonly produce over a short period pseudo, rather than true, hallucinations.

Visual hallucinations are most common. However, amphetamine psychosis may produce a picture similar to acute schizophrenia with prominent and persistent hallucinations, and cocaine psychosis is characterised by paranoid delusions and tactile hallucinations. Patients may interpret the peculiar tactile sensations, believing themselves infested by animals crawling over their bodies; the term 'cocaine bug' is often applied to this condition. Drug therapy with nasal congestants in infants, slimming tablets in adolescents, sympathomimetic amines, levodopa, benzhexol, chloral or barbituates, particularly in the elderly, may produce hallucinations in patients apparently responding in other respects to the prescribed treatment.

Drugs have been available and abused for centuries, Berserkir (Bare-shirt), the Norse hero whose ungovernable fury in battle has passed into legend, fed himself and his twelve sons on fly-agaric (muscarine). In a state of delirious excitement, disdaining armour, they would fling themselves into battle until ultimately collapsing in a state of exhaustion. Then, by drinking their own urine, they would reclaim their frantic valour. In the 18th Century, laudanum was cheaper than beer or gin, cheap enough for even the lowest paid worker; so in one Lancashire parish a single chemist could sell 200 lb of opium in small packets in one year and still say that this was less than half the demand (Hayter, 1968). In the 19th century efforts to reduce alcoholism in Ireland by means of ether were markedly successful, but the use of ether became so widespread that it was necessary to take steps to reeducate the public to the use of alcohol (Goodman and Gillman's *Pharmacopoeia)*. The present spate of solvent abuse and glue sniffing had arisen as a result of the widespread availability of chemicals in all walks of life, providing an alternative to alcohol as a means of escape, especially when access to alcohol has been limited by price, prohibition or laws such as those relating to teenage drinking.

From the beginning, Inquisitive Man has always been susceptible to the fruits of knowledge of good and evil. Poets, writers and the young, more unstable, intelligensia, have often yielded to temptation. Surprisingly, few visual artists have been consciously influenced by drugs. Chance hallucinations from drugs taken unwittingly or in the course of fevers cannot be said to have resulted in any major work of art. Modigliani is the obvious person to examine in this respect and can be viewed as a romantic genius, starving in a garret, the victim of drugs, alcohol and tuberculosis, yet painting and carving obsessively. He is a particularly difficult person to assess as many of his finest works of art were produced during the worst periods of his life.

Alcoholic hallucinations are particularly sterile as a source of artistic inspiration. Alcohol carries a dysinhibiting effect producing an initial sense of well-being, fluency, affability and warmth which can ease social relationships, in the case of Sir Joshua Reynolds and many others; but the boisterous elation, argumentativeness and maudlin feelings with increasing intoxication can prove self-destructive. Hallucinations due to alcoholism are known to all: those of acute intoxication are predominantly auditory with associated paranoid ideation. The poorly nourished sufferer from Korsakoff's psychosis may confabulate visions of pink elephants, and alcoholic liver disease cause yellow vision; but, most dramatically, the agitation and motor restlessness of acute withdrawal, delirium tremens, is attended by terrorising hallucinations which are mainly visual but can also be tactile, auditory, olfactory and vestibular — moving floors, rooms which spin or tip, etc. The hallucinatory state leads to delirium and disorientation and may be followed by a series of fits (e.g. rum fits). None of these varied experiences can have had any improving effect upon the work of any artist. Maurice Utrillo, a confirmed alcoholic by 19, spent long spells in hospitals and institutions and began to paint, under constraint from his mother Suzanne Veladon, for its remedial value. Some of his street scenes are excellent but his work remains uneven.

There is the celebrated studio brawl in 1938 between Oscar Dominquez, the inventor of decalcomania, Victor Brauner and Esteban Frances, in which Brauner lost an eye. Four years earlier he had painted a series of pictures featuring mutilations of the eye, including Self-Portrait with Extracted Eye. Impressed by the prophetic coincidence, he made a number of what he called 'magic' pictures, with titles such as Depolarisation of Consciousness, featuring female spectres symbolising the supernatural conflict between the artist and his demons.

Towards the end of his life, Jackson Pollock became an alcoholic and Peggy Guggenheim describes how he became quite hysterical, went up to her flat and drank from all the bottles she had purposely hidden, knowing his great weakness. He got so drunk that he undressed and walked quite naked into a party a friend was giving in the sitting room. Then he peed in the fireplace. Alcohol was in no way responsible for his automatic paintings but was the direct cause of his suicide.

All the Romantic writers thought that there was a strong link between dreams and the processes of literary creation; that dreams were part of one's professional equipment as a writer. Charles Lamb in *Essays of Elia,* writing on Witches and Other Night Fears, professed himself mortified by the poverty of his own dreams compared with those of his fellow poets (Hayter, 1968).

'There is Coleridge, at his will can conjure up icy domes, and pleasure houses from Kubla Khan, and Abyssinian maids, and songs of Aboro, and caverns where Alph the sacred river runs, to solace his night solitudes — where I cannot muster a fiddle. Barry Cornwall (B. W. Proctor 1787-1874) has his tritons and his nereids gamboling before him in nocturnal visions, and proclaiming sons born to Neptune — when my stretch of imaginative activity can hardly, in the night season, raise up the ghost of a fish-wife . . . The degree of the soul's creativeness in sleep might furnish no whimsical criterion of the quantum of poetic faculty resident in the same soul waking.'

Although Lamb took very little opium — he had experienced madness and was habituated to drink — the view that opiates were a legitimate source of inspiration was widespread at the time and lingers on in the mythology of addiction. Of the earlier known drugs, only the atrophic drugs such as belladonna were truly stimulant but they could leave the victim 'hot as a hare, blind as a bat, dry as a bone, red as a beet and mad as a hen'. The opiates were primarily sedative drugs, narcotics and analgesics with less direct stimulant properties.

Baudelaire spoke of the similarities and differences of opium and hashish. Both enfeebled the will-power, both riveted the attention inescapably on trivial and minute details, both magnified the sensation of time and space, both inclined the imagination towards visions of moving water — fountains, waterfalls, sea waves. But hashish was more vehement and disturbing than opium in its immediate effects: hashish was a confusing fury, opium a gentle seducer. Like De Quincey, he never suggests that opium directly stimulated imaginative writing but had 'some slight secondary purpose upon the faculty of dreaming'. Opium could give interesting dreams if you already had an interesting mind and the power to dream. De Quincey said he was a philosopher and therefore his opium dreams were philosophical; but the plain practical man who took opium would have either no visions at all, or visions of his plain practical affairs.

Even with the more modern hallucinogenic drugs such as mescaline, cannabis and lysergic acid 'the silken garment of the imagination' is not necessarily stirred. Panic reactions are just as common as the hallucinatory effects. To quote from *The Lancet* (1970), the effect of cannabis is not always euphoriant and the user sometimes experiences an acute depression, especially when approaching the drug with ambivalent anticipation. The resulting mood change resembles a transient neurotic depression, is frequently related to a preceding emotional problem, and usually ends spontaneously. The most common adverse response is a panic reaction, in over 75% of cases, in which the user interprets the physical or psychological effects as meaning that he is going mad.

Cannabis is a so-called soft drug. With the hard drugs — mescaline, marijuana and LSD — the reactions are even more emphatic and dangerous. Sympathetic overreaction, anxiety, tachycardia, sweating, depression, withdrawal or agitation, in short panic states, lead to extreme alterations of mood with depersonalisation, disturbances of the sense of position in space and alterations of visual, auditory and other sense. Pseudohallucinations are accompanied by heightened imagery and perceptions. Colours appear more vivid, textures more pronounced. The attention cannot be focussed but shifts rapidly so that the individual becomes passively receptive to the input of surging, shifting impressions. The course of these reactions is usually uncomplicated. However, if there is an acute panic reaction during a bad trip, with or without paranoid delusions, catastrophes can occur with sudden death, suicidal or homicidal impulses (Dimijian, 1976). Such eventualities are even more likely if the drug has been taken unwittingly and without the subject's knowledge (Stone, 1973). In such circumstances hallucinations take the form of mental representations so intense as to become mental presentations.

In an age when we automatically assume that all chemicals reach us in a state of purity, there is no guarantee that heroin, LSD, morning glory seeds, angel dust or dimethoxymethylamphetamine (DOM) or any other stimulant drug approaches any exact scientific standard. In an article on drug abuse in the United States of Amercia, Caplan, Mier and Banks (1982) state that heroin is often diluted with a variety of adulterants, including talcum, starch, curry powder, Vim, Ajax, caffeine ('Chinese heroin'), strychnine, mannitol, quinine or lactose and given by injection either subcutaneously (skin popping) or intraveneously.

At greater and greater risk, using stronger and stronger drugs, people have sought a visionary experience surpassing that of De Quincey:

'I have been transported into Asiatic scenery. Under the connecting feeling of tropical heat and vertical sunlights, I brought together all creatures, birds, beasts, reptiles, all trees and plants, usages and appearances, that are found in tropical regions, and assembled them together in China or Hindostan. From kindred feelings, I soon brought Egypt and her gods under the same law. I was stared at, hooted at, grinned at, chattered at, by monkeys, by paroquets, by cockatoos. I ran into pagodas, and was fixed for centuries at the summit, or in secret rooms; I was the idol; I was the priest; I was worshipped; I was sacrificed. I fled from the wrath of Brama through all the forests of Asia; Vishnu hated me; Seeva lay in wait for me. I came suddenly upon Isis and Osiris; I had done a deed, they said, which the ibis and the Crocodile trembled at. Thousands of years I lived and was buried in stone coffins, with mummies and sphinxes, in narrow chambers at the heart of eternal pyramids. I was kissed, with cancerous kisses, by crocodiles, and was laid, confounded with all unutterable abortions, amongst reeds and Nilotic mud.'

With lysergic acid (LSD), the strongest hallucinogenic drug, the experience may not end following a successful trip, with vivid memories supplanting the side actions or with an unsuccessful 'bad trip'. Flashback reactions can occur months after the drug effects have worn off, precipitated by acute stress, panic at the risk of permanent brain damage or due to the potentiating effects of hashish, marijuana or even alcohol. When the person has been repeatedly subjected to LSD the flashbacks can persist as chronic, irreversible or slowly reversible phenomena. The majority of flashbacks, especially the perceptual ones, are not unpleasant and are often recorded as a free LSD trip but others can evoke somatic and emotional distress. Some of the visual perceptive phenomena have infiltrated into both primitive and sophisticated art forms.

Many of the visual flashbacks arise as phosphenes or eigengrau, similar to the non-specific luminous perceptions that occur when the eyes are closed. In the chronic phase these can be induced by emerging into a dark environment. Closing the eyes, pressure on the eyeball or other stimuli may provoke flashes of bright colours, sparkles, visual fireworks, geometric patterns, images within images (pareidolias), positive after images, negative after images and formed images (imagistic phosphenes) with haloes, waving, rolling or jumping, leaving trails of luminosity in their wake.

Phosphenic phenomena are curious but not revealing. The other flashback phenomena involve the recall of vivid memories. It was a theme of the introductory chapter that hallucinatory phenomena, studied in otherwise healthy individuals, could provide scientific insight into the workings of the human brain. There is no better example than that of flashbacks. Flashbacks may occur as a post-traumatic stress experience, reliving a war scene or hostage situation; as a temporal lobe epileptic hallucination; and especially as the result of taking an hallucinogenic drug. They can even occur as a 'cued' retrieval in the course of one's daily life: a particular smell or taste — dubbed by American scientists as the Sauce Bernaise syndrome — may trigger a recollection of the past; a forgotten dream, one which perhaps scarcely impinged upon the conscious mind, might be recalled by a chance meeting or event; a subjective mood, such as depression, may influence the nature of recalled experience; and with ageing or dementia, past events, forgotten for years, suddenly appear uppermost.

Memory surges can arise in a brain made toxic. The mumblings of a typhoid vigil, or of the delirious patient in a pneumonic crisis, appear to emanate from the fever. Hormonal flux in thyroid and other endocrine encephalopathies have a similar effect. Spontaneous changes in brain dopamine levels in post-encephalitic parkinsonism account for the 'thousands of memories suddenly crowded on to the mind' described by a patient of Zutt (1927) during an oculo-gyric crisis when the eyes were fixed for nearly twenty minutes in an involuntary upward stare. A similar experience was reproduced unwittingly in a 63 year old female patient of Sacks and Kohl (1970). She had had progressive post-encephalitic parkinsonism since the age of eighteen. Levodopa therapy resulted in a dramatic release from her parkinsonism and oculo-gyric entrancement but produced a state which they described as 'incontinent nostalgia'. She requested a tape recorder and over the next few days recalled the nightclubs and music halls of her youth. When the increased excitement (erethism) necessitated a reduction of the dosage of levodopa, she instantly 'forgot' all these early memories.

The association of drugs with the recall of memory can take many forms, as implied by the Latin tag 'in vino veritas'. The 'truth' drug has been used to dysinhibit memory traces and at times what is learned under the influence of a drug is best recalled under drug influence and poorly recalled when the drug is absent. Such a state-dependent effect figures in the plot of Wilkie Collins' novel of detection, *The Moonstone*. To reproduce the effect the central personage refrained from tobacco for several nights so that his sleep would be disturbed, he was reminded of the circumstances of the diamond's disappearance and finally rather more laudanum was added to the concoction of brandy and water than had been slipped into his drink on the first occasion.

Collins was closely associated with the visual arts. His father and brother were academicians and his Christian name derives from a family friend, the Scottish painter Sir David Wilkie. It is clear from Collins' description of the suffereings of Ezra Jennings that his knowledge of the opium habit came from knowledge of a close acquaintance and was only secondarily derived from the writings of De Quincey.

The recognisable impact of drug habituation upon literature and, hence by diffusion, upon art began with the publication of Samuel Taylor Coleridge's poem, *'Kubla Khan, a Vision in Dream'* in 1816 and was affirmed by the serialisation of De Quincey's *Confessions of an English Opium Eater* in 1821-4. In France, some of the literary fraternity came together to form the Clube des Haschichins whose membership included Charles Pierre Baudelaire, Theophile Gautier, Alexandre Dumas (père), Honoré de Balzac and Victor Hugo. Baudelaire wrote the *Poem of Hashish* in 1857 and the prose work, *Les Paradis artificiels* — a close copy of De Quincey's *Confessions* — in 1860. Frequent reference was made to the wheels, whirlpools, spirals and rainbows of the colour forms and multiple images, often so multiplied and superimposed that all harmony was lost; the brain fails to keep pace with its impressions, still less to codify and control them. Gautier devoted some of his literary output to art criticism but the only one to produce genuine visual art was Victor Hugo. The dramatic and surreal aspects of his sketches have already been described. Jacques Moreau (1845), a French psychiatrist of the time, wrote a monograph on hashish in which he developed the principle of objective experimentation in the study of mental disorders. He believed that the hallucinatory state resulted from excitation of the brain which enabled imagined thoughts and memories to become transformed into sensory impressions of visions and sounds — 'the hallucinating person hears his own thoughts as he sees, hears the creations of his imagination as he is moved by his memories and, what is even more extraordinary, certain combinations of thought are transformed into sensory impressions, being endowed with the property of acting physically upon our senses in the manner of external stimuli'.

The major Romantic artists, Martin in England and Bresdin, Gustave Moreau and Redon in France, have been accused of seeking their visions in opium but only one painter of that era made a specific effort to obtain inspiration from drugs. Ernest Meissonier (1815-1891), arch rival of Courbet, hoped for splendid hallucinations when he took hashish but to his great disappointment he saw nothing but regular, symmetrical designs: 'C'était à se croire dans un jardin de la Nôtre et je me disais avec désespoir: dans cette ivresse, je n'aurai doue jamais d'imagination'.

Drugs were undoubtedly available to the surrealists and avant garde of the artistic community living in the vicinity of Montmartre at the turn of the century. From 1908 to 1914 Paul Alexandre, a doctor and collector of contemporary art who believed in the moderate use of drugs, started an artist's colony on the rue du Delta in Montmartre where he organised weekly hashish evenings. He supported and is perhaps most closely associated with Amadeo Modigliani, a man not noted for his moderation (Shapiro, 1976). During the First World War and in its aftermath, the cult hero of the Surrealists was Jacques Vaché (1896-1919), a young soldier, wounded in the leg who was befriended by André Breton. Under his influence Breton decided to undertake an intense study of psychology. Vaché was a simple soul who cared only for films, opium and the absurd. Each day he would wear a different uniform complete with a monocle. He died ignominiously from an overdose of opium.

In the artistic circle of the Bateau Lavoir, the dominant personalities were undoubtedly the poets, writers and critics who provided the verbal ambience of the Surrealist movement. They launched their manifestoes, proclaimed the omnipotence of the dream and the disinterested play of thought. Their commentaries spread in advance of the less mobile works of art. Their automatic writing could be read and discussed. Their pranks, surrealist games, seances and experimentation generated the noise and ephemera of the movement. However, were it not for the universality and permanence of the visual manifestations, which represented the only true art of the movement, surrealism would have disappeared into an historic vacuum.

On the subject of drugs, the Surrealist Manifesto is equivocal. Claims were made that 'we do not smoke, we do not snuff, we do not give ourselves injections, but we dream' whilst, at the same time, boisterously asserting that the doors of the dream (i.e. their source of inspiration) are opened by the enhancement of alcohol, tobacco, ether, opium, cocaine and morphine. The likely truth is that stimulants were used, though perhaps not regularly, by the writers and only occasionally, if at all, by the majority of artists. Painters were slower to gain popular recognition. For long periods they remained in poverty, dependent, as were artists of former generations, upon dealers and collectors for a limited livelihood. Compared with their journalistic contemporaries, we know very little of their way of life. Only a few, such as Pablo Picasso, were able to achieve early success and we know from Penrose that Picasso, along with Cocteau and others, tried opium.

Picasso had his own reasons for refraining from its continued use. His friend, Wiegels, hung himself after an overdose of ether. Picasso found opium 'the most intelligent of all odours'; whilst under its influence his imagination and vision became more acute but his desire to paint diminished seriously. With his early success, his circle of friends and patrons was more extensive than other artists. He visited Italy in 1917 and worked with Cocteau and Diaghilev on the ballet *Parade,* later marrying the ballerina Olga Koklova.

Jean Cocteau (1889-1963), a French dandy and intellectual in the mould of Oscar Wilde, normally produced and designed the sets for his own plays and films, and illustrated his own poems. For the Diaghilev ballet he sought to bring in the cubist influence of Picasso and their collaboration lasted for several years. In 1925, Cocteau, at the height of his powers, became addicted to narcotics and for the next five years was completely dependent on opium. As a director and producer of the ballet, his sensitivity to music remained exact and in his writings, later incorporated in the *Art and Poetry of Opium Addiction* (1957), he retained an astonishing intuitive clarity and precision. Peggy Guggenheim's autobiography contains a description of the scene when she visited him in his hotel room as he lay in bed smoking opium. Later they dined together. Throughout the meal he preened himself vainly before a mirror. The purpose of her visit was to invite him to exhibit thirty original drawings he had made for the decor of his play, Les Chevaliers de la Table Ronde. His painting was never his major oeuvre and represented little more than a mannered reflection of Picasso.

Only one of the later Surrealists, the introverted Henri Michaux (1899-) deliberately undertook to draw and paint under the influence of mescaline. After a Jesuit education he studied medicine, literature and music and joined the merchant navy. Then, in 1922, he began to write, becoming a recognised poet. Not till 1937 did he take up painting seriously, evolving by automatism a personal style of gouaches on a black background known as fond noirs. These phantomismes created an ambiguous world of psychic images, myths and phantoms. Briefly in 1948-9 he executed a series of lively water-colours in various shades of red, but the brooding images returned in 1950 with an assemblage of black and white Indian Ink drawings which he named Mouvements, the basic mood of which was one of speed and panic.

These were followed in 1955 by drawings inspired by mescaline. He described an elated, hypersensitive state. Through the stimulus of the drug, his plastic technique changed to a form of rhythmic calligraphy of undulating ideograms that intermix and seemingly pulsate on the pictorial surface without distinct centres of interest. As an example of the all-over style they are reminiscent of the works of Jackson Pollock and Cy Twmbly. The outcome is a boring, formless monotony, lacking variation. They are failures. In Henry Osborne's opinion (1981) they do not communicate the state and by artistic standards they lack the impact of a revelation. In the latter years of his life, from 1960 onwards, Michaux produced fewer and fewer works under the influence of mescaline, he no longer felt the previously induced ecstatic sensitivity and turned to colour compositions in acrylic paint and to abstract calligraphy.

The inspiration of primitive art is varied. The artist may be steeped in the culture of his society. He may enter into a trance conjured by the ju-ju spirits, or work under the influence of Yagé, ayahuasca or peyote. The phantasms, demoniacal nightmarish activity, brightly coloured geometric patterns may be fashioned by tradition, hypnotic influences or by drugs.

Yagé is a climbing plant of the Brazilian forests used as an intoxicant and a remedy for beri beri. Visual hallucinations are conspicuous. Blue splashes before the eyes, succeeded by malaise, vertigo, euphoria and confusion, are in turn followed by vivid and extraordinary visions. Of interest are the alleged metagnomigenic or clairvoyant properties of the plant, used when guidance is sought on the whereabouts of their enemy, the location of ambushes, the approach of strangers, propitious hunting grounds or the most suitable partner in marriage. Reichel-Dolmetoff (1972) describes how the Tukaro Indians of the Amazon regions of Columbia frequently decorated their houses and pottery with large geometrical paintings of their Yagé imagery.

Another drug of the same region, ayahuasca, produces an alkaloid similar to harmine. In religious orgies, a preliminary stage of excitement and eroticism is followed by vertigo and simple visual hallucinations. A third drug, bufotenin, derived from toadskins and taken as an Amazonian narcotic snuff, can produce sensations of flying through the air.

Mexican art has been influenced by the visual hallucinations excited by the peyote cactus from which mescal alkaloids are derived. Among the Huichol Indians, their artistic designs consist of concentric tunnel arrangements. Peyote-induced hallucinations are used to communicate with their gods and the visions are interpreted as a totally separate and valid reality producing a double consciousness so that the patterns of the hallucinations appear with equal clarity to that of the real world to which they attach themselves.

Chapter Eleven

Deceiving the Eye — Beguiling the Mind

'Art is ruled uniquely by the imagination'.
Bernadetto Croce. *Aesthetic.* (1902).

ALL painting is of necessity illusory — 'imitation by the use of colours' (Philostratus). What is natural or imagined is represented and given the appearance of life in terms of lines and degrees of colour. A painting is two dimensional, monocular rather than stereoscopic, and static. The painter can accomplish his task only by giving tactile values to retinal impressions (Berenson, 1896). Images are its only wealth, it does not classify objects, it does not pronounce them real or imaginary, does not quantify them, does not define them: it feels and presents them (Croce, 1902). As Liotard (1781) has said in his treatise on the principles and rules of painting, 'painting is the most astounding sorceress; she can persuade us through the most evident falsehoods that it is pure truth'. In a work of art the artist's emphasis is upon the subject matter, he clothes the bare bones of perspective, shading, texture and movement so that the conscious mind of the viewer will accept implicitly the manner of their expression. If the artist savours overmuch the skill of presentation, he is in danger of encroaching upon illusion which is an applied science rather than art. In such circumstances, for the work to succeed, the craftsmanship itself has to be good, 'but the choice of subjects is not'. (Diderot). Two excellent books analyse and discuss this subtle distinction: *Art and Illusion* by E. H. Gombrich and *Illusion in Art* by M. L. d'Otrange Mastai.

An artist must use his own visual judgment to present perspective. An imperfection or distortion is commonly used to accentuate the quintessence of a painting — a feature most highly developed by the cartoonist. We apply our visual powers carelessly: rapidly scanning what is before us, selecting at a subconscious level things which appeal to our senses or, more probably, to our preconceived notions, and we monitor our findings, not by a more meticulous examination of the whole panorama, but by the intrusion of visual memories and visual interpretations. The above statement is but a modern affirmation of Ptolemy's Optics:

'The sense of sight discerns the difference of shapes, wherever they are without delay or interruption, employing careful calculations with almost incredible skill, yet acting unnoticed because of its speed. When the sense cannot see the object through its own mode of action, it recognises it through the manifestations of other differences, sometimes perceiving truly and sometimes imagining incorrectly.'

Too exact a perspective can seem optically imperfect without the addition of artificial corrections such as the architectonic device of entasis (bulging the centres of columns and rounding straight horizontal lines). There is an ambivalence of perspective fixing both the exact dimensions and position of objects and at the same time the illusion which recreates them. Every artist to some degree employs certain established expedients to develop perspective. When his indulgence in such trickery exceeds the minimum exigencies of representation he is liable to enter upon illusionism or *trompe l'oeil*. Illusion for its own sake borders on gimmickery but illusionism is possible within a masterpiece and the artist's skill in illusion can be as praiseworthy as, and no more reprehensible than, his ability to heighten a colour or expurgate trivial detail.

Within the frame of a two dimensional picture several stratagems can be employed with honesty to indicate depth. Near objects will partially obscure far objects. The convergence of parallel lines provides a linear perspective. Foreground objects stand on the lowest horizontal of the ground plane and as distant objects recede into the background the ground plane occupies a higher horizontal. Similarly, foreground objects in the sky or attached to the ceiling are at the very top of the picture and distant ones of the same elevation fade and fall towards the middle. Just part of a foreground figure may occupy most of the picture, a distant figure in its entirety appear as a simple dot. If the scene is painted from an aerial perspective far objects can be distinguished from those nearer to view because they are hazy and tinged with blue. Shadows add depth. Through skilful shading objects appear round or sqaure. Near objects and patterns are proportionately larger than those far away. Gradients in texture add verisimilitude. Vermification or rustication, devices borrowed from architecture, suggest strength or solidity.

Various forms of artifice, amounting to subterfuge, aid the establishment of perspective — a surrounding alcove, a partially drawn curtain, a fly on the wall, or Parrhasio's trick of simulating a broken glass pane in front of a picture. A Ferranese Madonna and Child of the 15th century is bordered by the jagged fragments of the canvas. In *trompe l'oeil classique,* engravings or drawings are depicted against wooden backgrounds. A very dark, night-black or candle-lit background leads to an intensification of reality. With chiaroscuro, the exaggerated contrast of light and dark to all effects abolishes the middle distance. Selected objects, exposed to direct light, are depicted in relief and thrust forward into the foreground, so much so that we almost feel as if we could reach out and touch the arranged still life. In reduced light all colours which approach brown remain unseen. The contents of the dark void cannot be easily gauged, and the suggestion of considerable depth naturally contributes to the impression of three dimensionality. Scenes set in Spanish inns, for example eavesdropping upon a group of plotters, offer an unexpected feeling of sinister silence achieved by the harsh, almost cruel, juxtaposition of highlights and shades. In portraiture, chairoscuro may suggest supernatural powers or an aspect of severe aloofness. If the atmosphere is made to appear foggy or smoky — sfumato — the clarity of the boundaries is lost and edges become hazy and indefinite. Thus, through the use of subdued tones and colour, a three dimensional illusion of atmospheric thickening can be achieved. To depict masonry, friezes, or sculpture, monochromic underpainting with alteration of tones in grey or greyish colours — grisaille — is often used. A wider range of colours with two or three tones — generically known as camaieu — enables an artist to deploy his illusionistic talents to suggest on canvas a whole multitude of bas relief subjects in bronze, marble, terra-cotta, onyx or even wood.

The term *trompe l'oeil* is applied to any decorative artefact or painting whose main criterion of success is its ability to deceive the eye as to the material reality of the objects presented. Painted mural or ceiling decoration may suggest additional architectural features — quadratura. In the 17th century, painters who specialised in such work were called 'Quadraturisti'; they sometimes collaborated with other artists on the decoration of large spaces. Inserted pictures set within an overall framework to decorate a vault or ceiling were called 'quadro riportato'. Michelangelo raised illusionism to a metaphysical plane when painting the ceiling of the Sistine Chapel. By crowding a vehement host of superhuman figures within the narrow compass and angular projections of the vault he achieved a sense of movement through the entire canopy of heaven. 'The simulated stone heaves like a sea, in a complex maelstrom of shifting planes. Not one inch of the surface appears level; even the sense of direction has become confused, and one wonders if one has not been transported into a mysterious fourth dimension' (d'Otrange Mastai, 1975). In a *trompe l'oeil* painting, the artist strives relentlessly to achieve a perfect duplication of reality to the point of delusion. Component objects unnaturally arranged can appear with intense reality through the use of minute detail and the careful rendering of tactile and tonal values — the head of a lion appears to burst through a postage stamp, the preacher's hand and bible extend out of the painting beckoning the viewer, or in hunting genre, a brace of partridges and a gun hang from hooks in front of a panelled wall. A cartellino or inscription within or below the picture persuades the viewer to look in at the picture and so draws its contents forward.

Many forms of *trompe l'oeil* have achieved recognition as stylised forms of art:

Memento mori or vanitas — usually an allegorical skull set among memoribilia,

Cut out or silhouetted chantourné, which in 18th-century Holland frequently took the form of illusionistic dolls,

Cabinets de curiosité,

Construzione legittima — a living room in perspective, with perhaps a further scene glimpsed at in the reflection of a mirror,

Culte de la nature — illusionistic idyllic landscape or garden vistas framed in architectural settings,

Devant de cheminée — a realistic representation of whatever objects might naturally be placed in an empty hearth,

Papyromania — obsessional, illusionistic representation of paper,

Quod libet (what you will) — a medley of objects, often stylised with a common theme or allegorical meaning, e.g. letter rack or contents of a pouch (vide pouche),

Xenia — originally from xenion, a kind of triptych, refers to objects arranged as on an easel.

Easel paintings were incorporated by Magritte into landscapes depicted partly in their natural state and partly as though painted on canvas placed on an easel, the difference being discernable only when the viewer looks more closely at the painting.

Many artists employ illusionistic techniques to indicate emotions. The enigmatic smile of the Mona Lisa is suggested by leaving indistinct the eyes and the curves of the mouth. Gombrich comments that Leonardo da Vinci achieves his greatest triumph of life-like expression by blurring precisely the features in which expression resides, thus compelling us to complete the act of creation; and Rembrandt would often leave the eyes of his most moving portraits in shadow because we are thus stimulated to supplement them.

The two most famed early specialists in *trompe l'oeil* were the French genre painters Jean Baptiste Cardin (1699-1779) and Jean Baptiste Oudry (1686-1755). Cardin's (the greatest painter of still life till Cézanne) illusionistic paintings range from The Game of Cards wherein the player seated in a circular masonry niche balances cards on each other to build 'houses', Blowing Bubbles in which a figure leans from a parapet to blow a bubble out of the picture, Les Attributs de la Musique — a chairoscuro still life of musical instruments — to one of the best known devant de cheminée, The White Tablecloth, placed upon a low table painted as though situated within a narrow rectangular opening.

Oudry's technical brilliance extended to tapestry designed hunting scenes, 'the finest evocation of natural scenery in 18th-century France'. Le Tabouret de Laque presents a richly caparisoned set of bagpipes. The Dog with a Porcelain Bowl, placed in an empty hearth, bristles with expectant movement. In another devant de cheminée, a large open book is propped against a pile of smaller books; but his renown rested in the main on his imitation of bas reliefs and some of his masterly still lifes of game suspended against traditional backgrounds.

The illusion of the appearance of movement has been suggested by painters throughout the centuries. Velàsquez in Hilanderos gives an uncertain glance at a spinning wheel which appears to catch the stroboscopic effect of rapid rotation. Movement is suggested at times by van Gogh's wildly swirling brush strokes. But the experience of movement as an illusory development stems from the Op and Kinetic art of Victor Vasarely, Bridget Riley and others. Designs shift, float and shimmer, sometimes with violent though illusory movement. The stimulated eye movements overload the retina with after images and moiré patterns. Two or three dimensional works both explore and exploit the fallability of the eye. Undulating lines give illusions of depth. The eyes seek out organised patterns. Retinal rivalry of red and green objects destroys such organisation to produce constant but inconsistent shifting effects. Subjective colours can arise from achromatic surfaces to movement or flicker (the Prévost-Fechner-Benham effect). Contingent after effects produced by patterns of black and white vertical and horizontal lines can actually produce a separation of colours: greenish — horizontal, reddish — vertical (McCollough, 1965). Similar colour after effects can be made contingent on the direction of movement, on line width, or on curvature. Through Op and Kinetic art, the science of illusion attempts a new artistic dimension, an extension of science into art, a new achievement or interest, masterpieces of invention rather than of art.

Visual puns first become evident in the early pictographs of hieroglyphic writing. The sketchy outlines could be subtly altered to suggest other characteristics. Coarser and more bizarre puns were the art format of the 16th-century painter, Guiseppe Arcimboldo, who assembled fruits, animals, trees and implements to build up symbolic portraits of the seasons. This bebased form of artistry has remained as a frequently imitated folksy representation, reproduced at fetes and harvest festivals, until the Surrealists sought inspiration from his inventions. Elsewhere they have survived as parlour entertainment: upside downs revealing two different profiles, ambiguous figures, e.g. Boring's mother-in-law — attractive lady or old hag? — Necker cubes, Ames' chairs, Kanizsa's triangle with illusory contours, Rubin's visual reversals, Mach's depth reversing figures, Fraser's spirals, Poggendorf, Ponzo and Zollner distorted lines, and Muller-Lyer arrows.

The magical perspective presented by the technique of anamorphosis has many attractions. The underlying principle of negative perspective was initially used by Leonardo in his notes. Satirically, a Queen's head viewed from a different direction could suggest a skull. The distorted skull of Holbein's Ambassadors has an allegorical significance. The 16th-century portrait of Edward VI, attributed to Cornelius Anthonisz, seen from the front presents a weird appearance, but viewed close to the edge, as in a peep show, rectifies the distortion and a normal head protudes with plastic reality from an oblique panel. In the spy-conscious Elizabethan era, a similar likeness could be smuggled across frontiers and a cryptogram of meaningless squiggles emblazoned on a glass could yield a secret message reflected from its saucer.

A favourite optical illusion is the visual paradox presented by the impossible picture, described by Gombrich as ambiguity of the third dimension. Common devices producing a false perspective are staircases, waterfalls, columns and reversing mosaic patterns — none of which appear in William Hogarth's engraving of a fisherman (1754). Today the scientific counterparts include Penroses' impossible triangle and similar impossible prongs; but the Dutch artist, Maurits Cornelius Escher (1898-1972) has exhibited many illusory works based on mathematical and constructivist premises. His lithographs, woodcuts and mezzotints are filled with illusory space stations, waterfalls and houses, all giving an air of rationality to what is patently absurd.

The creation of illusion into a highly sophisticated art form, utilising all the techniques of the best *trompe l'oeil* artists, the visual punning of Archimboldo, ambiguous images and competitive interpretations, forms the basis of Salvador Dali's paranoiac-critical technique. But there is another aspect in addition. Cozens' blot drawings, Ernst's frottages, taking inspiration from the pattern of simple objects, and Rorschach's ink spots, used as personality tests and tests of psychotic states, have in common the obtaining of imaginative and illusory interpretations from what is otherwise dull and ordinary. Biomorphic illusionism was introduced to Surrealist thinking by Yves Tanguy (1900-55), with his unidentifiable amorphous objects strewn over irrational landscapes of spectral dream-space. The technique was too similar to Dali's own to be acknowledged, but he does acknowledge his debt to Max Ernst (1891-1976) for the development of frottage, applying a method analagous to brass rubbing to obtain a basis for pictorial designs from the texture of sacking, the grain of wood or the grooves of foliage. He studied the dazzling illuministic skills of the French 'pompier' paintings of the late 18th and mid 19th centuries, such as Jacques-Louis David's The Dead Marat, mentioning particularly the highly finished, though rarely admired, works of Ernest Meissonier (1815-91). Others have likened Meissonier's paintings of the Napoleonic campaigns to symphonies by Berlioz 'played without drums and with tin for brass'.

Salvador Dali (1904-) merits consideration because of the popularity of his works, their technical brilliance and ingenuity, and his sheer versatility — illusionistic quadratura cupolas (e.g. The Royal Hour ceiling of the Palacetta de Albeñez in Barcelona), photography, design, films and paintings. He demands consideration by virtue of his cultivated eccentricity, exhibitionism, megalomania, and his claims of psychiatric, even psychotic, insight into the realms of the imagination. He would seek the same relationship between his paranoiac-critical method and *trompe l'oeil* as oneiristic states are to dreams:

> 'The paranoiac activity offers us the possibility of the systematisation of delirium. Paranoiac images are due to the delirium of interpretation. The delirium which, in the dream is wiped out on waking, really continues into these paranoiac images and it is directly communicable to everybody . . . The illusionism of the most abjectly arriviste and irresistable imitative art, the usual paralysing tricks of *trompe l'oeil,* the most analytically narrative and discredited academicism, can all become sublime hierarchies of thought and the means of approach to new exactitudes of concrete irrationality.'

Elsewhere he declares that the only difference between himself and a madman was that he was not mad. He differed from other Surrealists, who looked to dreams and the subconscious, in that he sought to develop the Freudian and psychological interpretation of the subconscious, revelling in self analysis and swarming with fetishisms direct from Krafft-Ebing's case-histories. He would consciously explore the possibilities of organ transplants and obsessive sexual distortions. His paintings parade his obsessive fear of sex, leading to onanism and the threat of castration — as developed in his William Tell drawings. At their worst, Dali's paintings are liable to be mere psycho-pathological documents. His later autobiographical writings — the *Secret Life of Salvador Dali* and the *Diary of a Genius* — are liable to be no more than farragoes of absolute garbage.

The fascination of Dali's paranoiac method which dominated his painterly output from 1928 is the skill whereby numerous images are conjured forth within one configuration based on the 'sudden power of systematic associations proper to paranoia'. The viewer notes the brilliant execution of the work and by changing the focus of attention finds many possible meanings in each colour or form, possibly allegorical if one can always understand Dali's mind, but presenting a marvellous series of visual puns.

In the late 1940s Dali, the most outrageous and provocative of the artists associated with the Surrealist movement, began to turn towards religious subjects. In outlining his aims for painting the Christ of St. John of the Cross — now in the Kelvingrove Gallery in Glasgow — Dali explains in more rational terms his examination of perspective:

'My aesthetic ambition in the picture was completely the opposite of the Christs painted by most of the modern painters, who have all interpreted him in the expressionistic and contortionistic sense, thus obtaining emotion through ugliness. My principal preoccupation was that my Christ would be beautiful as the God that He is. In 1950 I had a 'cosmic dream' in which I saw in colour this image which in my dream represents the Nucleus of the Atom. This nucleus afterwards took on a metaphysical meaning. I consider it to be the very unity of the Universe — Christ. I saw the Christ drawn by St. John of the Cross. I worked out geometrically a triangle and a circle, which 'aesthetically' summarised all my previous experiments and I drew my Christ in this triangle.'

Chapter Twelve

Synaesthesia

'Les parfums, les couleurs et les sons se répondent'.
C. Baudelaire. *Correspondence.*

'The splashing over of impressions from one sensory modality to another'.
Gombrich. *Art and Illusion.*

THE phenomenon of synaesthesia, 'whereby a stimulus presented in one mode seems to call up imagery of another mode as readily as its own' (Vernon, 1937), represents a very special kind of hallucinatory activity worthy of analysis in depth. Although synaesthetic metaphor in poetry, e.g. 'the world lay luminous, every petal and cobweb trembled music', has received occasional literary and semantic examination, little has been offered by way of scientific or psychological analysis. Those with the gift may receive a sensory impression, translate it into a sensory percept within the same sensory modality, and then, in the course of extracting from it an emotional appeal or some equivalent higher sensory recognition, invoke other sensory percepts involving unrelated and apparently disparate modalities of sensation; for example, the blast of a trumpet may awaken waves of golden sound. These additional percepts are internal, unconnected to the stimulus in terms of neural mechanisms or pathways, and thus hallucinatory. Somehow those subject to such synaesthetic sensitivity are able to conjure forth a variety of secondarily associated memory traces — imagery and sensation belong to different sense modes. The result is a form of hallucination which many artists have been able to exploit with great facility: musicians such as Scriabin, Rimsky-Korsakof, Schönberg and Bliss; poets such as Rimbaud, Poe, Shelley and Swinburne; writers such as Huysmans, and painters such as Turner, Whistler, Kandinsky, Klee, Russolo and Wiertz.

There have been many attempts to explain this phenomenon. At its highest synaesthesia is the intellectual awakening of a whole range of mental imagery, deserving its synonyms: oratio colorata, Farbenhören, Farbinghören, audition colorée, colour-hearing, psycho-chromaesthesia — the skilful orchestration of a chain of mental associations where some of the intermediate links have dropped out of awareness. At its lowest synaesthesia is described as a primitive mechanism akin to eidetic imagery whereby a clear separation of the sensory modalities has yet to develop. And intermediate is the suggestion of an instability of the nervous system or loosening of bonds as seen in those with mental illness such as schizophrenia or as induced by intoxication with psychedelic drugs. Thus Sir Stuart Duke-Elder, the doyen of Ophthalmology, describes the phenomenon as psychological, if not sometimes psychopathic.

Révèsz (1922), in his studies of the psychology of music, describes three types of colour-hearing (Schollphotismen): (1) a sensationary type, when the subject actually sees colours while hearing music; (2) an imaginatory type, when he imagines colours; and (3) a nominal type, in which the name of a certain colour forces its way into the listener's conscience. With both coloured hearing and audible colour (Lichtphonismen) it is Révèsz' sensationary type with which we are principally concerned.

Synaesthesia as a special talent

The evolution of special talents is poorly understood. Little is known of the origin of those talents which are universally regarded as the highest attributes of civilised people, or why certain individuals, and not others, should be gifted with mathematical, literary and artistic ability. There is no apparent adaptive in being musical rather than tone deaf, and a colour-blind person may be less readily deceived by camouflage than an individual with full colour recognition. This aspect of natural selection was specifically discussed by Alfred Russel Wallace although he made little contribution to its understanding. Natural selection, depending on the survival of the fittest, can only act on useful or hurtful characteristics, eliminating the latter and keeping the former to a fairly general level of efficiency. It applies, with some approach to equality, among all savages — speed in running, bodily strength, skill with weapons, acuteness of vision, ability to follow a trail. Mathematical, musical or artistic talents — those specially developed faculties of civilised man — exist in only a small proportion of individuals and the difference of capacity between these favoured people and the average of mankind is enormous. Thus faculties are developed in civilised man which in their mode of origin, their function and their variations are altogether distinct from those other characteristics and faculties which are essential to him, and which have been brought to their actual state of efficiency by the necessities of his existence.

Wallace included speech among man's special talents developed outside the forces of natural selection, and it is probably speech which gives the clue to the development of all other special talents. The great evolutionary jump which man achieved was not a limited genetic mutation due to natural selection but the capacity for prolonged foetalisation whereby the brain was able to continue growing after birth. The result is that Man, though far from developing to the full the extraordinary potential of the human brain, has advanced above other animals by a series of unanticipated evolutionary strides as displayed by the spectacular evolution of language:—

'The natural laws governing the formation of guttural laryngeal sounds and mouth clicks do not account for the combination of sounds into words controlled by vocabulary. Similarly the rules regulating the development of vocabulary do not presuppose the formation of sentences controlled by syntax and grammar. At each stage the principles governing the isolated particulars of a lower level leave indeterminate conditions to be controlled by a higher principle. Consequently, the operation of a higher level cannot be accounted for by the laws governing its particulars on the next lower level' (Polanyi, 1968).

Vocabulary is not derived automatically from phonetics, nor grammar from vocabulary; a correct use of grammar does not anticipate style or content as in the plays and poetry of Shakespeare and Milton. Speech did not lead inevitably to writing or the written word to the advanced audio-visual devices of today.

Similarly, if we place synaesthesia among the special talents, we should seek an explanation among the stages involved in creative and imaginative thinking.

The basic physiology of synaesthesia

Scientists often shun the high-flown, preferring to seek an order of events from an understanding of the simplest and most basic concepts. Some scientists regard pain as the simplest modality of sensation but others believe that pain is a consequence of excessive stimulation of nerve receptors within the skin which normally respond to specific modalities of sensation such as touch, cold or warmth. These receptors have a low threshold to adequate or reasonable stimulation of their selective modality and a raised threshold to other kinds of stimulation. Other hypotheses consider the sensation of pain to be determined by and dependent upon the size of the nerve fibres involved and the pattern of their activation. Particular patterns of stimulation set up reverberating circuits within the spinal cord or at higher levels of the central nervous system perpetuating the stimulus in the form of pain. To date the most accepted hypothesis is one which suggests that sensory awareness to stimuli from the skin and sensory organs is determined by a gate control system modulated by the balance between painful and specific, non-painful impulses. Pain, when sufficiently intense, will burst through the gate to impinge upon conscience.

The word, synaesthesia, has a special and distinctive meaning with respect to spinal injury or amputation of limbs. Abnormal spread of sensation can occur and the term, synchiria, is applied when a stimulus such as a pin prick applied to the unaffected side of the body produces an unpleasant feeling bilaterally; allaesthesia or allochiria when the stimulus is felt only over the opposite affected side, and synaesthesialgia to a form of causalgia when a unilateral stimulus to the affected side causes pain in the unaffected side. As an extension of these definitions, synaesthesia is used where a stimulus to a normal area above the level of injury elicits two sensations, one well localised and the other on one or both sides of the damaged area.

Pain is observed for the most part by small, unmyelinated nerve fibres. Synaesthesia due to the build up of reverberating circuits and diffusion between nerve fibres may well occur in the higher levels of the central nervous system of children before the major fibre tracts are insulated from each other by the appearance of myelin sheaths around the larger nerve fibres. Thus a similar spread, blending or overlap of sensory impulses by ephaptic transmission, forms the battle of Werner's theory (1948) of synaesthesia being a primitive, undifferentiated perceptual experience which permits the linkage together of the separate realms of sensation. The facility for linking the varied sensory inputs is lacking or in abeyance in the highly differentiated and objectified forms of experience of most adults. In a similar vein, Wells (1918-9) has argued that colour-hearing is a primitive form of autistic thinking restricted to elementary sensory patterns in contrast to the more advanced forms of thought underlying symbol formation in dreams and hallucinations.

If synaesthesia arises physiologically in the immature nervous system, it is possible that it can occur in the adult nervous system either as the result of crude sensations that the body cannot analyse — thus flashes of light may follow pressure on the eyeballs or the presence of strong magnetic fields — or where there has been damage to a part of the nervous system. There are many reports of photisms, induced by sound, which always appear within a defective portion of the visual field (Jacobs *et al,* 1981). These photisms can vary from simple flashes of white light to complicated colourful hallucinations likened to a flame, a petal, oscillating lines, a kaleidoscope, or an amoeba. Other examples of auditory-visual synaesthesia follow damage to the optic nerve due to compression or disease, but it is also apparent that these experiences can also occur in normal individuals with intact visual pathways. However, the evidence that damaged sensori-neural systems are more prone to synaesthesia increases the suspicion that many forms of synaesthesia arise from diffusion of normal sensations away from their specific routes of transmission. Schizophrenia is characterised by a fragmentation of the boundaries between sensation, thoughts and memories and a similar situation can present under the influence of mescaline or other hallucinogenic drugs.

Synaesthesia psychoanalysed

The earliest reports of synaesthesia date back to the 17th century when John Locke in his *Essay Concerning Human Understanding* and John Thomas Woolhouse independently described blind people who perceived colours whilst listening to musical sounds. In 1881 two Swiss medical students, Bleuler and Lehmann, interviewed 596 people, of whom 76 (12.5%) had double sensations. These sensations were first recognisable in early childhood at around three or four years of age. When Eugen Bleuler re-examined his subjects 15 years later he found essentially no changes in the colours evoked by sounds, except that there was some reduction in the intensity and clarity of the photisms. He felt synaesthesia to be a physiological condition, present in everyone but available for conscious experience in only the minority of adults.

Bleuler's hypothesis has been challenged by other psychiatrists and psychologists who have emphasised that synaesthesia can be a symptom of mental disease with the secondary sensations overshadowing or obliterating awareness of the actual stimulus. Hug-Hellmuth declared that synaesthesia resulted from early childhood experiences whose memory associations are later repressed; and infantile sexual experiences, by stirring up pleasurable and painful emotions, can heighten synaesthesiae and cause them to become fixed in memories or fantasies.

A more modern hypothesis is that of Reichard, Jakobson and Werth (1949) who interpret the frequent occurrence of synaesthesiae among children as an important stage in the development of memory and the learning of language. Other psychological theories (e.g. Goldstone, 1962) differ from physiological explanations in that they place the element of confusion in synaesthesia at a conceptual level. The neural mechanisms for making intersensory distinctions may be 'built in' but the experience or perception of these distinctions is more probably of a learned, conceptual nature. Uninterpreted memory traces may thus remain as 'undifferentiated affective-perceptive engram conglomerates' (Mahler and Elkish, 1953).

Intersensory synthesis

The majority of adults who do not recall personal memories of synaesthesia may be tempted to dismiss the phenomenon as a purely semantic device. As Kerr and Pear (1932) remark, 'the use of a smile and metaphor may perhaps be regarded as the entrance door to synaesthesia'. Whereas the Maoris have 3,000 separately designated colours (Katz, 1935), other races with a relative poverty of vocabulary are forced to describe colours by analogy. Among the literary gifted, synaesthesia may reflect the richness of poetic metaphor or synaesthesia could be a verbal contrivance used by schizoid personalities prone to make clang or knight's move associations. Some of the people given to make synaesthetic relationships could be regarded as eccentric personalities or showmen as, for example, A. Wallace Rimington (1854-1918) with his colour organ seeking to translate music into sight and the Danish-American singer and scientist, Thomas Wilfred with his clavilux. The Italian futurist painter, Luigi Russolo (1885-1947) was obsessed by his Bruitistic musical instruments and his attempts to represent non-visual sensations by painting; and the Belgian artist, Antoine Wiertz (1806-65) painted portraits for bread and religious and historical compositions for honour. He refused to sell the latter, believing that they surpassed the masterpieces of Rubens, Raphael and Michelangelo. These large, uneven, macabre, apocalyptic designs were supposed to be viewed to the accompaniment of a concealed choir. Best known of all was Scriabin (1872-1915) with his colour symphony, *Prometheus: The Poem of Fire,* scored for a keyboard of light (clavier à lumière, tastiera per luce) projecting a play of scintillating colours on the ceiling of the darkened concert hall. Those not gifted with colour-hearing were left cold or puzzled. They were to be equally puzzled when Dame Edith Sitwell used the expression, 'Emily coloured primulas'. She explained that she meant pink: other conceived 'Emily' as a white pepper colour, or yellow, or even mauve.

Set against these slightly weird examples are many instances when the public have been prepared to accept synaesthesia, if only in terms of description. We can appreciate the 'perfumed colours' of artists such as Kandinsky, Klee and Chagall; and Ireland's composition *Scarlet Ceremonies* is accepted without demure. Arnold Bliss' *Colour Symphony* (1922) in which he labelled the movements, I Purple, II Red, III Blue, and IV Green more closely approximates to that of Scriabin except that he leaves the listener to relate the music to the proposed colour scheme. Green is described as the colour of emeralds, hope, joy, youth, spring and victory. When composing, Bliss always experienced a play of colour sensation (Lichtphonismen), and he relates that such a play of colour was especially vivid in his mind when working on this symphony. One of the earliest synaesthetic painters was a Lithuanian, M. K. Cuirlionis, a musical prodigy who suddenly turned to painting. His aim was to paint music. His colour compositions were conceived as symphonic movements with such titles as *Ocean Sonata, Sun Sonata, Snake Sonata*. However, Redon had already dubbed himself the peintre symphinique, and van Gogh forecast that painting promised to become more subtle — 'more music and less sculpture'. Or, as Kandinsky states, 'When I could see all my colours: I realised that painting possessed the same power as music'.

Two more recent works of art — Mondrian's painting Broadway Bougie Woogie and Walt Disney's film *Fantasia* are held by Gombrich to be excellent examples of synaesthesia. Few books on orchestration exist which do not make at least occasional use of colour suggestions and dyslexic children can be helped in reading by colouring various letters or combinations of letter. In all cultures heraldic associations abound: purple symbolising royalty or high birth; black, grief or penitence; green, dragons, wind or sour tastes; a red sound of low pitch is dark or bluish red, of high pitch yellow-red or orange. Wines may be robust, smooth with no edges on it, or possess a dry, flinty flavour. Noises can be 'penetrating' or 'jarring'. And Simpson and McKellar quote pains as green — mild and tickling; red — sharp, acute; and deep blue — throbbing and persistent.

Galton's scientific tract, *Inquiries into Human Faculty* (1883), is replete with schematised patterns whereby individuals recollect the days of the week, seasons of the year, numerals and other visualised forms. These mneumonics, number forms and kindred visual images appear to provide additional associations useful in the learning process. People with supposedly photographic memories reinforce the recollection of volumes of data by inapparent associations. Such is undoubtedly the case with Luria's famous mneumonist 'S' (1968) who possessed an outstandingly vivid, detailed and persistent visual memory, almost certainly eidetic, with an unusual degree of synaesthesia. He was considered to be weak in abstract thinking. Oswald (1960) regards these number forms — which do not come into view whenever a numeral is thought of but only in special circumstances — as aids to the comprehension of abstract concepts, particularly the concept of sequence. The visual mneumonics provide a semi-concrete representation allowing units with no inherent order to be arranged in an orderly fashion, giving them a 'sensory' character. An analogy can be made between these 'forms' and constructive acts of arranging the data of an abstract problem into a series of visual patterns until a key or solution to the problem is found. Just as the sequence of events in a particular month can be better remembered if related to a family birthday so it is possible to speed the process of mental arithmetic if one imagines multiples or the squares of numbers somehow highlighted.

Letters can be assigned colours: thus the French symbolist poet Rimbaud wrote a sonnet *Les Voyelles* in which he attached to each vowel the colour in which it appeared to him — 'a' black, 'e' white, 'i' red, 'o' green, and 'u' blue. Others see 'r' as flowering or moving and 'i' as sharp or bright. In fact, onomatopoeia can be a form of synaesthesia — sounds can indeed imitate or match visual impressions, words like 'flicker', 'blinking' or 'scintillating' are at least as good approximations in the language to visual impressions as 'tick-tock' or 'choo-choo' to auditory impressions.

Regardless of the frequent emphasis upon the literary associations of synaesthesia, there is sufficient physiological and psychological evidence to suggest that most synaesthesia is the outcome of genuine intersensory attributes. Gerard, Marshall and Saul (1936) found that the response to an auditory stimulus was increased whilst a light was shone in the eyes although there was no evidence of overflow of optic impulses into the auditory paths. However, intersensory spread or blending can arise in response to external stimuli, from memory associations or as irritative phenomena due to abnormal excitation within the nervous system. A clear example of synaesthesia of epileptic origin is presented by Jacome and Gummit (1979). Their patient had episodic seizures characterised by sudden pain over the right side of the face; simultaneously, he heard the word 'five' in both ears and saw the number '5' on a grey background before both eyes. These episodes occurred about ten times a month.

Philosophers repeatedly talk in terms of the harmonisation of the sensations and harmonisation of the emotions. Charles Henry (1926) held that not only could all the different arts be harmonised but they could bring about in the human organism a corresponding harmonising and transcendental experience or ecstacy. Ogden, Richards and Wood in *The Foundations of Aesthetics* put forward a theory of aesthetic experience or synaesthesis describing the experience of beauty in terms of a coming together or an equilibrium and harmony of impulses which have been called out in contemplation by the object sensed to be beautiful. Finally, the most quoted expert on synaesthesia, E. A. Hayek *(The Sensory Order,* 1952), asserts that all mental qualities — directly or indirectly — are so interrelated that any attempt to give an exhaustive description of any one of them would make it necessary to describe the relations existing between all of them.

Francisco Goya (1746-1828)
Sleep brings forth monsters

An Essay on the Pleasures of the Imagination

Thomas Addison (1712).

'When the brain is beset by an accident, or the mind disordered by dreams or sickness, the fancy is overrun with wild, dismal ideas and terrified with a thousand monsters of its own framing'.

(Hence Goya's picture: The Sleep of Reason Brings Forth Monsters).

EVERY one of the major illnesses of Goya's life, each striking with almost psychosomatic precision, appears to have coincided with a crisis in his development as a painter. The character of Goya, the man, is among the most impressive of all painters. His fortitude through serious illness and debility and his resilience through turbulent times — internal upheavals, invasion and revolution — demanding the fullest application of his considerable political awareness and social assets, are the more admirable because he presented overtly, in the most forthright manner throughout a long life, an uncompromising honesty of purpose. Spain was (to quote Tràgala, a song of the 1820 revolution) 'a country tied on an historical rack — the symbolic equivalent of its own Inquisition's instrument of torture'. He survived and thrived, indulging in the everyday pleasures and passions at the vortex of events — the anarchy of the Spanish court, the French Revolution, Spain as the battlefield of Europe, and the tragic aftermath of war. His art chronicles a blistering commentary of all levels of society throughout the 50 years of transition from 1774 to 1824. Licht, in a biographical study, 'Goya, the Origins of the Modern Temper in Art', claims that Goya through his art invented a language that conveyed the very principles of anarchy. At the same time he redefined the role of the artist who, with neither Church nor State to sponsor him, could no longer count on a recognised place within the structure of society, and was forced to create within a void.

Francisco Goya was born in 1746 at Fuendetos, a village near Saragossa, the capital of the province of Aragon, about halfway between Madrid and the French border. His father was a master gilder in semi-retirement. The parish priest, recognising the young Goya's talent at sketching people, recommended that he be apprenticed at the early age of 14 to the painter, José Luzàn, with whom he was to remain in Saragossa for four years. Goya as 'a broth of a boy' possessed all the characteristics of the Aragonese 'baturros' — toughness, obstinacy, impetuosity. For some years his riotousness and revolutionary character remained unbridled. He loved hunting, was an aficionarde of the bullfight and, as ringleader among like-minded youths, his escapades led to his being found one night with a knife in his back. José Luzàn, with the help of Francisco Bayeu, a painter at the court of Charles III, sought to enroll him in the Academy of San Fernando, the leading art school in Spain. However, he failed to gain entry on two occasions and we hear little of his progress until, at the age of 24, he left for Italy in the company of a group of bullfighters. He continued his training there, copying the Old Masters and gaining second prize in a competition at the Royal Academy of Fine Arts at Parma, but further exploits forced him to quit Rome in a hurry. He attempted to abduct a young nun from her convent. Only the intervention of some highly placed friends aware of his talents saved him from the death penalty.

On return to Spain, Goya received two commissions jointly with Bayeu, whose sister he married: firstly, to paint frescos for the new Pilar cathedral, and in 1778 — a year marked by a brief illness and some celebrated studies in the manner of Velàsquez — to design a series of cartoons of Spanish life for the Royal tapestry factory at Santa Barbara. Though expressing a zest for life in the style of the younger Tiepolo, one finds suspicious-looking characters reminiscent of the Caprichos even in these earlier pictures; however their charm, colour and brilliance was such that within two years he became Court Painter. From 1784 his success blossomed, with fashionable pictures and portraits. He gained the friendship of Charles IV, of Queen Marie Luisa's prime minister, Godoy, and his marriage did not prevent a legendary love affair with the Duchess of Alba.

Then, in 1792, came the great caesura with an illness lasting nearly a year. In March, 1793, Sebastian Martinez, writing to Goya's friend Martin Zapater said: 'Goya is slightly better but progress is sadly slow. The noises in his head and the deafness have not improved, but his vision is much better. He is no longer suffering from the disorders which made him lose his balance and he can walk up and down stairs with difficulty'. What seems to have happened was that Goya was struck down with giddiness, sickness, deafness and partial blindness, all of which appeared with chaotic and devastating suddenness. Exposure to cold and over-exertion when trying to mend the axle of a coach in which he and the Duchess of Alba were travelling have been suggested as the precipitating factors. The nature of the illness is uncertain. Meningitis remains a possibility. He was almost certainly at risk from syphilis and only one of his nineteen children survived childhood, but the fact that he recovered from illness and lived an active life for another 35 years suggests that this was an isolated event without further progression such as would be expected with neural or cardiovascular syphilis.

The probable explanation is more likely to be that proposed by my old chief, Sir Terence Cawthorne, namely the rare and curious Vogt-Koyanagi syndrome in which temporary inflammation of the inner eye is associated with permanent deafness, and often with loss of pigmentation of the hair and skin. Sir Terence describes five such patients, one of whom I saw when working for him. The infecting agent is believed to be a virus. Loss of pigmentation is by no means invariable, deafness and loss of vestibular sensibility are permanent though the uveitis clears up without any residual visual defect.

Two theories exist to explain the Vogt-Koyanagi and allied Vogt-Koyanagi-Harada syndromes, namely viral infection or the development of hypersensitivity of the body's antibodies to melanin and other pigment cells. These exist in the skin, eye, including the retina, inner ear and hair. The illness comes suddenly with cutaneous depigmentation, or deafness, or loss of vision or headache with fever and vertigo, or a combination of any of these. Individuals with certain tissue types are constitutionally more prome than the majority of the population to succumb to this condition but steroid treatment can arrest the progress of the disease.

Goya was left totally deaf. This sensory deprivation, and perhaps the partial sensory deprivation of his sight at the height of his illness, inaugurated an addition to Goya's art, namely the hideous, nightmarish, weird and colourless cartoon distortions which thrived alongside his more public art for the rest of his life. Brooding hallucinations replaced the discourse of the world with all the strength of Addison's prophetic words. When he resumed work at the end of 1793 he produced a series of pictures for the Academy of San Fernando based upon personal observation and continued his portraiture with renewed success but there was a new departure. In 1799 he advertised 80 prints in etching and aquatint 'censuring human errors and vices'. Each picture had a caption which deepened the ambiguity and sharpened the paradox of the subject. Goya had first considered their publication in 1797 as grouped drawings in sequences under the title of 'Sueños', dreams. Their subject matter could have derived something from the satires of Hogarth (1698-1764) and it is known that several of Goya's friends had visited England at that time. Piranesi has also used the title 'Caprices' for his pictures of French prisons. On 19th February 1799, after a sale of just two days, they were suddenly withdrawn; and, in 1803, at the prompting of Godoy, the plates were made over to the royal printer under threat of the Inquisition.

Twelve of the Caprichos involved transparent jibes at hereditary aristocracy; more than a dozen were seering attacks on the Church, its monks and priests — some overt, others in the forms of goblins and witches using the iconology of his friend, the playwright Morantin; and many of the remainder were a satire on sexual mores. His professed intention was to 'rake' the irrational, the superstitious and the inhuman in social life; but Goya himself talks of monsters coming into his drawings as though he had no control over them. Despite these hallucinations and the episodes of depression and paranoia which so often attend total, acquired deafness, Goya was at the height of his creative powers, producing over 700 paintings between 62 and 73 years of age, and it was said that some of his portaits were executed at a single sitting of but a few hours. His court paintings were realistic rather than flattering as with the picture of King Charles IV and his family and that of the Condesa de Chinchon painted with ears of corn in her hair (she did in fact go mad) but his relationship with the court was such that the King even learnt sign language to converse with him.

In 1808, Napoleon's troops occupied Spain and the War of Independence broke out. This inspired Goya's greatest painting, 'The Third of May, 1808', showing the irrational, predetermined brutality of the invaders. His etchings of 'The Disasters of War' show up all that is digusting and horrible in human conflict. In 1812, commissioned to paint the victorious Wellington, Goya became furious at the English General's inability to sit still, picked up the general's sword and chased him out of the studio.

In 1819 he suffered from a short illness but there are no recorded details. He continued his psychological exposé of the times with the 'Desparates' engravings, adding baffling and often startling proverbs. He moved into a small house on the outskirts of Madrid which became known as Quinta del Sordo. The house became famous for the series of Black Paintings painted in oils straight on to the plaster of its walls and filling up the spaces between doors and windows. Quite horrifying in their intensity and breathtaking in their genius, they were dashed off in bursts of violent energy. In 1876, a French nobleman, Baron Emil d'Erlanger bought the House of the Deaf Man and had the murals transferred to canvas to be exhibited in 1878 at the World Fair in Paris.

Goya left Spain for France along with many Spanish liberals in 1824, ostensibly on grounds of ill-health, but returned at the King's command to Madrid in 1826 to sit for his own portrait by Vincente Lopez. Far from being the ideal sitter, the aged, irascible Goya was constantly jumping up, offering criticisms and even adding a few brush strokes. Some of his paintings of his final years show a return to the old gay colours of earlier days, but in the spring of 1828 increasing trouble with vision and balance forced him to take to his bed and he died of apoplexy on April 16th 1828.

Opinions vary as to his mental state in later years. Professor Carstairs is altogether too melodramatic:

'He was an early exponent of black humour but in some of his most savage pictures this gives way to a fierce castigation of his own and his fellow creatures' baser impulses. This combination of pessimism, of preoccupation with cruelty, and of self-accusation is very characteristic of the mood of a person suffering from depression . . . His career was punctuated by periods of withdrawal from activity. Insomnia is the almost invariable accompaniment of this form of illness; and indeed darkness and night attend many of his lugubrious fantasies. It is noticeable, too, that there is a recurrent imagery of transfixion of the anus by swords, spears and other piercing implements. Here we have an all too literal expression of the oral-aggressive and anal-sadistic fantasies which are the (usually unconscious) accompaniments of severe depression.'

His letters give no sign of melancholia: they are full of fight, of high spirits, even when over eighty — 'I can't see, or write or hear — I have nothing left but the will — and that I have in abundance'.

I share the opinion of Kenneth Clark that he got a wry amusement out of his hallucinations of horror, deriving satisfaction from the reckless, masterly way he was able to transform them into the imagery of his art.

William Blake (1757-1827)
English poet, painter, philosopher and engraver

Developed Eidetic Imagery

BLAKE began his training as a draughtsman at the age of 10 and by 15 was apprenticed to an engraver, being already engaged in writing poetry. His art is noted for its esoteric symbolism, intense visionary quality and individuality, but is firmly based on a long tradition of figurative art — thus, besides illustrating his own poems, he used the Bible, Milton, Shakespeare and Dante as textual sources, all of which he interpreted in a highly personal manner.

He is noted also for the intensity of his imagery, spending his whole life in the elaboration of a symbolic universe so dense and complex that many aspects of it are still being elucidated by scholars. He did not draw from nature because, as he said repeatedly, his visions were clearer and more vivid than his optical perception of the world around him. The term 'eidetic imagery' can be more closely attached to Blake than to any other artist. The images are characterised by sharpness of definition, optical reality and involuntary appearance, often under conditions of nervous excitement producing a form of auto-suggestion.

As a child he had many imaginary illusory experiences: God put his head in at the window, the prophet Ezekiel was sitting under a tree at Peckham Rye, the tree was filled with angels. Working as an apprentice at Westminster Abbey, he saw a vision of Christ and the Apostles and at the Hercules Building, Lambeth, saw a vision of the Ancient of Day at the top of his staircase. Many imaginative children have these experiences. What is exceptional is that Blake, as part of his artistic training, kept and developed these intense powers of visualisation after the age of puberty (Kenneth Clark). Jaensch (1930) defines eidetic imagery as an intermediate stage between the perception of a thing and the pure memory image and not a mere sensory phenomenon, i.e. a positive after image occasioned by an external object. In part, at least, it is subject to laws other than those governing the sensory phenomenon e.g. it can be influenced by the will and under radical change such as susceptibility to imaginative influences and to creative fantasy. Thus Blake appears to have developed this facility as a positive form of Kim's game.

In favour of the eidetic imagery explanation are instances where one image blocks another. Two examples are described in detail by Varley, an early spiritualist who created an atmosphere like that of a mediumistic seance, and by Linnell. Varley, on hearing of the spiritual apparition of a flea, asked him to draw the likeness of what he saw. Midway through the portrait he left off and began on another part of the paper to make a separate drawing of the mouth of the flea before proceding with the first sketch. On another occasion he was requested to draw the likeness of William Wallace. 'The eyes of Blake sparkled, for he admired heroes. "William Wallace", he exclaimed, "I see him now, there, there, how noble he looks — reach me my things". Having drawn for some time with the same ease of hand and steadiness of eye as if a living sitter were before him, Linnell reported that Blake said: "I cannot finish him: Edward the First has stepped in before him". He then sketched Edward I, completed it and finished the head of Wallace'.

Against eidetic imagery is his saying that Imagination is surrounded by the daughters of Inspiration, and the following quotation: 'When the sun rises do you see a round disc of fire somewhat like a guinea — Oh, no, no, I see an innumerable company of the heavenly host crying "Holy, holy, holy is the Lord God Almighty" ' — thus mixing visual and auditory imagery.

He often expressed himself in terms that implied specific visual experiences but when asked where he saw his visions when out walking, he said 'Here madam' and touched his forehead. Many of his visions were involuntary, thus he believed himself to be in immediate contact with 'spirits' who revealed to him his vision and inspired his poems. He claimed that he conversed daily with his long-dead brother, saw him in his remembrance in the regions of his imagination and that it was Robert who revealed to him a new method of painting his own illustrated poems in colour. We can only conclude that in later life, by a process of detachment akin to yoga (Auguelles, 1975), he had developed a particularly strongly developed creative imagination coupled with an exceptional visual memory.

Joseph Mallord William Turner (1775-1857)

Lingering Perceptions of Nature

TURNER poses many questions of medical interest arising from his idiosyncratic and impressionistic use of colour. His contemporaries variously accused him of suffering from eye disease, sunstroke and madness. In middle life he was irascible and, after prolonged ill-health, became alcoholic. He employed the full range of available colours, with the exception of green, liberating colour from form and subject matter to achieve a heightened emotional effect. Thus be became the arch-romanticist of his time, but 50 of his most abstract paintings were only discovered as late as 1939 wrapped in tarpaulin in the archives of the National Gallery.

His phenomenal energy and creativity was apparent from an early age. Until 1796 he was essentially a watercolour landscapist employing great detail. His father, a barber and wig-maker, discovered that his son had a precocious gift for drawing that could be turned into a valuable source of income and directed and exploited his talent so that by 21 years of age he already had more orders than he could execute.

A Dr. Munro had a dual influence upon Turner, treating his mother for mental illness (? presenile dementia) and enabling Turner to copy the watercolour landscapes of John Robert Cozens, son of Alexander Cozens of 'blot' landscape fame. Cozens' colour schemes were restricted to grey and greenish grey but achieved remarkable atmospheric effects. The possible hereditary nature of his mother's insanity and his own bent towards cataclysmic art, with detailed portrayals of earthquakes and volcanic eruptions, led to frequent accusations of madness, Bedlam and imbecility until he was powerfully defended by the young Ruskin: 'Natural forces, both those that he had inherited from the Sublime as images of horror for himself, became the very essence of his art embodying in their forms also, the emotions he wished to communicate'.

Inwardly he appears as a very sympathetic person, close to those involved in the abolition of the slave trade and reflecting his personal anguish at his mother's illness in a passage from one of his verses, which simulated those of Thompson and Coleridge, wherein an account of madness is sandwiched between descriptions of natural cataclysms.

His revolutionary experimentation with colours and new tints came at an age, when, to quote the connoisseur, Sir George Beaumont: 'a good picture, like a good fiddle, should be brown', a respectability dependent upon the darkened varnish of the old Masters and the dark paintings of the 17th-century landscape artists. Patrick Trevor-Roper has examined the evidence relating to Turner's eyesight. His reading glasses are still preserved in the print room of the Ashmolean Museum. He was not myopic and there is no suggestion of cataracts. He attributes the presence of small patches of blue among a miscellany of reds to the wearing of brown-tinted spectacles and the later blurring of his compositions to astigmatism but dismisses the hypothesis of yellow vision (Xanthopsia) due to alcoholic cirrhosis*. After a flu-like infection the cause of Turner's ill-health was undoubtedly loss of teeth. Tenderness of his gums prevented his wearing of false teeth and his digestion gave way so that he existed for the most part on a diet of rum and milk. Thornbury tells of interviewing two boatmen who used to row Turner on his sketching expeditions on the Thames: 'It is still their unspeakable wonder how a man like that who always took a bottle of gin out with him for inspiration and never gave them any, could have been a great genius'.

Although Turner's elliptic scenery and suffused bursts of colour are frequently ascribed to dream-like inspiration, for the most part his robust imagination can be accounted for by his accurate observation of nature, not so much the actualities of the scene but its atmosphere — fiery sunsets,

---

*It is possible that gin drinking, without alcoholic cirrhosis could account for xanthopsia.

a storm on the Yorkshire moors which inspired Hannibal crossing the Alps. In his fuller description of a picture entitled Snow Storm, Peace and War, Turner relates how he got the sailors to lash him to the mast of a steamboat in the harbour's mouth for four hours. 'I did not expect to escape, but I felt bound to record it if I did'. There is a wealth of evidence testifying to the accuracy of his observation left by others who had the misfortune to be caught in the same storm as Turner and who afterwards saw them reproduced in his canvasses. He had an extraordinary memory for natural phenomena, the more violent they were, the more intensely were his powers of observation applied. A rare verbal impression, displaying his powers of perspective when on a fishing expedition may be used to underline the point:—

> 'Reflections not only appear darker but longer than the object which occasions them, and if the ripple or hollow of the wave is long enough to make an angle with the eye it is on these undulating lines that the object reflects, and transmits all perpendicular objects lower than the spectator. But in receding lines, as well as objects, rules seem to lose their power, and those guides to enable us to find some cause to near objects lose their application or become enfeebled by contraction to remote ones.'

'Mad' John Martin (1789-1854)
English painter of apocalyptyic visions

WAS he mad? Were his paintings an opium dream? No painter exerted a more popular and powerful influence upon the Romantic Imagination of his day. M. W. Bürger wrote in 1863: 'Martin got all Europe talking of him and is perhaps of all English painters the one who achieved the highest reputation on the Continent'. Widely acclaimed in his lifetime, hung in the famous houses — Deepdene, Stowe, Howick, Buckingham Palace — his works virtually disappeared from the public view for more than a century until 1972. At the time of his death the critics were more evenly divided:—

> 'At the touch of his pencil, as of a magician's wand, earth and heaven are riven, resolved as it were, into chaos, out of which a magnificent structure of his own creation is reared. No doubt his art was theatrical. He addressed the eye rather than the mind. He produced

his grand effects by illusion — perhaps, by imposition; — but it is not to be concealed that he did produce effects. Possibly it was scene painting — slight of hand; but it was also new. If easy, the style was his own. Nobody else had caught the trick by which he ravished the sense of the multitude and sometimes dazzled the imagination of calmer men.' *Illustrated London News*, 1854.

'Martin's mind was, no doubt, thrown off its balance during the last years of his life, when these pictures were painted; it had so long dwelt among the unearthly, that he lost all control over it in his works'. *The Art Journal*, 1855.

His pictures were enormous, grandiloquent, obsessed with spatial infinity and satanic heroism — cosmic, biblical, oriental. The public, along with the foreground figures, witnessed the vast, sublime, lofty scenes that capture a glimpse of the unearthly. Thomas Campbell (1849) was but one of many poets to add a verse to Martin's pictures, as The Last Man:

'I saw a vision in my sleep
That gave my spirit strength to sweep
Adown the gulf of time'
'I saw the last of human mould
That shall Creation's death behold
As Adam saw her prime'.

Even the titles of John Martin's major works, theatrically presented on public display and reproduced as etchings, engravings, book illustrations and mezzotints to satisfy popular demand, awaken the imagination:

Sadak in search of the Waters of Oblivion,
The Expulsion of Adam and Eve,
The Fall of Babylon,
Belshazzars Feast,
The Destruction of Pompeii and Herculaneum,
The Seventh Plague of Egypt,
The Creation,
The Deluge,
The Celestial City and River of Bliss,
Pandemonium.
The Great Day of His Wrath,
The Last Judgement,
The Plains of Heaven.

Each of his epic paintings was a 'mirror of literature, amusement and instruction reflecting the faults of previous civilisations'. The conjured atmosphere of the Deluge was reflected by his friend Bernard Barton (1828) in a long poem entitled 'Recollection of Martin's Deluge':

This Awful Vision haunts me still
In thoughts by day, in dreams by night;
So well hath Art's creative skill
There shown its fearless might.

The floodgates of the foaming deep
By pow'r supreme asunder riven,
The dark, terrific, arching sweep
Of clouds by tempests driven.

The beetling crags, which, on the right
Menace swift ruin in their fall,
Yet rise in memory's wistful sight
And Memory's dreams appal!

To those less impressed the canvasses presented a rather sickly surface, the figures were insignificant and the taste doubtful; to quote Dr. Syntax, 'I'll prose it here, I'll verse it there, And picturesque it ev'ry where'.

Was he mad? S. C. Hall, founder of the *Art Journal,* first used the phrase about Martin which Salvador Dali has since taken to his own, 'He possessed the genius that to madness nearly is allied'.

He was born near Haydon Bridge in Northumberland where the sheer and impressive stormy landscapes provided many a backcloth in his paintings. His father was more or less permanently out of work. His mother, Isabella, claimed on her deathbed that the fame of her four sons would sound from pole to pole and credited herself with special visionary powers which she passed on to William and Jonathan whose everyday decisions came to be inspired by their waking dreams (Feaver, 1975).

All four sons were either mad or eccentric. John remained close to his brothers throughout his successful career aiding their eccentricities and funding their failures. Richard, the least well known, was a Quartermaster in the Army before publishing a book of poems. William became an inventor, Christian philosopher and pamphleteer: The Spiritual Thunderstorm of Divine Truth, The Thunderstorm of Dreadful Forked Lightening. He described his miner's safety lamp as 'noble and safe' compared to Humphry Davy's 'infernal machine of destruction' and had John appear before the Select Committee on Safety in Mines to explain their Ventilation. Jonathan's renown was as an arsonist and as Bedlam's prize criminal lunatic. 'Having perceived on the night of 2nd February, 1829, that "the Lord was determined to have me shew his people the way to flee from the wrath to come" Jonathan Martin climbed into York Minster and spent four hours getting a fire going using prayer books and furnishings from the choir for kindling. Then, carrying the tassels for the canopy of the bishop's throne, he made for home and sanctuary in the Tyne Valley near Hexham where he was arrested four days later'. John Martin paid the costs of his defence and subsequently his living expenses in Bethlem Hospital where he remained preoccupied with anti-clerical stratagems for many years before making a dramatic attempt to escape shortly before his death in 1838. Three months later his son Richard, John's nephew and house guest, cut his own throat in the belief that his breath was turning the family black.

John Martin left school aged 14 to become apprenticed for seven years to a coachbuilder in Newcastle, gilding coats of arms on carriage doors. However, he quit after a year to work for a Piedmontese refugee, Boniface Musso, who had established himself in the town as a teacher of fencing, perspective and enamel painting. In 1805, when Musso's son Charles took a job in a china painting works in London, Musso and Martin sailed down the coast to join him. Later Martin was to work for William Collins, a painter and engraver in the Strand.

By the age of 22 Martin was self employed, supporting his paintings by teaching and hack topographical work. Many of his early large scale works were widely exhibitied but failed to sell for some years; but by personally supervising the production of mezzotints he developed a major source of income. His opulence was nevertheless dented in the 1830s by the expenses of Jonathan's trial, William's inventions and his own public disputes. Some of his early paintings failed to achieve automatic acceptance at the Royal Academy and he turned his back on that institution, exhibiting elsewhere in London or in Birmingham at the Scottish Academy. He used his skills as a draughtsman in an attempt to improve public amenities, patenting a rope cable, embankments for the Thames, a London connecting railway and advising on a pure water supply — superadding beauty to utility — from Denham through Bayswater, the Serpentine, Buckingham Palace, Green Park and St. James'. By 1840 he had planned a major sewage works for London and made drawings for the first underground railway. In 1845 he sketched plans for a double decker bridge across the Menai Straits showing a train crossing on the upper level, ships scattered on the Menai waters below and on the road deck carts drawn by elephants *(Proc. Soc. Antiquities,* Newcastle, series iv, no 4, 1928).

Over the last 15 years of his life his fortunes improved as he took to illustrating books on such themes as Paradise Lost, Biblical Stories, Journeys to the Holy Land and scientific discoveries. Prehistoric dragons were depicted in their natural surroundings. The mezzotints of his Coronation Picture of 1838, a ceremonial piece set in St. Paul's remained unrivalled as a popular print until George Baxter's The Opening by Queen Victoria of her 1st Parliament in 1841. His eyesight had begun to deteriorate but the large epic scenes were still produced with theatrical flourish. Whilst working The Beating of Jacob and Esau he suffered a stroke rendering him speechless and unable to write. He went on holiday to the Isle of Man, died there and was laid to rest in Spittall Vault of Kirk Brodden churchyard.

Were his paintings an opium dream? There are many circumstantial factors which link John Martin's name with the opium addiction of his time. He remains the only major painter considered alongside the literary figures of his day in Alethea Hayter's 'Opium and the Romantic Imagination'. Adults and children took Laudanum, Mithridate, Carminative, and Quieting Syrup. Wilberforce and Clive used opium to ease their bowel pains, Shadwell for gout, Coleridge for neuralgia. Others, such as De Quincey and Byron, were unwilling or unable to give it up and four of Poe's heroes were depicted as suffering from its effects. Martin's towering architectural visions were likened by Charles Lamb to images derived from dreams. The hauntingly naive picture 'Sailor in Search of the Waters of Oblivion' was reproduced by Keats in Hyperion, Shelley's Fame in Canto I of the Revolt of Islam is variously ascribed to Coleridge's Kubla Khan and Martin's Joshua Commanding the Sun to Stand Still.

Keats and Shelley indulged, but were probably not habituated to opium, but one line from the Revolt of Islam — 'a hue like that when some great painter dips his pencil in the gloom of earthquake and eclipse' — an obvious reference to Martin — was reproduced by De Quincey as an epigraph of his description of the pains of opium in The Confession of an English Opium Eater. Baudelaire in Paradis Artficiels 'faithfully rendering the colour of an opium landscape . . . here indeed the dull sky and veiled horizon which overshadow the brain enslaved by opium' could be seized upon as a critique of Martin's artistic style.

Many scenes from Martin's works could be ascribed readily to the effects of opiates: Satan presiding over the infernal council, the destruction of Sodom and Gomorrah, the Flight into Egypt and others, but there is no direct evidence of any of the Martins using these household tranquillisers and sedatives despite the remarkable similarity of their visionary extravaganza to those of known opium eaters (Hayter, 1968). Aldous Huxley has a more mundane explanation. Martin and even Keats were fascinated and inspired by improvements in the technology of magic lanterns, by de Loutherbourg's Eidophusikon with the sunset fury of the brightest stained glass and the dioramic scenes whereby the intense beamy quality of coloured images on a white sheet in a darkened room captivated the imagination. His art fell from fame as still photography revealed the biblical lands not as they grew in the imagination of children but in reality as found by the early archaeologists.

Dante Gabriel Rossetti (1828-82)

The Great Insomniac

THE trials and tribulations of insomnia are best described by recourse to the life of Dante Gabriel Rossetti. Until nearly 40 years of age, Rossetti was a particularly robust individual, dominating his household, family, friends and the pre-Raphaelite Brotherhood. His reputation as a poet and artist — imaginative though somewhat lax in execution — was at its zenith.

In 1866 various friends began to show concern for his health but met with repeated denials. However, in the following year he complained of intense insomnia which was to remain with him for the rest of his life. He talked of restlessness, irritability, extreme lassitude and irresolution when any effort was required of him; he would throw himself down on the ground and refuse to stir any further when out for a walk, he could never bring himself to tackle the picture he had brought with him to work on. Sunlight and artificial light became intensely painful, producing sensations of giddiness, so much so that he attended Sir William Bowman, the great ophthalmologist of the day, who was unable to find anything organically wrong, attributing the trouble to weakness, overstrain and nervousness. At a later stage, he suffered heavy perspiration when walking any distance, he still could not sleep, and his hands upon which his livelihood depended trembled alarmingly. In his poems he describes the anguish of those sleepless nights:—

> 'Ah, but if you knew how time has dragged, days, nights!
> All the neighbour-talk with man and maid — such men!
> All the fuss and trouble of street-sounds, window-sights:
> All the worry of flapping door and echoing roof; and then,
> All the fancies . . . Who were they had leave, dared try
> Darker arts that almost struck despair in me?
> If you knew but how I dwelt down here! quoth I:
> "And was I so better off up there?" quoth She.'

Lizzie Siddall, his wife and the focus of many of his paintings and poems, had died in 1862. The following years were periods of brooding and seances. There was in the 1860s in Victorian England a renewed interest in psychic and occult studies. A passion for dabbling in the unseen and for probing the mysteries of the human soul, living and departed, sought to satisfy the unanswered questioning of the heart with a medley of fresh pseudoscientific superstitions. Hypnosis, mesmerism, electro-biology and spiritualism, with its claims to communion with the souls of the departed, became an obsession with many people, and attracted for a time even the most level headed and sceptical.

'It is clear that Gabriel — as indeed other members of his family — was throughout life attracted to the world of spirits, or of the spirit, both in the nobler heights of Christian and Catholic tradition and revelation and the more trivial and dangerous sphere of "bogey's — spirits unquiet or evil — Doppelgänger, ghosts, vampires and their kindred ghouls" (Helen Rossetti Angeli, 1942). The medium, Mary Howitt, devoted herself for a time to communing with the spirit world and poured out page after page of undecipherable jargon, claiming to be inspired or 'automatic' (which it apparently was) addressed from the dead to Gabriel Rossetti. Angeli suggests that this activity did not seriously affect Gabriel who was not infrequently heard to denounce 'spirits' or even 'bogeys' for playing tricks on him, making off with mislaid belongings.

Most biographers are agreed in ascribing his insomnia to manifestations of guilt. He suffered from urethral stricture, no doubt venereally acquired, which required catheterisation from time to time. William Rossetti commented that he minded this not at all 'I have seen him resume painting within five minutes of the slight operation'. Lizzie Siddall Rossetti had been conscious of his infidelities and committed suicide taking an overdose of laudanum. As an act of penitence he buried the manuscript of his poems in her tomb; in April, 1870, he had the coffin exhumed to recover his work. And, finally, in addition to a succession of mistresses grossly inferior in status, he elected Janey Morris, wife of his friend William Morris, to a new ideal beloved in his art and poetry. If there is an alternative medical diagnosis to guilt as the cause for his insomnia, it could be that he suffered from 'masked' hyperthyroidsim. His sister Christiana Rossetti developed Graves' disease with an obvious goitre, weight loss, hyperactivity, tremor, protruberant eyes and sweating. In 'masked' hyperthyroidism the weight loss is rarely evident and apathy, neurasthenia and depression may obscure the underlying disease.

Whatever the cause of his insomnia, the culmination was an increased habituation to the hypnotic, chloral, so that by 1879 he was taking 92 grains nightly. The action of this potentially lethal dose was potentiated by swigging it down with whisky (the original knock-out, Mickey Finn combination). Even an attempt at mesmerism failed to break the habit. He became over sensitive to scurrilous attacks from the minor poet Robert Buchanan, became deluded (perhaps even before the chloral habit according to William Stillman) and by 1869 there was daily talk of suicide. Horace Gregory describes his depression:—

> 'Rossetti was beginning to suffer the early stages of melancholia which followed his wife's death; he was haunted by rumours of her suicide, and had the feeling that whether she committed suicide or not, he was responsible for her death. He had begun to have hallucinations of her presence in the chattering of swallows and starlings and in the noise of doves. The habit of taking laudanum and dose of chloral at night brought fewer hours of sleep than half-awakened dreams. When Rossetti in his deepest fits of melancholia believed himself persecuted by Lewis Carroll and felt that he was an object of ridicule in the *Hunting of the Snark,* his instincts did not lead him far astray. If the Bellman of the poem was only faintly reminiscent of Rossetti's leadership of the Aesthetic Movement, in *Alice in Wonderland* the mad tea party did resemble the dinners at Rossetti's Tudor House in Cheyne Walk'.

Browning's *Fifine at the Fair* which he treated as a pasquinade was almost certainly written in good faith but Robert Buchanan's viscious pamphlet 'The Fleshy School of Poetry' (1871) castigating the sonnets of Rossetti's work 'The House of Life' as 'a voluptuous and morbid deviation from healthy forms of life', 'a sickening desire to reproduce sensual moods', and 'a hotbed of nasty phrases' has some substance. His poem Jenny, 'Lazy, laughing, languid Jenny, fond of a kiss and fond of a guinea' is one of the longest poems ever written about a prostitute; and Nuptial Sleep would nowadays be regarded as an elegant example of soft porn:

> 'At length their long kiss severed, with sweet smart:
> And as the last slow sudden drops are shed
> From sparkling eaves when all the storm has fled,
> So singly flagged the pulses of each heart,
> Their bosoms sundered, with the opening start
> Of married flowers to either side outspread
> From the knit stem; yet still their mouths, burnt red,
> Fawned at each other where they lay apart.'

That Rossetti became hallucinated and paranoid is beyond question. In 1872 his brother William records, 'From his wild ways of talking — about conspiracies and what not — I was astonished to perceive that he was, past question, not entirely sane, After a consultation with Dr. Marshall, Dr. Hake and Sir Henry Maudsley, it was arranged to take him to Roehampton to Dr. Hake's own 'house'. During the cab journey from Chelsea to Roehampton, Rossetti swore that the cabbie had been ringing a bell on the roof specifically to annoy him and next day he ran out of the house to challenge some passing gypsies on their way to a Bank Holiday fair. That night Rossetti went to bed and heard a voice in the night, "which twice called out to him a term of gross and unbearable obloquy".' (William Rossetti).

In Dr. Hake's house he attempted suicide by swallowing a whole bottle of laudanum which he had secretly obtained and hidden away. After prolonged coma he was revived with an enema of black coffee but suffered from a pressure palsy affecting his left leg. This took several months to recover. Even so, as his health improved, he was once more able to dominate his family and continue his artistic and poetic work.

It is noteworthy that despite his visionary art and his earlier poems, such as Sudden Light, which describes a variety of olfactory, visual and auditory *déjà vu* sensations, his hallucinations throughout the years of insomnia were invariably auditory; for example, the chiming of cobwebs upset him. Auditory hallucinations can be indicative of schizophrenia but his personality remained intact. If the hallucinations had been due to the withdrawal effects of alcohol taken with his medication, he might have had delirium tremens; but then the hallucinations would have been visual 'quickly moving small animals such as rats and snakes have always been described as typical, together with the emotional reaction of terror they arose. But the illusory animals seen in the bed clothes are often huge as small; and though they may be threatening, others seem comical, humorous, or in sexual play with one another' (Mayer-Gross, Slater and Roth, Clinical Psychiatry) The likely diagnosis is of Alcoholic Hallucinosis with episodes of delusion, depression and paranoia coinciding with excessive consumption; the personality remains intact, guilt feelings predominate and the hallucinations are invariably auditory. In all he also suffered from three fits which could have been due to alcohol or drug withdrawal.

His health showed an unremitting deterioration from about 1877. In addition to his urethral stricture he also complained of a troublesome, bulky hydrocoele. His consumption of hypnotics, alcohol and analgesics increased. His poetry did not lose its fluency but a picture of Janey Morris 'The Day Dream, 1880' shows a deterioration in his art. A contemporary, Sir Thomas Hall Caine, wrote: 'As to Rossetti's delusions, I certainly do not know more than I am told, but then I think I know the chief cause of them. It was not chloral, although that was a contributing agent, but sleeplessness. After the death of his wife (with all that meant to him) he never slept naturally until about four months before his death'. In fact four months before he died he developed a left hemiparesis and is recorded as suffering from 'horrible dreams, restless until 9 a.m., then asleep for 2 hours, delirious towards evening' (15th Dec. 1881).

The final illness was diagnosed as uraemia (kidney failure). Although the term Bright's disease was used by his doctors, the failure of his kidney is more likely to have arisen from a combination of recurrent urinary infections related to his stricture and as a secondary effect of his medication. The secretion of chloral depends upon the kidneys but it does not direct damage to them; however, various analgesics do damage kidney tissues and these include willow bark, salicin, which was used in the 18th century and sodium salicylate which started to be used for fevers and pain in the 19th century. Salicylates produce an acidosis, depleting the electolytes of the blood and producing dehydration, all of which can harm the kidney tubules and impair their function. His death can thus be attributed in part to the measures he took to overcome his insomnia.

Arthur Symons, one of the early biographers of Rossetti, wrote that he lived a life of unreality:

'Rossetti with all his keen practical intelligence, was never wholly awake, had never gone outside that House of Dreams in which the only real things were the things of the imagination . . . He died of too much dreaming, of too passionate a desire after beauty, which at last literally took his sleep from him, and set him wandering about the streets at night, and closed him finally upon a drugged atmosphere of hallucinations. He was not powerful enough to turn out the guests of his brain, when they had come to haunt him like phantoms'.

Another biographer, Baum, concludes that 'without the dual outlet of poetry and art, the man would have gone mad.'

Gustave Moreau (1826-1898)

Phantasmogoria of the Imagination

MOREAU's biblical and mythological fantasies, exotically detailed with sumptuous trappings and mysterious lighting, appear somewhat perverse to modern taste. We sense an aura of incense and hashish, which we can accept, and a psychological disquietude which we cannot. Many of his contemporaries also were critical of his overheated colours, 'almost candied', the look of them recalls old Cordova leather or faded old tapestries, but to others he was, as Professor at the Ecole des Beaux Arts, a teacher of genius, intelligent and tolerant, possessing a powerful imagination 'controlled by a thinking mind', though occasionally — as he said — he gave way to the enthusiasm and divine frenzy of art. For Moreau, imaginative history painting was the only kind of painting that existed.

Of the three artists of that period who conjured forth a romantic yet horrific imagery — Moreau, Bresdin and Redon — Huysmans, in *A Rebours,* lavishes his greatest praise for Gothic invention upon Gustave Moreau as the 'creator of disquieting and sinister allegories made more to the point by the uneasy perception of an altogether modern neurosis'. Huysmans also admired his technical brilliance, claiming that 'never at any period had water colours been thus made to bring forth from the paper such glittering gems, such gleams of stained glass flashing in the sunlight, such fabulous and dazzling displays of fabrics and flesh'. Zola's appreciation was more grudging, for although he described Moreau as possessing a talent 'so stunning that one hardly knows what category to assign it to', he also found a hatred of realism which Zola felt represented a backward movement in the sphere of the imagination. Among the Surrealists, Moreau came to be claimed as a worthy ancestor whose dream-like compositions pointed the direction of their thoughts. More directly he inspired his many pupils, who included Matisse and Roualt.

Moreau led a very quiet and private life, the large part of which must have been utterly blameless. He lived with his mother until her death at the age of 82, by which time he was already 58. For the previous twenty years she had been deaf and he communicated with her through scraps of paper. When her death eventually occurred he fell into a 'dreary despair' and it was feared that his mind would give way. He was never at any time beset by money worries and did not develop as an artist until his fortieth year. His apprenticeship included four years touring with his mother and various relatives in Italy. He returned to France to enlist in the National Guard in the defence of Paris during the Franco-Prussian War of 1870. He lived out the horrors of the siege and then, in June 1871, as a result of the nervous strain of the war, he obtained a permit to leave Paris with his mother to visit a spa specialising in treatment for nervous disorders. The war, or his nervous condition, had a lasting effect on him and contributed to his withdrawal from society. Between 1870 to 1872 he produced very few works and in later years, although he became prolific, he rarely exhibited. Nonetheless, honours were poured upon him and at the age of 60 he was elected Professor of the Ecole des Beaux Arts.

There is a richness, a heaviness and an opulence about Moreau's work which Mario Praz has likened to Wagnerian music . . . 'he composed his pictures with the style of symphonic poems, loading them with significant accessories in which the principal theme is echoed, until the subject yielded the last drop of its symbolic sap'. The basis of his art according to Emile Zola lay in his talent for taking subjects which have already been treated by other artists and recasting them in a different, more ingenious way. Moreau himself was very clear as to the nature of his own ability:

'Work, incessant experiment, the development of my person through effort, the pursuit of the better, the rare, the invisible in art. The happy strokes of the workman's tool becoming even grander, freer, more ideal each day. The designs of the brain, its dreams, wrought out conceptions combined ad infinitum, once the initial code is lighted on. The inward visions and the infinite combinations of this art, a sacred language and the most ideal of all beneath its apparent materiality.'

Two charges are commonly laid against Moreau: that he was an addict and a homosexual. Jean Paladilhe, Curator of the Gustave Moreau Museum, describes him as an almost legendary figure, the alchemist of painting, a recluse seeking inspiration in hashish and indulging in an intellectual narcissism, and Paul de Saint-Victor (1876) describes him as 'an opium smoker who presumably has the hands of a goldsmith at his service', but there is a suggestion that his indulgence in drugs was a relatively late and benign involvement, thus Huysmans regards Bresdin, not Moreau, as having a brain 'clouded by opium'. The most damning criticism of him as a homosexual was also probably late and benign. His best friend Henri Rupp married and became a widower. Some time around 1890 Rupp came to live with the artist, acting for him as a kind of steward. By that time Moreau was 64 but that did not prevent Comt. Robert de Montesquiou the dandy who served Huysmans as the powerful model for des Esseintes likening Henri Rupp to Leonardo da Vinci's favourite disciple Francesco Malzi in exactly the same relationship with all that implies. It is the nonsense of our own age to regard every bachelor as a pervert. But without castigating Moreau's morals it is difficult not to read into his amazing repertory of erotic and fantastic imagery — chimeras with extra breasts, the prudery with which all pudenda are just covered — as essentially ambiguous, homosexual or onanistic. The critic, Edward Lucie-Smith, went so far as to write that Moreau's women, like much of his other imagery, are part of a powerfully imaginative celebration of male fears of castration and impotence. In Moreau's own commentary on the Chimeras he wrote:

'This Isle of Fantastic Dreams encloses all the forms that passion, caprice and fancy take in women. Women in her primal essence, an unthinkable creature, mad on mystery and the unknown, smitten with evil in the form of perverse and diabolical seduction'.

P. L. Mathieu points out that for Moreau, as for his contemporaries, woman was beauty, an object of cool Platonic and even fetishistic adoration and at the same time she was the instrument of man's perdition. In choosing his models, Moreau used to take the hands of one, the head of another to produce an idealised image. In some pictures one is hard put to say whether the figure represented is a man or a women and often he would omit any precise indication of sex. Thus he was obliged to clear matters up for the benefit of a purchaser, declaring that a certain painting was of an Arab youth, a poet and a singer . . . 'they are said to resemble women so much that one can hardly tell the difference, hence your mistake'. He could carry such ambiguity so far that Victor Bombert said that his work was the immobilisation of life and animation of the inanimate

. . . figures possessed no emotion, no movement, luxe, calme et volupte. A notable exception were the eyes. Breton, a man whose tastes were decidedly heterosexual, remained fascinated by the eyes of Moreau's women.

'Les Isolés. Vincent van Gogh' (1853-90)

'He who does not smell of a smouldering bomb and of compressed vertigo is not worthy to be alive'

Antonin Artaud (1965) *'Van Gogh, The Man Suicided by Society'*.

WHERE is there a statue to a critic? Perhaps just two deserve such recognition: the young Ruskin who in 1843 sprang to the defence of Joseph Mallord William Turner, and Albert Aurier who died aged twenty-seven in 1891 after revealing to the world the genius of Gauguin and van Gogh. Alas, van Gogh's recognition came just six months before he died. He had struggled for ten lonely years, driven by an intense inner energy, quite unable to sell his works. On reading the article in *Mercure de France* entitled 'Les Isolés. Vincent van Gogh', van Gogh showed his pleasure in a characteristic response. His long letter to Aurier combines his thanks with a wide ranging yet highly appropriate display of knowledge of art history, colour theory and admiration for other artists. He was later to recoil from the publicity as he had recoiled from the mockery of the townsfolk of Arles when he first became ill.

Aurier's critique remains one of the most penetrating appraisals of van Gogh:

'What particularises his entire work is the excess, excess in strength, excess in nervousness, in violence of expression . . . He reveals a powerful being, a male, a bold man, often brutal and sometimes ingenuously delicate . . . This can be seen in the almost organistic excesses of everything he has painted: he is a fanatic, an enemy of bourgeois sobriety and of trifling details, a kind of drunken giant, better able to move mountains than to handle bibelots, an ebullient brain which irresistibly pours its lava into all the ravines of art, a terrible and high strung genius, often sublime, sometimes grotesque, almost always on the edge of the pathological'.

Although the world regarded him as a failure and misfit, mad and uncouth, a different picture emerges from his letters. A creative psychopath he may have been, but his genius was founded on a deep understanding, wide reading, knowledge and exceptional intelligence. His letters to his brother Theo, to Gauguin and to Theo's wife, Jo, especially document his thoughts, passions, emotions and obsessions with a freedom and lucidity not apparent from his awkward exterior. The letters provide an insight into the intentionality behind the gusto and excesses of his works. They reflect the driving forces within him: religion and art.

The zeal of his early religious observance and his translation of the Bible and Saint Thomas à Kempis into Dutch, German, English and French, and the reawakening with even greater furore of his 'impassioned expressions' to obtain a permanent artistic achievement. Sir Edward Elgar, after he had read the letters of van Gogh, commented that 'Vincent might just as easily have become a thinker, a poet, a hero or a saint as a painter — it may be thought, in fact, that he became all these at once'. Finally, they provide the vital account of the history of his illness. As a commentary on his life and times, many regard them as literary masterpieces. In the words of his biographer, M. E. Tralbaut (1969), 'If he had never handled a brush, he would still have shown himself to be a writer of remarkable range with an especial gift for observation and description'.

The van Gogh family had been highly successful. A remote ancestor, also called Vincent van Gogh (1674-1746), had been a painter. His immediate relatives, though often dogged by ill-health, were distinguished in the Army, Navy and Civil Service; many had been preachers and three uncles (Cornelius, Hendrik and Vincent) were art dealers. One (Uncle 'Cent) had joined forces with the Paris firm of Goupil et Cie before entering into semi-retirement. Only his father, a devout man but a poor preacher, had difficulty in attaining a position consistent with the standards of the family. His mother was a keen naturalist and could draw pleasingly; but, by and large, her relatives, several of whom suffered from epilepsy, were less accomplished. His brother Theo was to die within a year of his own death from tuberculosis and nephritis. His sister Willhelmien became schizophrenic in the latter part of her life.

Vincent was the eldest of the six surviving children. He was commonly regarded as the most difficult within the close-knit family: red-headed, self-willed, temperamental and inclined to wander off to collect beetles or whatever interested him at the time. He drew little and painted. His mother applauded his efforts, but he would hide them self-consciously. At twelve years he was sent to boarding school at Zevenbergen. He was homesick at first but showed no signs of maladjustment. Similarly, the testimonial his parents received from N. C. Tersteeg, shortly after he started work with the art dealers Goupil and Co. in the Hague, when aged sixteen, states that 'everybody liked to deal with Vincent'. However, psychologists have suggested an abnormal childhood — a substitute child for an earlier Vincent van Gogh, born a year earlier only to die within a few days of birth, and whose tombstone lay in the churchyard at Zundert.

When at the age of twenty he was transferred to London, he bought a top hat. 'You can't be in London without one'. He was lonely at first but serious and hard-working, patient and helpful in dealing with requests.

His early letters to his younger brother Theo, who had also become an art dealer, bear witness to a deep interest in his work and a piquant appreciation of the English art scene. On a short holiday in Helvoit he drew a great deal, his mother commenting that it is a delightful talent which can be of great value to him.

He made many friends in London, culminating in his falling in love with his landlady's daughter. But when he discovered that she was secretly engaged he accepted the fact with difficulty and his mood altered drastically. He moved elsewhere and lived alone. It is at this stage that we first see a different van Gogh, an awkward, pubescent dreamer. He was no longer successful at selling pictures. He was inclined to question the taste and explain their faults to potential customers. After a brief interlude in Paris he returned to London and was put in charge of the Goupil picture gallery. By now he no longer desired to be an art dealer; his abiding passion was religion and the Bible. As a son of the Manse, he felt that this was his true vocation. He left Goupil but returned to England to teach temporarily in Ramsgate. 'There were many bugs, but the view from the school window made one forget them'. He received no salary apart from board and lodging but his eyes were set upon becoming a missionary to the East End of London.

When the school transferred from Ramsgate to Isleworth with no prospect of a salary, van Gogh was engaged by the Rev. Mr. Jones, a Methodist minister, as a sort of curate. His duties were diverse. He collected money owed by parents to the small school and had the opportunity to preach. He was happy at Ramsgate, ecstatic at Isleworth. 'When I was standing in the pulpit, I felt like somebody who, emerging from a dark cave underground, comes back to the friendly daylight'. He felt he had an identity of his own. This first sermon, and there were others, has been preserved in his letters to Theo. The text shows the strength of his faith as well as considerable power of expressing himself in English. However, the work offered no future prospect and he decided to seek a job in Holland. 'There are many things that make it desirable . . . the salary would certainly be better than at Mr. Jones' and it is one's duty to think of that, because later in life a man needs more . . . as to religious work, something of that will unfold in me'.

Through family influence he obtained a post in a bookshop in Dordrecht. He started in an exemplary manner but was not interested in learning the trade. His preoccupation was religion, attending services of all denominations, reading the Bible and making copious notes late into the night. He smoked his pipe constantly. He drew and pinned pictures over the walls of his lodgings. He lived ascetically and recognised himself as an eccentric. Again the family accepted a further change of direction. He was to go to Amsterdam to stay with Uncle Jan, commandant of the naval dockyard with whom he went for long walks round the city, and through the influence of another uncle, Pastor Stricker, he began to study theology under a young teacher, Mendes da Costa.

By July 1878, Vincent had overturned the last chance he had for an orthodox career. He was by now twenty four years of age. Had he become a perpetual student unable to settle to anything? Was he a drop-out who had lost his way? He appeared to have a clear direction which he desired to pursue. Was he the equivalent of a bright student who needed psychological help with his studies and examinations? His energies and interests were active enough but they appear to have been misplaced. Everything in his background suggested that he should not have been beaten by Greek verbs, Latin, algebra and mathematics as a stepping stone to his ambition. He had a friendly relationship with his teacher. It was perhaps symptomatic that he should have made a habit of chastising himself masochistically whenever he felt he had neglected to study. He would rise early, never going to bed before midnight. He was constantly walking about Amsterdam looking for rare books, going on country excursions, and drawing landscape maps. The letters from Amsterdam, despite their constant preoccupation with religion, contain a surprisingly large number of descriptions of pictures. These descriptions, moreover, are of considerable aesthetic value. Had he exhausted himself psychologically? Whatever conjectures we may make, the result was that he gave up the opportunity to qualify for the ministry in order to undertake more lowly evangelical missionary work. Tralbaut suggests that ostensibly Vincent abandoned his thoelogical studies in order to become a mission worker but he may also have been unconsciously leaving the door open for his artistic career. This supposition is not far fetched. His work at Borinage in the poor mining area of South Belgium was to bring him into contact with the same strata of society with which at a later date he hoped to identify as the Peasant Painter.

Van Gogh entered into missionary work with an intensity and depth of feeling that was later to be the hallmark of his painting. He was much distressed by the poverty he saw around him. He throw himself wholeheartedly into treating the suffering following a series of firedamp explosions in the mines, working incessantly and tearing up his own clothes to make bandages. His charity knew no limits. He gave all he had, his clothes, his shoes, and even his bed, living more roughly than those about him, neglecting himself, his health, his appearance and the essential dignity required of a mission worker. In his own words, 'They think I'm mad because I wanted to be a true Christian'. The profound sensitivity which he had shown to the conditions of the Borinage did not endear him to the Church authorities. He appeared too disreputable, his behaviour too good and too eccentric. However, in dispensing with his services, they chose to highlight his apparent inability to preach. His earlier presumed success as a preacher at Isleworth probably lay in the fact that he was then a young teacher showing an ability to speak and give a sermon in a foreign tongue. He was expected to be fluent in French at the Borinage. It has been suggested that in his evangelism he modelled himself on his father who was a poor preacher and that he developed a comparable inferiority complex when preaching. To many he appeared as a rough featured, nervous, restless man with an extraordinary way of pouring out sentences, once he got started, in Dutch, English or French. When thus excited he looked more than a little mad. If challenged he was apt to be suspicious and morose.

Not only was he forced to give up missionary work because he could not survive unaided, but his eccentricity, his inability to form close human contacts and above all his unwillingness to adapt to the demands of the society to which he belonged, gradually turned him away from religion. Without the continued support of his family and without his irresistable temptation to draw, which by now became his primary obsession in life, he would have been a broken man. His brother Theo is remarkable in realising before anyone else that he had potential, if not genius, as a painter. Theo began to support him economically, though it was some while before Vincent realised that the source of his benevolence was Theo and not his rich uncles. At this stage also he was able to return to his parents and they looked upon him with sympathy and puzzlement. His mother would comment: 'I am always so afraid that wherever Vincent may be or whatever he may do, he will spoil everything by his eccentricity, his queer ideas and views 'of life'. His father could still say: 'It grieves us so to see that he literally knows no joy of life, but always walks with bent head, whilst we did all in our power to bring him to an honourable position. It seems as if he deliberately chooses the most difficult path.'

The beginnings of his artistic career began with van Gogh attending the Brussels Academy as a partially registered student in the company of Anton van Rappard. After six months he returned home and became interested in the drawings of the French caricaturist, Gavarni (1804-66). Whilst in London Gavarni had contrasted graphically the life of the poor of London with that of the rich (1849), later embodying his satire in the character of Thomas Vireloque (1851-3) of whom Théophile Gautier said: 'This tatterdemalion of the hedgerows, however limited his outlook, sees life with an eye as penetrating, as profound and cynical as Swift or Voltaire'.

Vincent's life at home was notable in two other respects. He fell in love with his recently widowed cousin, Kee, who spurns his advances. He follows her to her home and attempts to burn his hand in remorse. And he quarrelled with his father having turned against religious observance. His reaction was to live in the Hague with a prostitute, Clasina (Sien) and her children. He had bought new clothes for Brussels; now he became shabby and dirty and off-hand in his manner. Even so he sought the friendship of a distant cousin, Anton Mauve, a successful painter who taught him to use water colours; and he made the acquaintance of other contemporary Dutch painters. He could be friendly with his fellow artists but could never accept their criticism.

In January 1882, he was ill with fever, insomnia, depression and gonorrhoea. Tersteeg and Mauve tried to influence him to leave the drunken Clasina and he developed a persecution mania towards them. However, he eventually took himself off to the peat fields of Drenthe. From the artistic view this was a successful interregnum. After the manner of Albrecht Dürer he had a perspective frame made for him by a carpenter and blacksmith but the loneliness of Drenthe impaled even van Gogh. He returned to Neunen.

He continued to paint seriously. He renewed his friendship with van Rappard and started to teach painting to three people at Eindhoven. This calm scenario was disrupted by the affair of Margot Bergmann, a neighbour who fell in love with him. Her family objected and to his deep distress she tried to poison herself. Also, in March 1885, his father died suddenly. The period is notable however for van Gogh's first great painting, the Potato-Eaters and his involvement with the colour theories of Delacroix. He learnt the piano so as to compare the notes with Prussian blue and dark green all the way to cadmium yellow (see Synaesthesia).

In 1885, Vincent van Gogh finally left his native Holland and went as a mature student to the art centres of Antwerp and Paris. The deep meaning of his art was already his own. His Potato-Eaters goes far beyond genre, beyond bourgeois realism. It incorporates a message that van Gogh took from Millet, that modern art should use themes from peasants' life to convey old religious feelings in secular terms (Pollock and Orton, 1978). His intolerance of criticism, his voracious background reading, his impatience and the tension between human emotions reflected in his art and the still imperfect means of expressing it, made him outwardly an unsatisfactory student but there is a discernible maturation and filling out of his art, the use of brighter colours, the widening of subject matter which was to achieve its full vigour in the Cloisonism of his works at Arles.

In Antwerp he spent his allowance on models and paints. His teeth were bad and his stomach suffered. He did not eat, becoming malnourished and ill. When he went to Paris in the summer of 1886 he recovered from his depression and physical debility and no longer called attention to himself by any extravagant clothes or artistic eccentricity. Among the artists such as Toulouse-Lautrec he showed himself as a lively and agreeable companion. Increased sociality was accompanied by indulgence in social vices: In Antwerp prostitutes and syphilis, in Paris alcoholism. Later in Arles, where he could afford to eat more freely, retsina and absinthe were added.

In February 1888, depressed by the winter skies, van Gogh took Lautrec's advice and went to Provence where the brilliant Midi light enchanted and dazzled him. 'I left Paris seriously sick at heart and in body, and nearly an alcoholic because of my rising fury at my strength failing me'. With the warmer colours and easier living he was able to utilise the more expansive ideas garnished from his exposure to Impressionism, the art of Japan which was the rage throughout Europe, and the pontillisme of Seurat and Signac. The first months in Arles represent the zenith of his achievement. He displayed one of the most extraordinary bursts of artistic energy the world has ever seen. On some days he seemed to be creating masterpieces as fast as he could paint. He hoped to set up an artists' co-operative in Arles and in particular to attract Gauguin to join him. His letters indicate a rich variety of moods and enthusiasms; but by October there were signs of crisis. He had no inclination for drawing, he complained of fatigue and an immoderate need for sleep. His handwriting became uneven. He pinned all his hopes on Gauguin's arrival.

With two complex and difficult personalities living in close proximity the period of grace did not last long. Gauguin, the more sarcastic and robust, was to participate in the onset of van Gogh's 'psychiatric' illness.

The first manifestations were unconsciously revealed in the portrait Gauguin painted of him. Van Gogh could only comment 'It is indeed I, but I having gone mad'. That evening he threw a full glass of absinthe at Gauguin who dodged the blow, took up van Gogh bodily in arms and carried him across the square to their lodgings. Van Gogh fell asleep within seconds and did not wake until the morning. Upon waking he said very calmly, 'My dear Gauguin, I have a vague memory of having offended you last evening'. The next evening, again without reason, van Gogh came at Gauguin with an open razor. Gauguin turned upon him, he stopped, lowered his head and ran back into the house. He was next seen in a brothel where he offered the lower lobe of his ear to a girl he had often visited by the name of Rachel, saying 'Guard this object carefully'. The police were informed and next morning they went to Vincent's house where they found him unconscious in bed and took him to the hospital.

Theo took the first train from Paris to Arles and found Vincent in a pitiful condition suffering from an acute nervous breakdown. He seemed lucid at times, and then, a few moments later, he would ramble off into philosophical and theological argument. Sometimes all the miseries of his past would well up in him; he wanted to cry but he could not do so. He remained in hospital from December 24th to January 7th and felt so well recovered that only ten days after he had left hospital he started on a portrait of Dr. Rey who was still treating his ear. In February he wrote to Theo that 'yesterday I went to see the girl I had gone to when out of my wits. They told me there that in this country things like that are not out of the ordinary. She had been upset by it and had fainted but had recovered her calm'.

Of the biographers, Tralbaut's explanations of the incident of the ear are particularly germane. From his study of the town archives, he found that at the time of Vincent's visit to Arles hardly a week went by without somebody having an attack of madness and being confined to an institution. These lunatics must have formed a surprisingly high percentage of the town's small population. He suggested that overindulgence in absinthe, alcohol and tobacco can make a man take leave of his senses. He also quotes two ingenious explanations for the incident with the ear. Firstly it was a custom of the bull ring for the toreador to cut off one of the bull's ears and present it to his love; and secondly, if at this stage van Gogh was subject to auditory hallucinations, his quarrel with Gauguin could have been accompanied by an imaginary voice in his ear whispering 'kill him'. So he attacked his friend but later recalled the biblical injunction 'and if thine eye offend thee, pluck it out'. The notoriety of the incident was followed by the mockery and pestering of the younger townsfolk, leading to a petition demanding his incarceration. Over the following months he had three fainting attacks and two relapses, one of two weeks and one of eight weeks. In May, out of desperation he thought it safer to seek voluntary confinement.

In the asylum of Saint Paul de Mausole at Saint Rémy de Provence he was told 'exactly what I already thought, that I must wait a year before thinking myself cured, since the least thing might bring on another attack. 'That year he suffered four bouts of 'madness', two of six weeks duration and two of only a week's duration. He painted more slowly than before, possibly because he was sedated with bromides but between attacks his personality, artistic skill and critical faculties remained intact. What then was the nature of his periods of madness? We have the clearest evidence from his own accounts:

'I am again — speaking of my condition — so grateful for another thing. I gather from others that during their attacks they have also heard strange sounds and voices as I did, and that in their eyes too things seemed to be changing. And that lessens the horror that I retained at first of the attack I have had, and which, when it comes on you unawares, cannot but frighten you beyond measure. Once you know that it is part of the disease, you take it like anything else. If I had not seen other lunatics close up, I should not have been able to free myself from dwelling on it constantly. For the anguish and suffering are no joke once you are caught by an attack. Most epileptics bite their tongue and injure themselves. Rey told me that he had seen a case where somewhere had mutilated his own ear, as I did, and I think I heard a doctor here say, when he came to see me with the director, that he also had seen it before. I really think that once you know what it is, once you are conscious of your condition and of being subject to attacks, then you can do something yourself to prevent your being taken unawares by the suffering or the terror. Now that it has gone on decreasing for five months, I have good hope of getting over it, or at least of not having such violent attacks. There is someone here who has been shouting and talking like me all the time for a fortnight, he thinks he hears voices and words in the echoes of the corridors, probably because the nerves of the ear are diseased and too sensitive, and in my case it was my sight as well as my hearing, which according to what Rey told me one day is usually the beginning of epilepsy. Then the shock was such that it sickened me even to move, and nothing would have pleased me better than never to have woken up again. At present this horror of life is less strong already and the melancholy less acute. But I have no will, hardly any desires or none at all, but hardly any wish for anything belonging to ordinary life, for instance almost no desire to see my friends, although I keep thinking about them. That is why I have not yet reached the point where I ought to think of leaving here. I should have this depression anywhere.' 592. 25th May, 1889.

In an earlier letter (574, Jan 28th 1889) he wrote, 'the unbearable hallucinations have ceased, and are now getting reduced to simple nightmares, in consequence of my taking bromide of potassium, I think'. Dr. Peyron in September 1889, wrote to Theo that he was 'quite recovered, he has completely regained his lucidity of mind and that he has resumed painting as he used to do. His thoughts of suicide have disappeared, only disturbing dreams remain, but they tend to disappear too, and their intensity is less great. His appetitie has returned, and he has resumed his usual mode of life''.

Despondent and overwhelmed with the company of madmen van Gogh wanted to leave Arles to move nearer to Paris. This was convenient for Theo; and Albert Aurier's articles gave him the opportunity to renew his contacts with other painters such as Lautrec and Pissarro. Theo arranged for him to stay ar Auvers-sur-Oise under the supervision of a Dr. Gachet, an expert in melancholia, homeopathic medicine and the therapeutic use of electricity but more importantly a respected amateur painter and engraver known to the art world by his pseudonym, Paul van Ryssel. Dr. Gachet had already gathered a remarkable collection of French impressionists including the works of Cézanne, Pissarro, Renoir, Guillamin, Monet, Manet, Sisley and Daumier.

Van Gogh explored the countryside around Auvers, was greeted with friendship and respect, and was soon to produce a remarkable series of landscapes, still-lifes and portraits. He was able to visit Theo in Paris and meet Aurier and Toulouse-Lautrec. Theo was uncertain of his future with Goupil and Co. Should he set up on his own? His health was poor and his son ill. By contrast, Vincent had stopped drinking and recognised that he was doing better work as a result; but the risk of a further attack still existed. It was to come quite unexpectedly. He quarralled with Dr. Gachet because he had hung without framing a picture by Guillaumin. This apparent lack of respect to Guillaumin made him furious and it became an idée fixe. A few days later on Sunday July 27th van Gogh left the Gachet's, returned to the Ravoux hotel where he was staying and went out almost immediately. As night was falling he returned limping, clutching his belly, saying 'I shot myself . . . I only hope I haven't botched it'. He died on the Tuesday morning,

The exact nature of van Gogh's illness remains open to debate. Two diagnoses, epilepsy and schizophrenia have been most frequently mooted. He was initially admitted to hospital at Arles with the diagnosis by Dr. Urpur, the director, of acute mania with generalised delirium, but the house-surgeon of the same hospital, Dr. Rey, spoke of epileptic crises and Dr. Payron, director of the asylum at Saint Remy, talked of attacks of epilepsy.

Epilepsy is a symptom; the type of epilepsy depends upon the part of the brain where the attack is initiated. If van Gogh had epilepsy then the probable diagnosis is of psychomotor epilepsy of temporal lobe origin, the cause of which is not always apparent. He suffered from blackouts, having three without warning in April 1889 and on other occasions had prolonged loss of consciousness often preceded by irrational behaviour. It matters not that he did not have grand mal attacks i.e. the form of epilepsy described in the Bible. The diagnosis of epilepsy would explain the virtual total recovery between attacks and the preservation of personality and abilities intact between bouts. Brief hallucinations can occur, and people with temporal lobe epilepsy can develop a schizo-affective disorder in many respects similar to schizophrenia.

The epileptic attacks as such were controlled by treatment with bromides. Bromide of potassium was introduced initially to calm mania and to prevent mentally subnormal retardates from masturbating as this was felt to cause even greater retardation. The drug proved highly successful in the treatment of epilepsy but has since been abandoned because it is both cumulative and toxic eventually causing headaches, lethargy, disorientation, hallucinations, loss of memory and dementia.

The diagnosis of idiopathic epilepsy of temporal lobe origin does not explain van Gogh's prolonged psychotic states with active hallucinations, lasting at times for weeks on end, nor does it explain his suicidal tendencies. It is possible that the epilepsy was symptomatic due to a tumour or abscess within the brain. A tuberculosis abscess, in particular, is a distinct possibility. The time scale between onset and demise is appropriate but there was no evidence of a progressive decline in intellect, increasing drowsiness or progressive neurological manifestations. We know he had contracted syphilis at Antwerp. The time scale for tertiary sphyilis producing G.P.I. (general paralysis of the insane) and dementia is too short but it is possible that the blackouts were due to 'congestive' attacks from meningo-vascular syphilis.

In favour of the diagnosis of schizophrenia is the fact that his sister Wilhelmien was similarly afflicted. His early behaviour is probably confirmatory. In matters of love he was prepared to over-react. He placed his hand in the fire when rejected by Kee. When he quarrelled with his father, the Rev. Theodorus van Gogh thought he may need confinement in an asylum. But there is conflicting evidence about his early life. He did make relationships, even though some were bizarre. There is just one early hallucination. When nursing back to health a severely burned miner from the Borinage, he experienced a vision of the martyred Jesus in the person of this same victim. This hallucination is not necessarily indicative of schizoid tendencies, merely evidence of the intensity of the situation that followed the mining disaster. The diagnosis of schizophrenia readily explains the psychotic episodes with hallucinations, the paranoia of his quarrels, his self-mutilation, suicidal gestures such as eating his paints when in the asylum and his eventual suicide. The diagnosis does not readily explain the blackouts nor the preservation of his personality quite intact between bouts of psychotic behaviour.

There is a third diagnosis for which I claim no originality but which seems most applicable to the situation. Van Gogh was never a healthy individual. He had frequent illnesses, often neglected his food and became malnourished. Pipe tobacco can be carcinogenic, can raise the blood levels of cyanide, and in the presence of malnutrition can be particularly harmful. In Paris he became alcoholic and in Arles became addicted to the local drink, absinthe. Absinthe is an iridescent green, bitter and highly aromatic preparation that was popular in 19th-century France. Degas' picture of the Absinthe drinker (L'Absinthe) (1876) is well-known. The main ingredient is an extract of a herb, artemisia absinthium (wormwood), which was thought to be a cure-all that invigorated the brain and quelled fevers. In 1915 it was prohibited in France and has since been banned in most countries as a health hazard. Nowadays the popular drink is flavoured with anise rather than absinthe, but retains the name of the man who first produced absinthe on a commerical scale, Pernod.

To make absinthe an extract is prepared by steeping the pungent herb in alcohol and distilling the spirit. Fennel, licorice, sweet flag, angelica root or dittany leaves may then be added to moderate the bitterness and achieve the desired colour. There were almost certainly local variations in the production of absinthe and whatever was used in the neighbourhood of Arles may have contributed to the increased toxicity and accounted for the higher incidence of madness under the Midi sun than elsewhere. A person in a poor physical state would normally be more susceptible and interactions could occur with cyanide, bromide or other chemicals within the body.

The drink is prepared at the table with due ceremony. Absinthe is poured (1½ oz.) over a lump of sugar held on a perforated spoon and for each measure of absinthe five portions of water are then poured. Wormwood is addictive. Some researchers have noted similarities between the effects of absinthe and those reported with marijuana (Bell, 1984). The manifestations can include vertigo, seizures, hallucinations, stupor, delirium and even death. In contrast to the hallucinations of schizophrenia which are predominantly auditory (less than 5% visual), drug induced hallucinations are frequently a combination of visual and auditory experiences such as those from which van Gogh suffered. The young houseman, Dr. Rey, when talking of epileptic crises, was speaking from his limited experience, not of the whole range of epilepsy, but of attacks of fits and madness related to the locality of Arles and presumably caused by inibition by susceptible persons of its local beverage.

Van Gogh's life is best summed up in the words of his friend, Anthon van Rappard, 'Whoever had observed this toiling, struggling, and sorrowful existence could not but feel sympathy for a man who demanded so much of himself that it ruined both body and mind. He belonged to that stock from which great artists are born.'

Giorgio (de) Chirico b. 1888

Founder of Metaphysical Art

DE CHIRICO was born in Greece where his father was a railway engineer and absorbed Greek classical forms and mythology. On the death of his father the family returned to Italy and thence to Munich where he, and his younger brother, Alberto Savinio, completed their education. His brother became a musician, wrote phantasmagorical poetry and in later life also painted. Both were influenced by the paintings of Böcklin, Klinger and Kubin and by the philosophy of Nietzsche and Schopenhauer.

In 1911 de Chirico moved to Paris. The early months were dogged by a nervous disorder with extreme crises of melancholia and chronic intestinal upsets but he developed a friendship with Guillaume Appolinaire and the Surrealists, at the same time developing his own independent form of painting which he successfully exhibited and sold.

He returned to Italy in 1915 to enlist, but an exacerbation of his enteric illness, depression and probably hepatitis caused his transfer to a Neuropsychiatric unit of a Military Hospital together the Futurist painter Carlo Carrà. Carrà adopted de Chirico's metaphysical painting but de Chirico in his turn acquired a greater feeling for the simplicity of things and the magical beauty inherent in them — before the meeting he had transported them too quickly to the grandiloquent region of his visual dreams, overemphasising their metaphysical significance (Haftman). After leaving hospital he was briefly ill with Spanish flu in 1918. In the 1920s, apart from a brief interlude which included his metaphysical novel, *Hebdomeros,* he rejected, in a paranoid fashion, modern movements in art and copied Italian classical styles but his claustrophobic interiors reflect his hospital internment.

De Chirico regarded as Metaphysical all painters who reveal the fantastic quality of the most solid things and raise them to a magnificent realism of visual dreams — la nostalgia, le solitude, il sogno (dream) — but his own memories and other writings are notable for the variety and apparent authenticity of his visual experiences:

(1) Recurrent dream from childhood;

It is my father who thus appears to me in my dreams, and yet when I look at him he is not at all as he was when I saw him alive in the time of my childhood. Nevertheless it is he. There is something far off in the whole expression of his face, something which perhaps existed when I saw him alive, and which now, after more than 20 years strikes me with full force when I see him again in a dream.

(2) Lilliputian dream;

I have a confused memory of my brother: I remember him as small, very small, disturbedly small, like certain alarming people one sees in dreams.

(3) The dual identity of certain objects;

Every object has two appearances: one, the current one, which we nearly always see and that is seen by people in general; the other, a spectral or metaphysical appearance beheld only by some rare individuals in moments of clairvoyance and metaphysical abstraction as in the case of certain bodies concealed by substances impenetrable by sunlight yet discernible, for instance by X-ray or other powerful artificial means.

(4) *Jamais vu, déjà inconnu;*

Let me recount how I had the revelation of a picture that I will show this year at the Salon d'Automne, entitled Enigma of an Autumn Afternoon.

One clear autumn afternoon I was sitting on a bench in the middle of the Piazza Santa Croce in Florence. It was of course not the first time I had seen this square. I had just come out of a long and painful intestinal illness, and I was in a nearly morbid state of sensitivity. The whole world, down to the marble of the buildings and the fountains seemed to be convalescent. In the middle of the square rises a statue of Dante draped in a long cloak, holding his works clasped against his body, his laurel-crowned head bent thoughtfully earthward. The statue is in white marble, but time has given it a grey cast, very agreeable to the eye. The autumn sun, warm and unloving, lit the statue and the church facade. Then I had the strange impression that I was looking at all these things for the first time, and the composition of my picture came to my mind's eye. Now each time I look at this painting I again see the moment. Nevertheless the moment is an enigma to me, for it is inexplicable. And I like to call the work which sprang from it an enigma.

(5) Telepathy;

During the night before my visit to the painter Laprade I dreamt that I saw a landscape somewhat similar to the banks of the lakes of Lombardy and Lake Garda. In the foreground were a few trees and some pink blossom; in the background was a stretch of water like a mirror. When I entered Laprade's studio the next day, I saw, exactly opposite the door, standing on an easel, a painting which represented a landscape identical with the one I had seen in my dream.

(6) Oneiristic experiences;

(a) I see again as twilight scenes associated with long illnesses, like typhus, and wearisome convalescence.

(b) I had gone to sleep in barracks. One night, in my sleep, I heard a loud noise and dreamt that I saw two hens as big as ostriches. I woke up and suddenly realised that the terrible disease (Spanish flu) had attacked me too.

(c) Swallowed a few sulphomamide tablets and then immediately ate the roast chicken. The first part of night was disturbed, I had nightmares. I saw in my dreams one of my uncles who had died in Florence 18 years earlier and in my dream I reopened a discussion that I and my brother, Alberto Savinio, often had with my uncle about the Old and New Testaments.

(To what extent these were drug or metabolically induced can be gauged by his statement of the treatment he received in childhood for high temperatures: Purge with castor oil, disinfection of the intestine with a good dose of salol, total fasting; after the purge had acted a very light broth with all the fat removed, quinine, massage of the chest and the spine with hot oil in which camomile flowers had been boiled, mustard poultices, made with the French variety called Rigolo, applied to spine and chest; the application of ventouses, also called cupping, and linseed poultices mixed with powdered mustard).

(7) Excessive use of dream symbolism;

De Chirico is said to show a tendency to transmute visual experiences into allegories: thus many of his works are presented as dreams — The transformed dream, The dream of the poet, The endless voyage, The double dream of spring, The purity of a dream — or as enigmas — The joys and enigmas of a strage hour, The enigma of a day, — of fatality, — of the oracle, — of the hour, — of an autumn afternoon.

Pablo Picasso (1881-1973)

Dyslexia and Minor Hemisphere Dominance

'After perpetual wanderings, through dark or dazzling rooms, the irrational took its first rational step with Picasso's painting: that first step was a last a raison d'etre'. Paul Eluard.

OF PICASSO's intelligence there has never been any dispute. No painter has ever been so well versed in the history of art. His technical brilliance and ingenuity have made him the great academic joker among artists. Symbolism and allegory surface in his Guernica painting. Myth, dream, history, incongruous juxtaposition, the absurd and the literal provide the elements of fantastic art in the Minotauromachy. He could be faithful to the clean lines of Ingres within hours of the destructive outlines of the Dora portraits. Nonetheless, by conventional standards he would have been written off academically.

Roland Penrose describes how Picasso's parents were worried by his backwardness in elementary education, particularly in arithmetic. Even the rudiments of reading, writing and sums gave him great trouble and he played truant, escaping to his father's studio to a form of learning he loved. By definition he was dyslexic. When Picasso was eight years of age, his father, Don Jose Ruiz Blasco, was appointed Lecturer in Art at La Guarde Institute in Corrunna. Picasso had to change school. 'Don Jose realised that something must be done to save his son and himself from disgrace and approached a man who was a very good friend and also a very indulgent schoolmaster. He arranged with him for an examination to be held. Faced by his examiner, little Pablo could only answer that he knew nothing, strictly nothing. The patient professor insisted that he should write down a column of four or five figures but even this was impossible. Determined to help, the master wrote the figures on the blackboard and told Pablo to copy them. That indeed was precisely what Pablo could do and, forgetting his own way of making figures, he copied stroke for stroke the numbers on the board with delight. The addition had to be made, and this again would have defeated him had he not noticed that the master, carelessly or on purpose, had written the correct answer on his blotting paper. The opportunity was quickly seized by Pablo, who with great care drew in the figures that completed the sum'. (Penrose).

Although he lived in Paris for 50 years, his command of the French language remained poor and when he married the Russian ballerina Olga Koklova, their mutually inadequate grasp of a common tongue contributed to the breakdown of their marriage.

Later in life he tried to write surrealist automatic verse and even a short play in French. Such verse need follow no form of conventional grammar. However, spelling mistakes were made with simple words such as 'J'attendrais' and his punctuation was unacceptable.

In right handed people the major speech and language centres lie in the left cerebral hemisphere. This hemisphere is chiefly concerned with processing information as discrete ideas dependent on their phonetic and temporal order and the right hemisphere with the synthesis of information into unified percepts in which the temporal aspects are superseded by spatial relationships. With left handed individuals the separation is not as clear cut. For the majority of those with genetically determined left handedness, i.e. with a family history of left handedness, the speech centres lie in the left hemisphere, but the unilaterality of speech is not as distinct as in most right handers. However, a proportion of left handers are truly left handed and have the speech and language centres within the right hemisphere. Where left handedness has been acquired, for example as the result of brain damage at the time of birth, in utero or in the early years of life, some plasticity of the nervous system is evident and the right hemisphere may take over speech and language function. In this respect, the various faculties of learning compete for 'space' in the healthy areas of the brain. The cerebral hemisphere concerned with speech and language is loosely regarded as the dominant hemisphere and the minor hemisphere or non-dominant hemisphere carries less precisely examined abilities such as an awareness of spatial relationships.

Picasso was left handed, although able to draw with almost equal facility with either hand, or simultaneously with both hands. Whether this handedness was genetically determined or acquired, we cannot be certain. From the contrast between his linguistic abilities and his spatial abilities we can only surmise that somehow the development of his 'minor hemisphere' (which could be either the right or the left hemisphere), particularly as illustrated by his ability to develop new spatial relationships in Cubist art, was far superior to the maturation of the corresponding 'major' side of his brain. Another Cubist, Robert Delauney, the founder of Orphism, was also dyslexic.

Among the hypotheses to explain the causation of dyslexia is that of brain damage. In Picasso's case, we know that his birth was not straightforward. The midwife made a near fatal misjudgement. The child appeared to her to be stillborn and she abandoned it on a table so as to give all her attention to the mother. Fortunately, Don Salvador, his uncle and a qualified doctor, was also present at the birth and, noticing that the child did not breathe spontaneously, blew cigar smoke into its face to stimulate repiration, saving the infant from asphyxia.

This explanation can account for dyslexia but not for the superior development of lesser hemisphere abilities. A low Apgar score, reflecting the child's vitality immediately after birth, is associated with an increased risk of brain damage; but if the left hemisphere had been damaged it is improbable that the right half of the brain would have succeeded in developing the way it did. The brain of an infant is capable of plasticity of function and, in the event of damage to the primary language zones, linguistic function will compete with other functions for immature or 'uncommitted' cortical space making it likely, on the basis of the Goldman 'competition' hypothesis, that Picasso's extraordinary development of minor hemispheric functions would not have occurred. A major factor in brain maturation is believed to be the types of stimulation received. Picasso's brain may be more correctly regarded, not as one with an impairment, but as one with an unusual concentration of functional ability of a particular type. We are tempted to ask, as was popular among the old style phrenologists, whether his insatiable egotism and hypersexuality — if that is truly so — are due to right brain predominence or whether his seemingly haphazard sequencing of artistic styles (mixing representational and abstract art), wives and mistresses, was due to a failure of temporal sequencing! Picasso's major talents — superb draughtsmanship, visual originality, and powers of construction are undoubtedly those associated with the minor, non-dominant cerebral hemisphere.

Blakeslee, *The Right Brain* (1980), makes two claims: that the right side of the brain is associated with creativity through the healthy co-operation of intuitive and logical thought, and that dreaming is primarily a right brain activity — full of images that lack a logical time sequence. Wilder Penfield was able to induce dream-like states more readily through stimulation of the right than the left hemisphere.

Picasso's art is not overtly based upon either dreams or theoretical concepts. Although friendly with, and the contemporary of, many Surrealists, he claimed always to have been the essence of reality. 'I paint things as I think of them, not as I see them'. 'I don't search, I find'. He would fantasise on a painting, producing many preliminary sketches as with Guernica, or discuss styles, materials and approaches at great length as he did with Braque at the beginning of Cubism, but mostly he left theorising to others. 'When you start a painting', he said, 'You need an idea, but it should be a vague one'. The picture which heralded in Cubism, 'Les Desmoiselles D'Avignon', originally had other figures, including that of a sailor, in the foreground. He used shapes to provide depth, based on the style of Cézanne, but the most potent ingredient was probably Negro art, deforming the conventional Renaissance vision. He was prepared to experiment with anything which intrigued him sufficiently.

The spectre of drugs is raised whenever an artist's vision borders on the fantastic. Early in his career, Picasso's attitudes were shaped by the suicidal death of a young German painter called Wiegels, as a result of excessive doses of ether. He had been a contemporary in the Spanish Schools of Art. Penrose explains that along with Cocteau and others Picasso tried opium. 'Opium', says Picasso, 'has the most intelligent of all odours', but it not only the suicide of Wiegels that put a stop to its use. While under the influence of the drug, Picasso found that his imagination and vision became more acute but his desire to paint what he saw diminished seriously. This threat of blissful steriliy influenced him most.

Picasso's art absorbed the human experience of an entire epoch. The roots of his art encompass all European art, child art and primitive art. The Blue period when the colours were reduced to a lyrical dominant colour with a dreamy, melancholy, unreal atmosphere to depict poor people with great emotional concentration, owes much to Redon and Carrière. The poetic sadness of the Rose period with few colour contrasts but greater variation follows that of Puvis de Chavannes, Toulouse-Lautrec, Dégas and even Gauguin. These were followed by a return to traditional Spanish art and an obsessional preoccupation with Negro and other forms of Primitive art before the origination of 'bizarreria cubiques' and the exploration of the whole keyboard of Cubist inventions. The Ballet, Naturalism after Ingres, Classical, Realistic and Troupe L'oeil effects flowed from his hands, his pen, his brush, varying and intermingling. He took to sculpture — abstract and realistic — as a diversion, not, as with Dégas, because of any lessening of his vision or talents with other forms of art. Two World Wars, political pressures — Guernica and the Peace Dove, commercial success and social demands seem to have reinforced his desire to produce more and more pictures, sometimes even as an escape from those around him. The style of his art often reflected the new female seeking attention. Fortunately his health remained robust to near the end and disease factors rarely impinged on his work.

Paul Klee (1879-1940)

Imagination and Physic Improvisation

'Art plays an ingenious game with ultimate things'.

'An artist's way of life, as seen from the outside, can tell us much about the character of his creativity'. Paul Klee. *Creative Credo.*

FOR KLEE, art is a sample of creation, a unity of conscious and unconscious, and 'wholly embedded in them is a third factor, myself'. The individuality and personality of Klee shines through his work as with no other artist. He remained throughout his life an accomplished aesthete and polymath, a continually potent graphic artist, painter, musician, poet and highly articulate writer. Music was the abiding passion of the family home. His father was a German musician who married and settled in Berne. The household was bilingual. His mother was French from Besancon, with a smattering of Mediterranean blood. He played the violin to concert standard, married a musician and throughout his life the evenings were devoted to music. 'Klee the painter', as his friend Feininger remarked, 'is unthinkable without Klee the musician'.

His slow development as a painter, even more than that of his friend Kandinsky, cannot be ascribed to an immaturity of approach, rather to the tremendous feats of assimilation of knowledge and experience he appeared to require before he reached a zenith of apparently effortless creativity. Behind a robust Bernese accent he remained gentle and sensitive. Klee's own temperament, as described by Sir Herbert Read, was physically introverted and metaphysical in its modes of expression. His paintings are sometimes taken to be pure whimsy but in fact they almost always have their point of departure in something that he had observed with particular precision in the world around him. Thus his work, for all its fantasy and superreality, was never escapist. Humour, sometimes sardonic, more often gay, predominates (Read, 1964). He gave to painting an enexplored world whose frontiers, before his time, had been crossed only by poetry, music and mathematics. His world is poetic but absurd (San Lazzaro, 1957).

He was recognised as an outstanding pupil when he first attended Prof. Knirr's private school of art in Munich at the age of 19. However, at the Academy of Fine Arts under the 'painter prince' of Munich, Franz von Stuck, he lost confidence in his means of self-expression and toyed with the idea of becoming a sculptor. Read castigates the rigidity of Klee's teachers 'from whom he derived no inspiration, no insight, no aesthetic revelation' but Stuck's semi-abstract, symbolistic contributions to the Jugendstil, with mythological and erotic motifs and colouring designed to set the mood of the composition, aided Kandinsky, who was also a pupil at the Academy, in his exploitation of colour.

At this stage of his career, Klee's idiosyncratic approach to art was already evident. In 1902 when on a visit to Italy he was more impressed by the Aquarium at Naples than by the splendours of Rome. He enjoyed the ports, such as Genoa, with their multitude of ships from all over the world. The statues, heroic monuments and churches of the Renaissance appealed to him less than old Siena with its basilicas, Byzantine and early Christian art, Coptic weaving and ancient calligraphy.

His first significant works were etchings in black and white, an amalgam of assimilated ideas derived from the fifteenth century and from artists such as Goya, Blake, Doré, Böcklin, Toulouse-Lautrec and even Picasso. He held a one-man show in 1910 and illustrated Voltaire's *Candide* in 1911. He tentatively tried his hand at water colours painted on glass; but even in 1911 when he joined the Blaue Reiter group, which included Kandinsky, Marc and Macke, he still had not mastered colour. In due course, the visual and mental impressions gained in a brief fortnight's visit to Tunisia in

1914, in the company of Moillet and Macke, awakened in him a delicate, even lyrical, sense of colour and provided some of his most characteristic abstractions. From there on he was able to say, 'Colour and I are one, I am a painter'. Even so he did not emerge as a commercial painter until, after a period of conscripted service in the German air force, he was demobilised in 1919.

Suddenly in his fortieth year the success which had previously eluded him blossomed: he was the subject of two monographs and the Munich art dealer Goltz staged an exhibition of 362 works which made Klee internationally famous. It was this exhibition, rather than his association with Kandinsky or the Blaue Reiter groups which led to Walter Gropius' invitation to teach painting at the Bauhaus. An insight into the freedom of composition which Klee attained, enabling him to produce nearly 8,000 works over the next 20 years, can be obtained from certain remarks of San Lazzaro on Klee's ambidexterity: 'He drew and painted with his left hand, but wrote with the right. He could write and draw with both simultaneously, working either from right to left or from left to right. For heavy work he preferred to use his left hand . . . He had trained his hands to an extraordinary degree, drawing automatically, independently of his will had his reason not intervened at a certain point and given meaning to the creative act.'

He would doodle freely with one or both hands — a form of Surrealist automatism, certain relationships in the consequent blot or maze — the dimensions of lines, the juxtaposition of certain harmonies of colour — would then allow him to experiment actively with the incomplete form to find an inner cohesion, reflecting a cerebral symmetry, and imaginatively perfect the task. His pictures were microcosms. From 1921 they crystallised out as mosaic-like compositions with small geometrical forms, irregular quadrilaterals and simplified natural forms 'binding the individual elements together in a proportionate relationship which seems to be based on the science of numbers' (Haftmann). This approach enabled his art to be highly experimental with an infinity of themes, incorporating each and every new development in technique with one exception — his format rarely allowed for the illusion of space.

His creativity 'to make visible as form something which is in process of forming' appeared effortless: a natural mode of expression once certain conditions were satisfied. The emphasis was upon feeling. He did not decide on a construction in advance; he looked for an underlying order which would yield up a construction after he had found it. 'The heart', he said, 'must do its work undisturbed by reflective consciousness. To know when to stop is of the same importance as to know when to begin. To continue merely automatically is as much a sin against the creative spirit as to start work without true inspiration'. Colour became more and more important to him. He soon discovered that the artist's attitude to the colours in his paint box is more important than an exact topography of nature. Colour, as Runge explained, has always something mysterious about it that cannot be properly understood. Colours are the most irrational element in painting. For Klee they provided a frail, delicate quality amounting to a feeling of magic.

At the Bauhaus, the close working relationship with other artists including Kandinsky, Itten, Feininger, Schlemmer and Moholy-Nagy enlivened his approach. The discipline of providing regular and methodical lessons of the fundamentals of painting, having to instruct and theorise on his own technique, proved exceedingly productive and vastly furthered his vision and thinking. In preaching on the richness of simplicity he had to demonstrate how it could be achieved. The reduction of art to fundamental forms — the dot, the line, the circle and the spiral — enabled him to show how a work of art is built up: developing character from movement, opening up the inner workings of an object as it expands beyond its initial appearance. His writings bear witness to his success as a teacher.

He extended the surrealist search of automatism or 'psychic improvisation' to primitive art: 'he went to the primitive and tried to civilise it'. He was interested in discovering how a primitive instinct finds a formal structure appropriate to content, thus giving a clue to the formative powers of the unconscious. He examined psychopathic art. But, most especially, he looked closely at the drawings of children, and of his own son Felix. He took the shapes and perspective of children, cloaking them with delicate colour and extracting something magical, spiritual or even humorous from so doing. 'As a child plays at being grown up, so the painter initiates those forces which created and still are creating the world'. The fantastic images, as with his picture of the Golden Fish, develop new metaphors through colour. He looked for new shapes in Nature to produce almost cubistic mosaics, inspired more by Delauney than Braque. He used hypnagogic imagery:

'Before falling asleep we recall a number of things, lines of the most varied kinds, spots, dabs, smooth planes, dotted planes, wavy lines, obstructed and articulated movement, counter movement, plaitings, weavings, bricklike elements, scalelike elements, simple and polyphonic motifs, lines that fade and lines that gain strength (dynamism), the joyful harmony of the first stretch, followed by inhibitions, nervousness'. *(Creative Credo, 1920).*

As political pressures affected even the workings of the Bauhaus, forcing him to leave for the Düsseldorf Academy, where he accepted a lowly post taking over the basic materials and techniques, he became more remote and lapsed into a meditative detachment. He was to be cast out of Germany, fleeing to Berne as a result of Nazi threats. His works were included in the notorious exhibition of degenerate art in 1937. His highly sensitive response to these and similar provocations was to produce one of the most telling symbolic works of art, a symbol of all hostages to political misfortune, The Letter Ghost: on the back of a simple envelope he drew the eyes, mouth and nose, and at the sides the outlines of the shoulders, of a sad humanoid — 'an oblique but unforgetable image that makes us feel that a man is trying to escape from the tensions of sleep, only to find that fear has impregnated the very blankets that he tries to pull up to his chin'. At that time, not to get a letter often meant the arrest, if not the death, of the person who had gone to the mailbox as a free human being the week before.

Exile meant immense disappointment, much mental trauma and a need for a fresh start after the loss of his possessions. He applied for Swiss nationality but it was rejected until after his death. Friends described his last years in Berne as a gentle, magical apparition floating amid the crowd. Following a brief illness, believed to be an attack of measles, he became seriously ill 'fading away like a leaf in autumn when the sap runs dry' due to scleroderma — a wasting, lingering fate with a drying of secretions. He continued to paint and draw and remained prolix in creativity but his art reflected a state of severe physical and mental strain with acute depression.

It is understandable that initially he should seek to restore his fortunes theough the rapid production of larger paintings displaying a new toughness of approach; but unlike the majority of depressed persons who find difficulty with any form of expression, especially through art, his biographers describe Klee's dynamic energy and the remarkable efflorescence of his art in his last five years (Lynton, 1964). With a personality such as Klee's, whose mental functions are habitually based on feeling rather than on thought, sensation or intuition, one would expect the manner of his art to alter profoundly (Read). His technical and formal mastery remained unaffected. Earlier playfulness was replaced by a more powerful and morbid seriousness, including bitter satire. There was a darker scale of colour, harsh and simplified; and yet his colours continued to shine forth with a mystical glow. Outlines became rounded and taut. He chose coarser materials with which to work: parchment replaced fine paper, oils on sacking, pastels on linen, and poster paints on a variety of surfaces. Towards the end a pre-occupation with the malign and malevolent gave way to a whole hierarchy of angels. As stated in one of his peoms, full of subtle, untranslatable puns, 'one of these days I shall lie in nothingness, besides an angel of some kind'.

Apart from the asceticism and psychic interest of his later works, various critics have stressed their importance in the development of modern art (Douglas Hall). His disjunctive method of composition, his abnegation of the necessity to focus on a point or an episode of a painting, represent one of the very few innovations in painting since Cubism.

Wassily Kandinsky (1866-1944)

Synaesthesia

'The Dance of the Intellect amongst Paints'

FAR from being the archetypal artist, the bespectacled, militaristic, almost Prussian figure of Kandinsky is a composite of the many roles which preceded, paralleled and were subservient to his universally recognised achievement as an artist of unusual sensitivity. His manner and his prescriptive, dogmatic lecturing style were those of a lawyer, professor, diplomat, state official, Director of the Moscow Museum and Pictorial Culture, Founder of the Russian Academy of Artistic Sciences and Assistant Director of the Bauhaus.

His upbringing was suitably broad and elitist. Born in Moscow, he grew up in Odessa on the Black Sea, where his father, a prosperous tea-merchant, had gone for reasons of health. He sought academic success, but also played the cello and drew. From 1886 he studied law and political science at Moscow University. Whilst still a student he journeyed in 1889 on behalf of the Society for Natural Science, Ethnography and Anthropology of Moscow to the Northern Province of Vologda to report on the peasant laws and the survival of paganism among the Syryenian tribes, noticing the brilliantly coloured designs with which these primitive people bedecked the interiors of their homes.

In 1892, the year of his graduation, he married a cousin and in 1893 was appointed lecturer in Law at the University. He supplemented his salary by working in a managerial capacity for a firm which produced coloured art reproductions. With an assured academic future, he abruptly changed direction at the age of thirty, declined a professorial post in Law at the University of Dorpat in Estonia, left his wife and, financed by his family, travelled to Munich to study painting.

Munich was the great German cultural centre of the time. For the arts its pre-eminence was second only to Paris. At first he studied under Anton Azbé but soon moved to the better known Franz von Stuck whose idyllic, mythological paintings were inspired by Böcklin. Pupilage ill became him. In 1901 he set himself up as a teacher of art groups — Phalanx to be followed by the Neue Kunstlerverienigung of Munich (1909), and the influencial Blaue Reiter group (1911).

Gabriel Münter became his pupil and mistress with whom he travelled from 1903 to 1908 throughout Europe and North Africa — an aesthete making the grand tour, already an accomplished musician, poet, etcher and art critic. He produced no major works as a professional painter until the age of forty-two, that is until after years of trial and theoretical insight he had advanced ahead of others in painting the first abstract pictures: abstractions depending entirely on the emotional significance of colours and form without figurative suggestion. Whether he actually produced the first abstract painting can be debated: that he became the founder of abstract expressionism is beyond question.

Writing remained an important aspect of his life. *Concerning the Spiritual in Art* — later revised to conform with the requirements of Soviet Russia — was published in 1911, *On the Question of Form* in 1912, the autobiographical *Rückblicke* (reminiscences) in 1913 and a limited edition of his poems *Klänge* (sounds) in the same year. Typically his poems emphasise word-sounds rather than meanings. With the outbreak of war Kandinsky left Munich on 3rd August 1914, via Switzerland and the Balkan States, to return to Russia. There, with the shortage of materials, he did little painting but in the wake of the revolution applied his talents and theoretical ideas on the nature of art to practical projects within the system as Professor of the Moscow Academy of Fine Art, Director of the Museum of Pictorial Culture and founder of the Academy of Artistic Sciences but with the imposition of Socialist realism he chose to return to Germany, having married a second time to a young Russian girl, Nina de Andreevsky.

Gropius encouraged him to the Bauhaus in 1921 where he was to stay until its closure by the Nazis in 1933. As Paul Overy comments (1969) Gropius was presumably attracted by his admiration for Kandinsky as a painter and theorist, by his administrative prominence and no doubt found his plans for reorganising art education much to his personal taste. With Klee, Itten and Feininger he remained a moving spirit for the visual arts in this experimental centre for design. After its closure he moved to Paris where he lived for the rest of his life in the suburb of Neuilly-sur-Seine.

Kandinsky is a painter of colour and geometry rather than of Nature or reality. He does not deny Nature but is prepared to seek visual stimulation by capturing its energy. Nor does he deny the objective origination of any abstract painting, accepting that there could always be a possible conscious or subconscious foundation from which emanates the artistic essence. He brings to art a highly selective and developed mind which is remarkable for several reasons, each facet of which adds to a most unusual combination of circumstances to give him an unsurpassed appreciation of colour.

An artist induces others to see the world differently. The novelty of his view provides a new perspective. With flair, distortions and even imperfections of vision, can be turned to advantage; and shortsightedness (myopia) is no exception. Besides Kandinsky, Bonnard, Braque, Deraigne, Grosz, Matisse, Mondrian and Vlaminck were all myopic. The myope focusses minutely. Where clarity is achieved by glasses, outlines remain indistinct and blurred. A halo of luminosity may surround the object upon which attention is concentrated. Colours therefore appear with greater intensity compared with form or substance. Whereas the average person rarely recalls colours, colours retain a special importance to the myopic; especially to any myope with an artistic temperament who strives consciously to compensate for his optic impairment. He is more likely to be alerted to certain properties of colours which rarely impinge on the awareness of his normal (emmentropic) or farsighed (hypermetropic) contemporaries; one such is the Purkinje effect whereby in reduced light — as at dusk — blues and greens tend to glow brighter than reds or yellows.

Clarity of visual memory depends upon inner vision, not upon sharpness of sight: and Kandinsky, like Dickens, had the ability to walk along a crowded street and then recall every building, every feature or character of interest — the names of shops, their trade, their window displays and the people who flocked to their doors. Like Blake, Kandinsky was a strong visualiser who retained an eidetic imagery. It is a hard lesson, as Galton has said, for a child who is imaginative and retains eidetic imagery to distinguish between the real and visionary world. No wonder the childhood impressions of the Muscovite fairyland appealed to him. His eidetic imagery was also influenced differently, even from Blake, by the nature of his early myopia. In his autobiography he writes that:

'the first colours that made a strong impression on me were bright juicy green, white, carmine green, black and yellow ochre. These memories go back to the third year of life. I saw these colours on various objects which are no longer as clear in my mind as the colours themselves'.

As early as 1903 Kandinsky spent some time in Paris and was well versed in the artistic movements around him, but his personal art was more readily influenced by early Russian pictures, the mosaics of Byzantium and the Orient and by Bavarian glass painting than by Cubism, Constructivism, Fauvism etc.

As well as being unusually sensitive to the emotional association of colours, Kandinsky has a strongly developed power of synaesthesia, believing that synaesthesia develops as the strength of a modality of sensation increases to produce an emotional response stimulating a reverberation or echo among the other sensations. He possessed this gift from an early age. When one of his senses was stimulated another reacted. In his case he usually heard something when looking at a scene or even at a single colour, or saw a colour or scene when listening to music e.g. with a particular note or a particular instrument. He took the view that association alone will not explain the phenomenon. Each modality possesses an energy or vibration: 'it is only as a step towards the spiritual vibration that the physical impression is important' . . . 'Painting can develop the same energies as music'. Synaesthesia provided a visual language, which, he believed, would eventually communicate feelings more clearly than could any verbal language:

'Generally speaking colour directly influences the soul. Colour is the keyboard, the eyes are the hammers, the soul is the piano with many strings. The artist is the hand that plays, touching one key or another purposively, to cause vibration in the soul. It is evident, therefore, that colour harmony must result ultimately on purposively playing upon the human soul; this is one of the guiding principles of internal necessity.'

Art becomes a physic, intuitive process, a spiritual activity — its business to order man's vision of the world and through mystic colours to evoke the ideas of infinite space.

The emphasis upon synaesthesia spread to his other intellectual pursuits. He wrote a long theoretical essay on yellow sound and used the same title for a stage composition (Buhreukomposition) describing the effects of light, colour and darkness he wanted and the kind of music to go with them.

Kandinsky's colour theories were derived from Goethe and Rudolf Steiner. He spoke of the fundamental distinctions: the 'temperature' of colours and their tone (lightness or darkness). He defined as four major sounds: warm and bright; warm and dark; cold and bright; cold and dark. Temperature is determined by the tendency of any colour towards yellow (absolute warmth) or blue (absolute coldness). Colours also have meaning — yellow, typically earthy; blue, heavenly; yellow, aggressive, blue, retreats. The contrasts: white/black or red/green awake unconscious urges which may also arise through form as in his book, *Point and Line to Plane.* By contrast there was an affinity of yellow with white and blue with black.

Yellow is the most sensitive colour and is very easily sullied.

Pure green is the most restful colour, lacking any undertone of joy, grief or passion.

Yellow is brash and importunate. It pricks, it upsets purple.

Red has an unbound warmth but not the irresponsible appeal of yellow.

Orange brings red close to yellow 'almost to the point of spreading out towards the spectator'.

Black is a silence with no possibilities: in music it is represented by one of those profound and final pauses.

White acts upon our psyche as a great and absolute silence, like the pauses in music which temporarily break the melody.

In the process of developing his theories whilst at the Bauhaus in the 1920s, Kandinsky began to discipline the surging atmospheric effects of his early paintings by a system of planes and gradually eliminated the illusion of depth. The emphasis came to lie upon the 'perfumed' colours and increasingly he felt that the more abstract the form the clearer and more distinct is its appeal. Even in the last pictures of his Parisian period when almost eighty, he retained his taste for colour and the dazzling constellation of moving, thrilling and nervous forms.

References

Abell T (1845) 'Blindness, a personal account'. *Boston Medical and Surgical J.* 33: 408-412.

Abraham MD (1983) 'Visual phenomenology of the LSD flashback'. *Archives of General Psychiatry* 40: 884-889.

Abrahms MH (1934) *The Milk of Paradise.* London.

Addison T (1712) 'Essay on the Pleasures of the Imagination'. *The Spectator.* July 3rd.

Ades D (1972) 'Freud and Surrealist Painting'. In *Freud, The Man, His World, His Influence.* ed. J. Miller. Weidenfeld and Nicholson. London.

Ades D (1982) *Dali.* Thames and Hudson. London.

Allderidge P (1974) *Richard Dadd.* Academy Editions. London.

Ames D (1984) 'Self-shooting of a phantom head'. *British J. Psychiatry* 145: 193-194.

Angeli HR (1949) *Dante Gabriel Rossetti, his friends and enemies.* Hamish Hamilton. London.

Argüelles JA (1975) *The Transformative Vision.* Shambhala. Berkeley.

Aurier A (1891) *Mercure de France.*

Ayrton M (1971) *The Rudiments of Paradise.* Secker and Warburg. London.

Baudelaire C (1860) *Les Paradis Artificiels.* Paris.

Begbie H (1915) *On the Side of the Angels.* (see also *The Phantom Brigade,* 1930, Vivian APG, Benn. London).

Bell MH (1984) 'Absinthe'. *J. American Medical Association* 252: 1838.

Bender L (1954) *A Dynamic Psychopathology of Childhood.* Thomas. Illinois.

Berenson B (1896) *The Florentine Painters of the Rennaissance.* New York.

Berrios GE (1982) 'Tactile hallucinations: conceptual and historical aspects'. *J. Neurology, Neurosurgery and Psychiatry* 45: 285-293.

Berrios GE, Brook P (1982) 'The Claude Bonnet Syndrome and the problem of visual perceptual disorders in the elderly'. *Age and Ageing.* 11: 17-23.

Berrios GE, Brook P (1984) 'Visual hallucinations and sensory delusions in the elderly'. *British J. Psychiatry* 144: 662-664.

Biomedical Results from Skylab (1977) ed. RS Johnston and LF Dietlin. NASA. Washington.

Blake W (1969) *Complete Works.* ed. G Keynes. Oxford University Press. Oxford.

Blakeslee TR (1980) *The Right Brain.* Macmillan. London.

Bleuler E, Lehmann K (1881) *Zwangsmaessige Lichtempfindungen Durch Schall, und verwandte Erscheinungen auf dem Gebiete der anderen Sinnesempfindungen.* Fues' S Verlag. Leipzig.

Bleuler E (1913) 'Zur Theorie der Sekundärempfindungen'. *Z. Psychol. Physiol. Sinnesorg.* 65: 1-39.

Blumrich JF (1974) *The Spaceships of Ezekiel.* Bantom. New York.

Boas F (1955) *Primitive Art.* Dover Publications. New York.

Boiffard JA, Eluard P, Vitrac R (1924) *La revolution Surrealiste.* Paris.

Bors E (1979) 'Extinction and synaesthesia in patients with spinal cord injuries'. *Paraplegia* 17: 21-31.

Bragman LJ (1935-6) 'The case of Dante Gabriel Rossetti: a psychological study of a chloral addict'. *American J. Psychiatry* 92: 1111-1122.

Brain WR (1955) *Diseases of the Nervous System.* Oxford University Press. Oxford.

Bridgemen W, Hazard J (1955) *The Lonely Sky.* Holt. New York.

Brownfield CA (1965) *Isolation: clinical and experimental effects.* Random House. London.

Butler M (1978) *William Blake.* Tate Gallery. London.

Byrd RE (1938) *Alone. A classic of endurance.* Putnam. New York.

Calef V (1954) 'Colour in dreams'. *J. American Psycho-analysis Association* 2: 453-455.

Campbell PJ (1915) 'The White Comrade', in (1979) *The Canon's Mouth,* Hamish Hamilton. London.

Caplan LR, Mier DB, Banks G (1982) 'Current concepts of cerebrovascular disease: Stroke - stroke and drug abuse'. *Stroke* 13: 869-872.

Carlen PL, Wall PD, Nadvorna H, Steinbach T (1978) 'Phantom limbs and related phenomena in recent traumatic amputations'. *Neurology* 28: 211-217.

Carstairs M (1966) 'The Madness of Art'. *Observer Colour Supplement.* Oct. 12th.

Cawthorne T (1962) 'Goya's illness'. *Proceedings of the Royal Society of Medicine* 55: 213-217.

Chipps HB (1975) *Theories of Modern Art. A Source Book by Artists and Critics.* University of California Press. Berkeley.

de Chirico G (1919) 'On Metaphysical Art'. In (1971) *Memories.* trans by M Crossland. Owen. London.

Clark B, Graybiel A (1957) 'The break off phenomenon'. *J. Aviation Medicine* 28: 121-124.

Clark K (1976) *The Romantic Rebellion.* Omega Books. London.

Cohen BD, Rosenbaum G, Dobie SI, Gottlier JS (1959) 'Sensory isolation'. *J. Nervous and Mental Disease* 129: 486-491.

Cohen S (1970) *Drugs of Hallucination.* Palladian. London.

Collins W (1868) *The Moonstone.* Chatto and Windus. London.

Connolly J (1983) 'The Indication of Insanity'. In (1963) *Three Hundred Years of Psychiatry 1535-1860* ed. Hunter R, McAlpine I: pp 805-809.

Courthion P (1958) *Flemish Painting.* Thames and Hudson. London.

Critchley EMR, Denmark JC, Warren F, Wilson KA (1981) 'Hallucinatory experiences of prelingually profoundly deaf schizophrenics'. *British J. Psychiatry* 138: 30-32.

Critchley EMR (1983) 'Auditory experiences of deaf schizophrenics'. *J. Royal Society of Medicine* 76: 542-544.

Critchley M (1939) 'Visual and auditory hallucinations'. *British Medical J.* ii: 634-639.

Critchley M (1965) 'Acquired anomalies of colour perception of central origin'. *Brain* 88: 711-724.

Critchley M (1977) 'Ecstatic and synaesthesia experience during musical perception'. pp 217-232 In, *Music and the Brain.* ed. M Critchley and RA Henson. Heinemann. London.

Croce B (1909) *Aesthetic: Science of expression and general linguistics.* London.

Damas-Mora J, Skelton-Robinson M, Jenner FA (1982) 'The Charles Bonnet syndrome in perspective'. *Psychological Medicine* 12: 251-261.

Davis JM, McCourt WF, Solomon P (1960) 'The effect of visual stimulation during sensory deprivation'. *American J. Psychiatry* 116: 889-892.

Dement WC (1960) 'The effect of dream deprivation'. *Science* 131: 1705-1707.

Dimijian GC (1976) 'Differential diagnosis of emergency drug reactions'. In *Acute Drug Abuse Emergencies.* ed. PG Bourne. Academic Press. London.

Dobbs B, Dobbs J (1977) *Dante Gabriel Rossetti, an alien Victorian.* Macdonald and James. London.

d'Otrange Mastai ML (1975) *Illusion in Art.* Abaris Books. New York.

Duke-Elder S (1963) *A System of Ophthalmology.* Morsby. St. Louis.

Dunn DW, Weisberg LA, Nadell J (1983) 'Peduncular hallucinations caused by brain stem compression'. *Neurology* 33: 1360-1361.

Dyke SC (1963) 'Some medical aspects of the life of Dante Gabriel Rossetti'. *Proceedings of the Royal Society of Medicine* 56: 1089-1093.

Edgell HG, Kolvin I (1972) 'Childhood hallucinations'. *J. Child Psychology and Psychiatry* 13: 279-287.

Eliade H (1972) *Shamanism.* Princetown University Press. Princetown.

Erickson EH (1958) *Young Man Luther.* New York.

Esquirol E (1817) *Hallucinations.* (reprinted in *Des Maladies Mentales.* Bailliere. Paris 1938).

Ey H (1969) 'Disorders of consciousness in psychiatry'. pp 112- 136. In vol 3. *Handbook of Neurology.* ed. G Bruyn *et al.* Elsevoir. Amsterdam.

Feaver W (1975) *The Art of John Martin.* Clarendon. Oxford.

Fenichel O (1946) *The Psychoanalytical Theory of Neuroses.* Kegan Paul. London.

Fitzgerald RG (1971) 'Visual phenomenology in recently blind adults'. *American J. Psychiatry* 127: 1533-1539.

Flournoy H (1923) 'Hallucinations Lilliputiennes atypiques chex un vieillard atteint de cataract'. *L'Encephale* 18: 566-579.

Flournoy T (1900) *Des Indes A la Planète Mars.* Paris.

Flynn WR (1962) 'Visual hallucinations in sensory deprivation'. *Psychiatry Quarterly* 36: 55-63.

Foulkes D, Pivik T. Steadman HJ, Spear PS, Symonds JD (1967) 'Dreams of the male child'. *J. Abnormal Psychology* 6: 457-467.

Fraser D (1962) *Primitive Art.* Thames and Hudson. London.

Freud S (1901) 'On Dreams' In (1953-74) *Complete Psychological Works of S. Freud.* Hogarth Press. London.

Friedlander MJ (1943) *Art and Connoisseurship.* London.

Frisby JP (1979) *Seeing: Illusion, Brain and Mind.* Oxford University Press. Oxford.

Galton F (1883) *Inquiries into Human Faculty.* Dent and Dutton. London *(Inquiries into Human Faculty and its Development.* (1928) Dutton. New York).

Garma A (1961) 'Colour in Dreams'. *International J. Psychoanalysis* 42: 556-557.

Garralda ME (1982) 'Hallucinations in psychiatrically disordered children' *J. Royal Society of Medicine* 75: 181-184.

Garralda ME (1984) 'Hallucinations in children with conduct and emotional disorders'. *Psychological Medicine* 14: 589-596.

Gerard J, Marshall D, Saul P (1936) *Archives of Neurology and Psychology* 36: 675.

Gibson W (1953) *The Boat.* Houghton-Miffin (Riverside Press) Boston.

Gibson WS (1973) *Hieronymus Bosch.* Thames and Hudson. London.

Glasgow Art Gallery and Museum (1985) *Salvador Dali: Christ of St. John of the Cross.*

Goldman PS (1972) Developmental determinants of cortical plasticity. *Acta Neurobiologica Experimentalis* 32: 495-511.

Goldstone S (1962) 'Psychophysics, Reality and Hallucinations'. In *Hallucinations.* ed. LJ West. Grune and Stratton. New York.

Gombrich EH (1968) *Art and Illusion.* Phaidon. London.

Gombrich EH (1972) *Symbolic Images.* Phaidon. London.

Goode AW (1981) 'Microgravity Research'. *Lancet* i: 767-769.

Goodman LS, Gilman A (1955) *The Pharmacological Basis of Therapeutics;.* Macmillan. London.

Grant WB (1918) *We Have a Guardian.* London.

Green R (1983) 'Aviation psychology'. *British Medical J.* 286: 1880-1882.

Gregory H (1969) *The World of James McNeill Whistler.* Hutchinson. London.

Gregory RL (1970) *The Intelligent Eye.* Weidenfeld and Nicholson. London.

Greysmith D (1973) *Richard Dadd.* Studio Vista. London.

Grohman W (1957) *Paul Klee.* New York.

Guggenheim P (1974) *Autobiography.* New York.

Guilleminault GC, Billiard M. Montplaisir J, Dement WC (1975) 'Altered states of consciousness in disorders of daytime sleepiness'. *J. Neurological Sciences* 76: 377-393.

Guterman N (1959) *The Inward Vision: Watercolours, Drawings and Writings of Paul Klee.* Abrams. New York.

Haftmann W (1954) *The Mind and Work of Paul Klee.* Faber. New York.

Haftmann W (1965) *Painting in the Twentieth Century.* Lund Humphries. London.

Hall D (1977) *Paul Klee.* Oxford University Press. Oxford.

Halliday F, Russell J (1962) *Sir Matthew Smith.* Allen and Unwin. London.

Hammacher AM, Hammacher R (1982) *Van Gogh, A documentary biography*. Thames and Hudson. London.

Hammeke TA, McQuillen MP, Cohen BA (1983) 'Musical hallucinations associated with acquired deafness'. *J. Neurology, Neurosurgery and Psychiatry* 46: 570-572.

Hayek EA (1952) *The Sensory Order*. Routledge and Kegan Paul. London.

Hayter A (1968) *Opium and the Romantic Imagination*. Faber and Faber. London.

Heim A (1892) 'Remarks on fatal falls'. *Yearbook of the Swiss Alpine Club* 27: 327-337. (reprinted in *Omega* (1972) 3: 45-52).

Henry C (1926) *Generalisation du theorie du rayonnement*. Paris. (Also *Cercle Chromatique*. Verdun. Paris, 1888).

Hobbs R (1977) *Odilon Redon*. Studio Vista. London.

Hodin JP (1972) *Edvard Munch*. Thames and Hudson. London.

Hodin (1972) *Expressionism*. Thames and Hudson. London.

Horowitz MJ (1964) 'The imagery of visual hallucinations'. *J. Nervous and Mental Disease* 138: 513-523.

Hug-Hellmuth H (1912) 'Ueber Farbenhoeren'. *Imago* 1: 228-264.

Huysmans JK (1889) *A Rebours. (Against the Grain*. Illustrated Editions Co. New York).

Hyde HM (1964) *A History of Pornography*. Heinemann. London.

Jacobs L, Karpik A, Bozian D, Gothgen S (1981) 'Auditory-visual synaesthesia: Sound induced photisms'. *Archives of Neurology* 38: 211-216.

Jacome DE, Gummit RJ (1979) 'Synaesthesia seizures'. *Neurology* 29: 1050-1053.

Jaensch ER (1930) *Eidetic Imagery and Typological Methods of Investigation*. Harcourt Brace. New York.

Jaspers K (1963) *General Psychopathology*. Manchester University Press. Manchester.

Jesperson O (1922) *Language, its Nature, Development and Origins*. Allen and Unwin. London.

Jung, CG (1954) 'The Interpretation of Dreams'. reprinted in *Memories, Dreams and Reflections* (1963) Routledge and Kegan Paul. London.

Jung CG (1964) 'The Flying Saucers'. *The Collected Works of CG Jung*. ed. RFC Hull. vol 10, Princetown University Press. Princetown.

Kahn E, Demet WC, Fisher C, Barnack JE (1962) 'Colour in dreams'. *Science* 137: 1054-1055.

Katz D (1935) *The World of Colour*. Kegan Paul. London.

Kerr M, Pear TM (1932) 'Synaesthesia'. *British J. Psychology* 23: 2-7.

Kinsey AC (1948) *Sexual Behaviour of the Human Male*. Saunders. London.

Kinsey AC (1948) *Sexual Behaviour of the Human Female*. Saunders. London.

Klee P (1920) *Creative Credo*. Reiss. Berlin.

Klein R (1917) *Zeitschrift fur die gesamte Neurologie und Psychiatrie* 36: 323-340.

Koestler A (1959) *The Sleepwalkers, a history of man's changing view of the Universe*. London.

Kokoschka O (1912) *On the Nature of Visions*. trans Medlinger H. Thwaites J. London.

Kroll J, Bachrach V (1982) 'Medieval visions and contemporary hallucinations'. *Psychological Medicine* 12: 709-721.

Kubin A (1908) *Die Andere Seite (The Other Side)* Penguin edition (1983) London.

Lackner JR, Graybiel A (1983) 'Perceived orientation in free fall depends on visual, postural and architectural factors'. *Aviation, Space and Environmental Medicine* 54: 47-51.

Lance JW (1976) 'Simple formed hallucinations confined to the area of a specific visual field defect'. *Brain* 99: 719-734.

Lancet (1970) 'Unwanted effects of cannabis'. *Lancet* ii: 1350.

Lavater L (1572) *Of Ghostes and Spirites Wailing by Night*. Watkins. London.

Leading Article (1959) 'Sensory deprivation'. *Lancet* 2: 1072.

Lenneberg E (1967) *Biological Foundations of Language*. Wiley. New York.

Leroy R (1921) 'Le syndrome des hallucinations Lilliputiennes'. *L'Encephale* 16: 504-510.

Lessell S, Cohen MM (1979) 'Phosphenes induced by sound' *Neurology* 29: 1524-1527.

L'Hermitte J (1922) 'Syndrome de la calotte pédonculaire'. *Reveu Neurologique* 38: 1359-1365.

Licht F (1980) *Goya, the Origins of the Modern Temper in Art.* Murray. London.

Life Sciences Research in Space (1977). ed. Burke WR and Gyenne TD. European Space Agency Scientific and Technical Publication. Brance. Noordvijk.

Lindstrom M (1957) *Children's Art.* University of California Press. Berkeley.

Linn L (1954) 'Colour in Dreams'. *J. American Psychoanalysis Association* 2: 462.

Liotard JE (1781) *Traité des principes et des règles de la peinture.* (Reprinted 1945). Geneva.

Loevgren S (1971) *The Genesis of Modernism.* Indiana University Press.

Lorand S (1937) 'Fairy Tales, Liliputian Dreams and Neuroses. *American J. Orthopsychiatry* 7: 456-459.

Lowenfeld V, Brittain WL (1970) *Creative and Mental Growth.* Macmillan. London.

Lucie-Smith E (1972) *Symbolic Art.* Thames and Hudson. London.

Lucie-Smith E (1972) *Eroticism in Western Art.* Thames and Hudson. London.

Lukianowicz N (1960) 'Imaginery sexual partner'. *Archives of General Psychiatry* 3: 429-499.

Luria AR (1968) *The Mind of a Mneumonist.* London.

Lyton N (1975) *Paul Klee: Figures and Faces.* Thames and Hudson. London.

McCollough C (1965) 'Colour adaptation of edge detectors in the human visual system'. *Science* 149: 1115-1116.

McGee R (1984) 'Flashback and Memory phenomena'. *J. Nervous and Mental Disease* 172: 273-278.

McKellar P (1957) *Imagination and Thinking.* Cohen and West. London.

Mahler M, Elkish P (1953) 'Some observations on disturbances of ego — cause of infantile psychosis'. *Psychoanalytical Study of Childhood.* 8: 252-261.

Marius R (1974) *Luther.* Quartet Books. London.

Marks LE (1982) 'Synaesthetic perception and poetic metaphor'. *J. Experimental Psychology.* 8: 15-23.

Marsden CD, Parkes JD (1974) 'Narcolepsy'. *British J. Hospital Medicine.*

Massie S (1978) *The Land of the Firebird.* Hamish Hamilton. London.

Mathieu PL (1977) *Gustave Moreau.* Phaidon. Oxford.

Maury AL (1848) *Annales Medico-psychologiques.* 11: 26-31.

Mayer-Gross W, Slater E, Roth M (1954) *Clinical Psychiatry.* 3rd ed. Slater E, Roth M, ed. Bailliere, Tindall and Cassell. London.

Mehta M (1973) *Intractable Pain.* Saunders. London.

Mendelson J, Foley J (1956) 'Hallucinations in a tank respirator'. *Transactions American Neurological Association.* 81: 134.

Menzel DH, Taves EH (1977) *The UFO Enigma.* Doubleday. New York.

Miller TC, Crosby TW (1979) 'Musical hallucinations in elderly deaf patients'. *Annals of Neurology* 5: 301-302.

Mills L (1936) 'Peripheral vision in art'. *Archives of Ophthalmology* 16: 208-219.

Mitchell JV (1974) *Ghosts of an Ancient City.* Cerialis Press. New York.

Moore RF (1935) 'Subjective "lightning streaks".' *British J. Ophthalmology* 19: 545-547.

Nebel BR (1957) 'The phosphene of quick eye movement'. *Archives of Ophthalmology* 19: 545-58: 235-243.

Novak B (1969) *American Painting of the Nineteenth Century.* Pall Mall Press. London.

Ogden CK, Richards LA, Wood J (1934) *The Foundations of Aesthetics.* London.

Osborne H (1970) *The Oxford Companion to Art.* Oxford University Press. Oxford.

Osborne H (1981) *The Oxford Companion to 20th-Century Art.* Oxford University Press. Oxford.

Osborne J (1961) *Luther, a play.* London.

Ostwald PF (1964) 'Colour Hearing'. *Archives of General Psychiatry* 11: 40-47.

Oswald I (1960) 'Number forms, and kindred visual images'. *J. General Psychology* 63: 81-88.

Oswald I (1962) *Sleeping and Waking.* Elsevier. Amsterdam.

Ovcharro BW (1974) *Van Gogh in Perspective.* Prentice Hall. London.

Overy P (1969) *Kandinsky: The Language of the Eye.* London.

Paladilhe J (1980) *Gustave Moreau.* Paris.

Paree R (1916) *'Angel of Mons' Valse.* publ. Lawrence Wright Music Co. London.

Penrose R (1958) *Picasso, His Life and Work.* London.

Perruchot H (1955) *La Vie de Van Gogh.* Hachette. Paris.

Philostratus the Elder (AD 190) *Imagines.* trans by Goethe, 1818.

Piaget J (1974) *The Child and Reality.* Muller. London.

Pickford RW (1942) 'Rossetti's "Sudden Light" as an experience of déjà vu'. *British J. Medical Psychology* 19: 192-200.

Plant M (1978) *Paul Klee: Figures and Faces.* Thames and Hudson. London.

Polanyi M (1968) *Science* 160: 1308-1318.

Pollock G, Orton F (1978) *Vincent Van Gogh.* Hachette. Paris.

Prinzhorn JH (1971) *Artistry of the Mentally Ill.* Springer Verlag. Berlin.

Raabe P (1957) *Psychotic Art.* Routledge and Kegan Paul. London.

Read H (1931) *The Meaning of Art.* Faber and Faber. London.

Reichard G, Jakobson R, Werth E (1949) 'Language and synaesthesia'. *Word* 5: 224-233.

Reichel-Dolmetoff G (1972) In *Flesh of the Gods, the Ritual Use of Hallucinogens.* ed PT Furst. Praeger. New York.

Reitman F (1950) *Psychotic Art.* Routledge and Kegan Paul. London.

Renoir J (1962) *Renoir, My Father.* Boston.

Revesz G (1922) 'Uber audition colorée'. *Z. Agnew. Psychol.* 21: 308.

Rice D (1977) 'Landry-Guillain-Barrée syndrome'. *British Medical J.* i: 1330-1332.

Richardson J (1958) *Georges Braque.* Penguin. London.

Ritter C (1954) *A Woman in the Polar Night.* Dutton. New York.

Rokhline LL (1971) 'Les conceptions psychopathologiques de Kandinsky'. *L'Evolution Psychiatrique.* 36: 475-485.

Roth B, Brukova S (1967) *Experimental Medicine and Surgery.* 27: 187.

Russell J (1965) *The Meanings of Modern Art.* London.

Russell B (1946) *A History of Western Philosophy.* Allen and Unwin. London.

Rutter F (1927) *Masterpieces of Modern Art.* Modern Masterpieces Ltd. London.

Sacks OW, Kohl M (1976) 'Incontinent nostalgia induced by L-dopa'. *Lancet* i: 1394.

San Lazzaro G di (1957) *Klee.* Thames and Hudson. London.

Schachter N, Schmeidler GR, Staal M (1965) 'Dream reports and colour tendencies'. *J. Consultative Psychiatry* 29: 415-421.

Schmied W (1969) *Alfred Kubin.* London.

Schneider E (1951) *Coleridge, Opium and Kubla Khan.* London.

Scholes PA (1977) *The Oxford Companion to Music.* 10th ed. Oxford University Press. Oxford.

Seitz WC (1960) *Claude Monet 1840-1926.* Abrams. New York.

Shapiro T (1976) *Painters and Politics* (The European Avant Garde Society 1900-1925). Elsevier. Amsterdam.

Sherrington CS (1906) *The Integrated Action of the Nervous System.* Cambridge University Press. Cambridge.

Siegel RK (1984) 'Hostage hallucinations'. *J. Nervous and Mental Disease* 172: 264-272.

Silverman SM, Berman PS, Bender MB (1961) 'The dynamics of transient cerebral blindness'. *Archives of Neurology* 4: 333-348.

Simpson L, McKellar PH (1955) 'Types of synaesthesia' *British J. Psychiatry* 101: 141-147.

Slocum J (1901) *Sailing Round the World.* Sampson Low, Mouston and Co. London.

Soby JT (1966) *Giorgio de Chirico.* Arno Press. New York.

Spillane JD (1968) *An Atlas of Clinical Neurology.* Oxford University Press. Oxford.

Stockbridge WW (1982) 'Michigan's Space Shuttle pilot suffered motion sickness'. *Michigan Medicine* 81: 443-444.

Stone MM (1973) 'Drug related schizophrenic syndromes'. *International J. Psychiatry* 11: 391-437.

Susman MP (1964) 'Dante Gabriel Rossetti and his sister Christiana'. *The Medical J. of Australia* 2: 518-519.

Terr LC (1981) 'Psychic trauma in children'. *American J. Psychiatry* 138: 129-136.

Terraine J (1980) *The Smoke and the Fire: Myths and Antimyths of War* (1861-1945). Sedgwick and Jackson. London.

Todd JM (1964) *Martin Luther.* Burns and Oates. London.

Tolstoy LN (1898) *What is Art?* trans. A. Maude. London.

Tralbaut ME (1969) *Vincent Van Gogh.* Viking Press. New York.

Trevor-Roper P (1970) *The World Through Blunted Sight.* Thames and Hudson. London.

Uhthoff (1899) *Monatschrift fur Psychiatrie und Neurologie* 5: 240-249.

Unsigned (1984) 'The Angels of Mons'. *This England,* Winter pp 68-70.

Van Gogh V (1958) *Complete Letters (1886-1890)* Greenwich. London.

Verhoeff FH (1942) 'Moore's subjective "lightning streaks"'. *American J. Ophthalmology* 25: 265-268.

Vernon MD (1937) *Visual Perception.* Cambridge University Press. Cambridge.

Vike J, Jabbari B, Maitland CG (1984) 'Auditory-visual synaesthesia. Report of a case with intact visual pathways'. *Archives of Neurology* 41: 680-681.

Waetzoldt. (1935) *Dürer.* Phaidon ed (1973) London.

Wallace AR (1900) *Studies, Scientific and Social.* Macmillan. London.

Walton JN (1977) *Brain's Textbook of Diseases of the Nervous System.* 9th ed. Oxford University Press. Oxford.

Washton Lond RC (1980) *Kandinsky: The Developments of an Abstract Style.* Clarendon. Oxford.

Watson L (1979) *Lifetide.* Hodder and Stoughton. London.

Watson L (1966) *An Angel on Each Shoulder.* Hodder and Stoughton. London.

Wells F (1918-1919) 'Symbolism and synaesthesia'. *American J. Insanity* 75: 481-488.

Weisman AD, Hackett TP (1958) 'Psychosis after eye surgery'. *New England J. Medicine* 258: 1284-1289.

Werner H (1948) *Comparative Psychology of Mental Development.* International University Press. New York.

White NS (1980) 'Complex visual hallucinations in partial blindness due to eye disease'. *British J. Psychiatry* 136: 284-286.

Williams GA (1976) *Goya and the Impossible Revolution.* Allen Lane. London.

Wilson SAK (1933) *Diseases of the Nervous System.* Oxford University Press. Oxford.

Wilson S (1980) *Salvador Dali.* The Tate Gallery. London.

Worringer WR (1953) *Abstraction and Empathy.* Routledge and Kegan Paul. London.

Zaret BS (1985) 'Lightning streaks of Moore: a cause of recurrent stereotyped visual disturbances'. *Neurology* 35: 1078-1081.

Ziskind E (1964) 'A second look at sensory deprivation'. *J. Nervous and Mental Disease* 138: 223-232.

Zutt (1932) quoted by Jelliffe SE in *Psychopathology of forced movements and the oculogyric crises of Lethargic Encephalitis.* (1932). London.

Index